A SECOND COURSE
IN
CALCULUS

This book is in the

ADDISON-WESLEY SERIES IN MATHEMATICS

———————

Lynn H. Loomis
Consulting Editor

A SECOND COURSE IN CALCULUS

SERGE LANG
Columbia University, New York, New York

ADDISON-WESLEY PUBLISHING COMPANY, INC.

READING, MASS. · PALO ALTO · LONDON

Foreword

This volume is a continuation of *A First Course in Calculus*, and deals principally with functions of several variables.

The first chapter deals with vectors. The rest of the book separates naturally into two parts. The first part deals with the calculus of functions of several variables, and the second part deals with linear algebra. These are essentially independent, and the short Chapter XIII can be omitted entirely, without prejudice to the understanding of the rest of the book. However, it affords a beautiful crossing point of the algebra and analysis.

Thus, after covering Chapter I, there are two possibilities for the order in which one can read the rest of the book. One may cover immediately Chapters II through VIII, which essentially do for functions of several variables what the *First Course* did for functions of one variable. Or, one can cover Chapters IX, X, XI, XII, XIV, XV to get an introductory course in linear algebra. Each part will require approximately one semester. Thus the whole book may be used for a year's work. The order in which one covers the two parts will depend on the taste of the instructor, the mood of the students, and the requirements of the course.

The chapters on linear algebra are not meant to give a complete treatment of the subject. They are meant as an introduction to the notions of vector space, bases, linear mappings, matrices, and determinants. These notions have become so basic in mathematics (both pure and applied), that it is desirable to get acquainted with them as early as possible. Here again, the mood of the instructor and the degree of sophistication of the students will determine to what extent the emphasis in these chapters is computational or theoretical. At any rate, introducing students early to the notions of linear algebra makes it possible a year later to give better courses at a more advanced level on the calculus of functions of several variables (including the inverse mapping theorem, differential equations, multiple integration, etc.), and linear algebra (including quadratic forms, the dual space, etc.).

At the present level, multiple integration presents a real expository problem. It is absolutely impossible to develop any sort of theory coherently without some linear algebra, determinants, and techniques of uniformity. Thus I feel it is better to postpone this theory to the third year of calculus, which should essentially be a first course in analysis. On the other hand, various science courses (e.g. physics) require a minimum of technique in evaluating double and triple integrals. Thus the chapter on multiple integration simply states rigorously (without proof) certain computational recipes describing this technique. In addition to that, one must recognize that part of the purpose of such a chapter is geometric: To give the student practice in visualizing some three-dimensional figures and their boundaries. Strictly speaking, this is not entirely mathematical, but is still regarded as a requirement of the course. Pushed to extremes in a course of mathematics, it becomes extremely oppressive. I have tried to include just the right amount to carry out the responsibility that the course owes to other science courses, and yet preserve the overall coherence which I have sought to attain.

The chapter on complex numbers can be read immediately after Chapter I, and one could discuss vectors with complex coordinates. The last three chapters (applications to functions of several variables, determinants, and complex numbers) are logically independent, and the order in which they are treated permits some variations of emphasis for the course.

The size of the book is deceptive. Most instructors will find that there is more material than can be covered in one year, and some topics, obviously less important than others, can be omitted (for instance the discussion of parametrization by arc length, or Lagrange multipliers). The chapter on determinants has been written in such a way that a student can learn what determinants are, and can learn to compute them, without reading the proofs. In other words, determinants are characterized by their properties. To go through the proofs requires a fairly high level of abstraction or computation which is unavoidable. Thus the proofs may be omitted in the general case, although it is recommended that students go through them explicitly in the cases of dimension 2 and 3.

At some point during the first or second course, the instructor should give a discussion of proofs by induction. I find it inadvisable to give such a discussion at the very beginning. It is better to carry out such proofs in a natural context for a while, and then point out formally exactly what is involved. Hence I have stated the pattern of induction in an appendix, and anyone teaching the course can decide for himself precisely when he wants to discuss it. In teaching induction, I believe that (as with foreign languages) it is better to learn how to use the language first, and then formalize it, i.e. give its rules of grammar and syntax. Needless to say, the brighter the students are, the earlier they should be exposed to the formalization.

There is no reason why some of the contents of this book should not soon be taught in the secondary schools. This applies especially to Chapter I, to the calculus of matrices, determinants (suitably axiomatized), and complex numbers. The chapter on complex numbers could also be covered in the *First Course*.

It seemed advisable to insert an appendix on the sine and cosine functions, and angles, to show how their theory can be derived purely analytically. The section on sine and cosine could be read with the *First Course*, but to discuss angles, it is necessary to introduce some notions of linear algebra.

I have made great efforts to make the style of presentation as naive and unpretentious as possible, deliberately avoiding introducing more vocabulary than is necessary to understand the concepts with which we deal. In linear algebra, certain abstractions are both unavoidable and desirable. I hope that the reader will find neither too much nor too little.

SERGE LANG
New York, 1964

Contents

Chapter VI

Taylor's Formula

Chapter VII

Maximum and Minimum

Chapter VIII

Multiple Integrals

Chapter IX

Vector Spaces

Chapter X

Linear Equations and Bases

Chapter XI

Linear Mappings

CHAPTER I

Vectors

The concept of a vector is basic for the whole course. It provides geometric motivation for everything that follows. Hence the properties of vectors, both algebraic and geometric, will be discussed in full.

The cross product is included for the sake of completeness. It is *never* used in the rest of the book. It is the only aspect of the theory of vectors which is valid only in three-dimensional space (not 2, nor 4, nor n-dimensional space). One significant feature of almost all the statements and proofs of this book (except for those concerning the cross product), is that they are neither easier nor harder to prove in 3 or n-space than they are in 2-space.

§1. Definition of points in n-space

We have seen that a number can be used to represent a point on a line, once a unit length is selected.

A pair of numbers (i.e. a couple of numbers) (x, y) can be used to represent a point in the plane.

We now observe that a triple of numbers (x, y, z) can be used to represent a point in space, that is 3-dimensional space, or 3-space. We simply introduce one more axis. The next picture illustrates this:

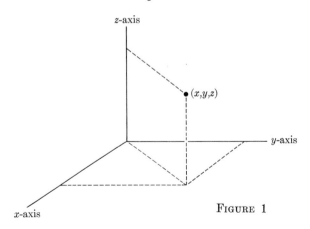

FIGURE 1

Instead of using x, y, z we could also use (x_1, x_2, x_3). The line could be called 1-space, and the plane could be called 2-space.

Thus we can say that a single number represents a point in 1-space. A couple represents a point in 2-space. A triple represents a point in 3-space.

Although we cannot draw a picture to go further, there is nothing to prevent us from considering a quadruple of numbers

$$(x_1, x_2, x_3, x_4)$$

and decreeing that this is a point in 4-space. A quintuple would be a point in 5-space, then would come a sextuple, septuple, octuple, ...

We let ourselves be carried away and *define a point in n-space* to be an n-tuple of numbers

$$(x_1, x_2, \ldots, x_n),$$

if n is a positive integer. We shall denote such an n-tuple by a capital letter X, and try to keep small letters for numbers and capital letters for points. We call the numbers $x_1, \ldots, x_n$ the *coordinates* of the point X.

We shall now define how to add points. If A, B are two points, say

$$A = (a_1, \ldots, a_n), \qquad B = (b_1, \ldots, b_n),$$

then we define $A + B$ to be the point whose coordinates are

$$(a_1 + b_1, \ldots, a_n + b_n).$$

For example, in the plane, if $A = (1, 2)$ and $B = (-3, 5)$ then $A + B = (-2, 7)$. In 3-space, if $A = (-1, \pi, 3)$ and $B = (\sqrt{2}, 7, -2)$ then

$$A + B = (\sqrt{2} - 1, \pi + 7, 1).$$

Furthermore, if c is any number, we *define* cA to be the point whose coordinates are

$$(ca_1, \ldots, ca_n).$$

If $A = (2, -1, 5)$ and $c = 7$ then $cA = (14, -7, 35)$.

We observe that the following rules are satisfied:

(1) $(A + B) + C = A + (B + C)$.

(2) $A + B = B + A$.

(3) $c(A + B) = cA + cB$.

(4) If c_1, c_2 are numbers, then

$$(c_1 + c_2)A = c_1 A + c_2 A \quad \text{and} \quad (c_1 c_2)A = c_1(c_2 A).$$

(5) If we let $O = (0, \ldots, 0)$ be the point all of whose coordinates are 0, then $O + A = A + O = A$ for all A.

(6) $1 \cdot A = A$, and if we denote by $-A$ the n-tuple $(-1)A$, then

$$A + (-A) = O.$$

[Instead of writing $A + (-B)$, we shall frequently write $A - B$.]

All these properties are very simple to prove, and we suggest that you verify them on some examples.

We shall give in detail the proof of property (3).

Let $A = (a_1, \ldots, a_n)$ and $B = (b_1, \ldots, b_n)$. Then

$$A + B = (a_1 + b_1, \ldots, a_n + b_n)$$

and

$$\begin{aligned} c(A + B) &= (c(a_1 + b_1), \ldots, c(a_n + b_n)) \\ &= (ca_1 + cb_1, \ldots, ca_n + cb_n) \\ &= cA + cB, \end{aligned}$$

this last step being true by definition of addition of n-tuples.

The other proofs are left as exercises.

Note. Do not confuse the number 0 and the n-tuple $(0, \ldots, 0)$. We usually denote this n-tuple by O, and also call it zero, because no difficulty can occur in practice.

We shall now interpret addition and multiplication by numbers geometrically in the plane (you can visualize simultaneously what happens in 3-space).

Take an example. Let $A = (2, 3)$ and $B = (-1, 1)$. Then $A + B = (1, 4)$. The figure looks like a parallelogram (Fig. 2).

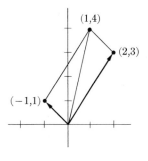 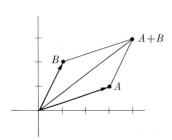

FIGURE 2   FIGURE 3

Take another example. Let $A = (3, 1)$ and $B = (1, 2)$. Then $A + B = (4, 3)$. We see again that the geometric representation of our addition looks like a parallelogram (Fig. 3).

What is the representation of multiplication by a number? Let $A = (1, 2)$ and $c = 3$. Then $cA = (3, 6)$ (Fig. 4a).

Multiplication by 3 amounts to stretching A by 3. Similarly, $\frac{1}{2}A$ amounts to stretching A by $\frac{1}{2}$, i.e. shrinking A to half its size. In general, if t is a number, $t > 0$, we interpret tA as a point in the same direction as A from the origin, but t times the distance.

Multiplication by a negative number reverses the direction. Thus $-3A$ would be represented as in Fig. 4(b).

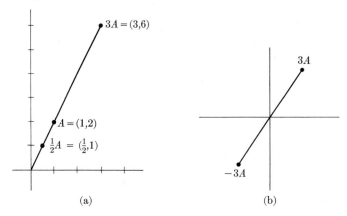

(a)   (b)

FIGURE 4

EXERCISES

Find $A + B$, $A - B$, $3A$, $-2B$ in each of the following cases.

1. $A = (2, -1)$, $B = (-1, 1)$ 2. $A = (-1, 3)$, $B = (0, 4)$
3. $A = (2, -1, 5)$, $B = (-1, 1, 1)$ 4. $A = (-1, -2, 3)$, $B = (-1, 3, -4)$
5. $A = (\pi, 3, -1)$, $B = (2\pi, -3, 7)$ 6. $A = (15, -2, 4)$, $B = (\pi, 3, -1)$

7. Draw the points of Exercises 1 through 4 on a sheet of graph paper.

8. Let A, B be as in Exercise 1. Draw the points $A + 2B$, $A + 3B$, $A - 2B$, $A - 3B$, $A + \frac{1}{2}B$ on a sheet of graph paper.

§2. Vectors

We define a *located vector* to be a pair of points which we write $\overline{AB}$. (This is *not* a product.) We visualize this as an arrow between A and B. We call A the *beginning point* and B the *end point* of the located vector (Fig. 5).

How are the coordinates of B obtained from those of A? We observe that in the plane,

$$b_1 = a_1 + (b_1 - a_1).$$

Similarly,

$$b_2 = a_2 + (b_2 - a_2).$$

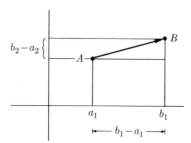

FIGURE 5

This means that

$$B = A + (B - A).$$

Let $\overline{AB}$ and $\overline{CD}$ be two located vectors. We shall say that they are *equivalent* if $B - A = D - C$. Every located vector $\overline{AB}$ is equivalent to one whose beginning point is the origin, because $\overline{AB}$ is equivalent to $\overline{O(B - A)}$. Clearly this is the only located vector whose beginning point is the origin and which is equivalent to $\overline{AB}$. If you visualize the parallelogram law in the plane, then it is clear that equivalence of two located vectors can be interpreted geometrically by saying that the lengths of the line segments determined by the pair of points are equal, and that the "directions" in which they point are the same.

In the next figure, we have drawn the located vectors $\overline{O(B - A)}$ and $\overline{AB}$.

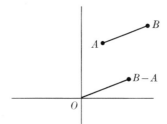

FIGURE 6

Given a located vector $\overline{OC}$ whose beginning point is the origin, we shall say that it is *located at the origin*. Given any located vector $\overline{AB}$, we shall say that it is *located at* A.

A located vector at the origin is entirely determined by its end point. In view of this, we shall call an n-tuple either a point or a vector, depending on the interpretation which we have in mind.

Two located vectors $\overline{AB}$ and $\overline{PQ}$ are said to be *parallel* if there is a number $c \neq 0$ such that $B - A = c(Q - P)$. They are said to have the *same direction* if there is a number $c > 0$ such that $B - A = c(Q - P)$, and to have *opposite direction* if there is a number $c < 0$ such that $B - A = c(Q - P)$. In a similar manner, any definition made concerning n-tuples can be carried over to located vectors. For instance, in the next section, we shall define what it means for n-tuples to be perpendicular. Then we can say that two located vectors $\overline{AB}$ and $\overline{PQ}$ are perpendicular if $B - A$ is perpendicular to $Q - P$. In the next figure, we have drawn a picture of such vectors in the plane.

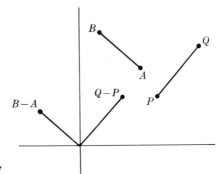

FIGURE 7

§3. *Scalar product*

It is understood that throughout a discussion we select vectors always in the same n-dimensional space.

Let $A = (a_1, \ldots, a_n)$ and $B = (b_1, \ldots, b_n)$ be two vectors. We define their *scalar* or *dot product* $A \cdot B$ to be

$$a_1 b_1 + \cdots + a_n b_n.$$

This product is a *number*. For instance if

$$A = (1, 3, -2) \quad \text{and} \quad B = (-1, 4, -3)$$

then

$$A \cdot B = -1 + 12 + 6 = 17.$$

For the moment, we do not give a geometric interpretation to this scalar product. We shall do this later. We derive first some important properties. The basic ones are:

SP 1. *We have $A \cdot B = B \cdot A$.*

SP 2. *If A, B, C are three vectors then*

$$A \cdot (B + C) = A \cdot B + A \cdot C = (B + C) \cdot A.$$

SP 3. *If x is a number, then*

$$(xA) \cdot B = x(A \cdot B) \quad \text{and} \quad A \cdot (xB) = x(A \cdot B).$$

SP 4. *If $A = O$ is the zero vector, then $A \cdot A = 0$, and otherwise $A \cdot A > 0$.*

We shall now prove these properties.

Concerning the first, we have

$$a_1 b_1 + \cdots + a_n b_n = b_1 a_1 + \cdots + b_n a_n,$$

because for any two numbers, a, b, we have $ab = ba$. This proves the first property.

For SP 2, let $C = (c_1, \ldots, c_n)$. Then

$$B + C = (b_1 + c_1, \ldots, b_n + c_n)$$

and

$$\begin{aligned} A \cdot (B + C) &= a_1(b_1 + c_1) + \cdots + a_n(b_n + c_n) \\ &= a_1 b_1 + a_1 c_1 + \cdots + a_n b_n + a_n c_n. \end{aligned}$$

Reordering the terms yields

$$a_1 b_1 + \cdots + a_n b_n + a_1 c_1 + \cdots + a_n c_n,$$

which is none other than $A \cdot B + A \cdot C$. This proves what we wanted.

We leave property SP 3 as an exercise.

Finally, for SP 4, we observe that if one coordinate a_i of A is not equal to 0, then there is a term $a_i^2 \neq 0$ and $a_i^2 > 0$ in the scalar product

$$A \cdot A = a_1^2 + \cdots + a_n^2.$$

Since every term is ≥ 0, it follows that the sum is > 0, as was to be shown.

In much of the work which we shall do concerning vectors, we shall use only the ordinary properties of addition, multiplication by numbers, and the four properties of the scalar product. We shall give a formal discussion of these later. For the moment, observe that there are other objects with which you are familiar and which can be added, subtracted, and multiplied by numbers, for instance the continuous functions on an interval $[a, b]$ (cf. Exercise 5).

Instead of writing $A \cdot A$ for the scalar product of a vector with itself, it will be convenient to write also A^2. (This is the only instance when we allow ourselves such a notation. Thus A^3 has no meaning.) As an exercise, verify the following identities:

$$\begin{aligned} (A + B)^2 &= A^2 + 2A \cdot B + B^2, \\ (A - B)^2 &= A^2 - 2A \cdot B + B^2. \end{aligned}$$

We define two vectors A, B to be *perpendicular* (or as we shall also say, *orthogonal*) if $A \cdot B = 0$. For the moment, it is not clear that in the plane, this definition coincides with our intuitive geometric notion of perpendicularity. We shall convince you that it does in the next section.

1. Find $A \cdot A$ for each one of the n-tuples of Exercises 1 through 6 of §1.

2. Find $A \cdot B$ for each one of the n-tuples as above.

3. Using only the four properties of the scalar product, verify in detail the rules giving $(A + B)^2$ and $(A - B)^2$.

4. Which of the following pairs of vectors are perpendicular?
    (a) $(1, -1, 1)$ and $(2, 1, 5)$ (b) $(1, -1, 1)$ and $(2, 3, 1)$
    (c) $(-5, 2, 7)$ and $(3, -1, 2)$ (d) $(\pi, 2, 1)$ and $(2, -\pi, 0)$

5. Consider continuous functions on the interval $[-1, 1]$. Define the scalar product of two such functions f, g to be

$$\int_{-1}^{+1} f(x)g(x) \, dx.$$

We denote this integral also by $\langle f, g \rangle$. Verify that the four rules for a scalar product are satisfied, in other words, show that:

SP 1. $\langle f, g \rangle = \langle g, f \rangle$.

SP 2. $\langle f, g + h \rangle = \langle f, g \rangle + \langle f, h \rangle$.

SP 3. $\langle cf, g \rangle = c\langle f, g \rangle$.

SP 4. *If $f = 0$ then $\langle f, f \rangle = 0$ and if $f \neq 0$ then $\langle f, f \rangle > 0$.*

6. If $f(x) = x$ and $g(x) = x^2$, what are $\langle f, f \rangle$, $\langle g, g \rangle$, and $\langle f, g \rangle$?

7. Consider continuous functions on the interval $[-\pi, \pi]$. Define a scalar product similar to the above for this interval. Show that the functions $\sin nx$ and $\cos mx$ are orthogonal for this scalar product (m, n being integers).

8. Let A be a vector perpendicular to every vector X. Show that $A = O$.

§4. *The norm of a vector*

The following inequality is called the *Schwarz inequality* and is fundamental in the theory of vectors.

THEOREM 1. *Let A, B be two vectors. Then*

$$(A \cdot B)^2 \leq (A \cdot A)(B \cdot B).$$

Proof. Let $x = B \cdot B$ and $y = -A \cdot B$. Then by SP 4 we have

$$0 \leq (xA + yB) \cdot (xA + yB).$$

We multiply out the right-hand side of this inequality and get

$$0 \leq x^2(A \cdot A) + 2xy(A \cdot B) + y^2(B \cdot B).$$

Substituting the values for x and y yields

$$0 \leq (B \cdot B)^2(A \cdot A) - 2(B \cdot B)(A \cdot B)^2 + (A \cdot B)^2(B \cdot B).$$

If $B = O$ then the inequality of the theorem is obvious, both sides being equal to 0. If $B \neq O$, then $B \cdot B \neq 0$ and we can divide this last expression by $B \cdot B$. We then obtain

$$0 \leq (A \cdot A)(B \cdot B) - (A \cdot B)^2.$$

Transposing the term $-(A \cdot B)^2$ to the other side of the inequality concludes the proof.

We define the *norm*, or *length*, of a vector A, and denote by $\|A\|$, the number

$$\|A\| = \sqrt{A \cdot A}.$$

Since $A \cdot A \geq 0$, we can take the square root. Furthermore, we note immediately that $\|A\| \neq 0$ if $A \neq O$.

In terms of coordinates, we see that

$$\|A\| = \sqrt{a_1^2 + \cdots + a_n^2},$$

and therefore that when $n = 2$ or $n = 3$, this coincides with our intuitive notion (derived from the Pythagoras theorem) of length.

In view of our definition, we can rewrite the inequality of Theorem 1 in the form

$$|(A \cdot B)| \leq \|A\| \, \|B\|$$

by taking the square root of both sides. We shall use it in this form in the proof of the next theorem.

THEOREM 2. *Let A, B be vectors. Then*

$$\|A + B\| \leq \|A\| + \|B\|.$$

Proof. Both sides of this inequality are positive or 0. Hence it will suffice to prove that their squares satisfy the desired inequality, in other words,

$$(A + B) \cdot (A + B) \leq (\|A\| + \|B\|)^2.$$

To do this, we consider

$$(A + B) \cdot (A + B) = A \cdot A + 2A \cdot B + B \cdot B.$$

In view of our previous result, this satisfies the inequality

$$\leq \|A\|^2 + 2\|A\| \, \|B\| + \|B\|^2,$$

and the right-hand side is none other than

$$(\|A\| + \|B\|)^2.$$

Our theorem is proved.

Theorem 2 is known as the *triangle inequality.* (Cf. Exercise 11.)

THEOREM 3. *Let x be a number. Then*

$$\|xA\| = |x|\,\|A\|$$

(*absolute value of x times the length of A*).

Proof. By definition, we have

$$\|xA\|^2 = (xA) \cdot (xA),$$

which is equal to

$$x^2(A \cdot A)$$

by the properties of the scalar product. Taking the square root now yields what we want.

We shall say that a vector U is a *unit* vector if $\|U\| = 1$. Given any vector A, let $a = \|A\|$. If $a \neq 0$ then

$$\frac{1}{a}\,A$$

is a unit vector, because

$$\left\|\frac{1}{a}\,A\right\| = \frac{1}{a}\,a = 1.$$

We shall say that two vectors A, B (neither of which is O) have the *same direction* if there is a number $c > 0$ such that $cA = B$. In view of this definition, we see that the vector

$$\frac{1}{\|A\|}\,A$$

is a unit vector in the direction of A (provided $A \neq O$).

We mention in passing that two vectors A, B (neither of which is O) have *opposite directions* if there is a number $c < 0$ such that $cA = B$.

Let A, B be two n-tuples. We define the *distance* between A and B to be $\|A - B\| = \sqrt{(A - B) \cdot (A - B)}$. This definition coincides with our geometric intuition when A, B are points in the plane.

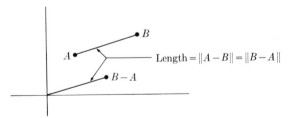

FIGURE 8

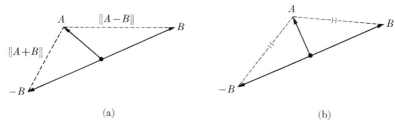

We are also in position to justify our definition of perpendicularity. Given A, B in the plane, the condition that

$$\|A + B\| = \|A - B\|$$

(illustrated in Fig. 9b) coincides with the geometric property that A should be perpendicular to B. This condition is equivalent with

$$(A + B) \cdot (A + B) = (A - B) \cdot (A - B)$$

(take the square of each side), and expanding out, this equality is equivalent with

$$A \cdot A + 2A \cdot B + B \cdot B = A \cdot A - 2A \cdot B + B \cdot B.$$

Making cancellations, we obtain the equivalent condition

$$4A \cdot B = 0$$

or

$$A \cdot B = 0.$$

Let A, B be two vectors and $B \neq O$. Suppose that we can find a number c such that $A - cB$ is perpendicular to B, or in other words,

$$(A - cB) \cdot B = 0.$$

We then obtain

$$A \cdot B = cB \cdot B,$$

and therefore

$$c = \frac{A \cdot B}{B \cdot B}.$$

Thus the number c is uniquely determined by our condition of perpendicularity. Conversely, for this number c, we clearly have $(A - cB) \cdot B = 0$.

We define cB to be the *projection* of A along B. If B is a unit vector, then we have simply

$$c = A \cdot B.$$

Our construction has an immediate interpretation in the plane, which gives us a geometric interpretation for the scalar product. Namely, assume $A \neq O$ and look at the angle θ between A and B. Then from plane geometry we see that

$$\cos \theta = \frac{c\|B\|}{\|A\|},$$

or substituting the value for c obtained above,

$$A \cdot B = \|A\| \, \|B\| \cos \theta.$$

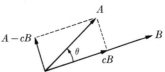

FIGURE 10

In view of Theorem 1, we know that in n-space, the number

$$\frac{A \cdot B}{\|A\| \, \|B\|}$$

has absolute value ≤ 1. Consequently,

$$-1 \leq \frac{A \cdot B}{\|A\| \, \|B\|} \leq 1,$$

and there exists a unique angle θ such that $0 \leq \theta \leq \pi$, and such that

$$\cos \theta = \frac{A \cdot B}{\|A\| \, \|B\|}.$$

We define this angle to be the *angle between A and B*.

EXERCISES

1. Find the length of the vector A in Exercises 1 through 6 of §1.

2. Find the length of the vector B in Exercises 1 through 6 of §1.

3. Find the projection of A along B in Exercises 1 through 6 of §1.

4. Find the projection of B along A in these exercises.

5. In Exercise 6 of §3, find the projection of f along g and the projection of g along f, using the same definition of projection that has been given in the text (and did not refer to coordinates).

6. Find the norm of the functions $\sin 3x$ and $\cos x$, with respect to the scalar product on the interval $[-\pi, \pi]$ given by the integral.

7. Find the norm of the constant function 1 on the interval $[-\pi, \pi]$.

8. Find the norm of the constant function 1 on the interval $[-1, 1]$.

9. Let $A_1, \ldots, A_r$ be non-zero vectors which are mutually perpendicular, in other words $A_i \cdot A_j = 0$ if $i \neq j$. Let $c_1, \ldots, c_r$ be numbers such that

$$c_1 A_1 + \cdots + c_r A_r = 0.$$

Show that all $c_i = 0$.

10. Let A, B be two non-zero vectors in n-space. Let θ be the angle between them. If $\cos\theta = 1$, show that A and B have the same direction. If $\cos\theta = -1$, show that A and B have opposite direction.

11. If A, B are two vectors in n-space, denote by $d(A, B)$ the distance between A and B, i.e. $d(A, B) = \|B - A\|$. Show that $d(A, B) = d(B, A)$, and that for any three vectors A, B, C we have

$$d(A, B) \leqq d(A, C) + d(B, C).$$

§5. Lines and planes

We define the parametric equation of a straight line passing through a point P in the direction of a vector $A \neq O$ to be

$$X = P + tA,$$

where t runs through all numbers.

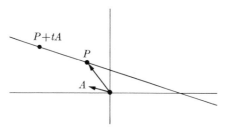

FIGURE 11

Suppose that we work in the plane, and write the coordinates of a point X as (x, y). Let $P = (p, q)$ and $A = (a, b)$. Then in terms of the coordinates, we can write

$$x = p + ta, \qquad y = q + tb.$$

We can then eliminate t and obtain the usual equation relating x and y.

For example, let $P = (2, 1)$ and $A = (-1, 5)$. Then the parametric equation of the line through P in the direction of A gives us

$$x = 2 - t, \qquad y = 1 + 5t.$$

Multiplying the first equation by 5 and adding yields

$$5x + y = 11,$$

which is familiar.

In higher-dimensional space, we *cannot* eliminate t in this manner, and thus the parametric equation is the only one available to describe a straight line.

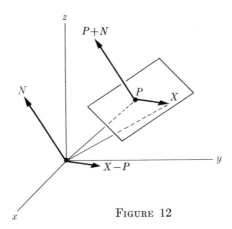

FIGURE 12

However, we can describe planes by an equation analogous to the single equation of the line. We proceed as follows.

Let P be a point, N a vector $\neq O$. We define the *hyperplane* passing through P perpendicular to N to be the collection of all points X such that $X - P$ is perpendicular to N, thus:

$$(X - P) \cdot N = 0,$$

which can also be written as

$$X \cdot N = P \cdot N.$$

We have drawn a typical situation in 3-space in Fig. 12.

Instead of saying that N is perpendicular to the plane, one also says that N is *normal* to the plane.

Let t be a number $\neq 0$. Then the set of points X such that

$$(X - P) \cdot N = 0$$

coincides with the set of points X such that

$$(X - P) \cdot tN = 0.$$

Thus we may say that our plane is the plane passing through P and perpendicular to the *line* in the direction of N. To find the equation of the plane, we could use any vector tN (with $t \neq 0$) instead of N.

In 3-space, we get an ordinary plane. For example, let $P = (2, 1, -1)$ and $N = (-1, 1, 3)$. Then the equation of the plane passing through P and perpendicular to N is

$$-x + y + 3z = -2 + 1 - 3$$

or

$$-x + y + 3z = -4.$$

Observe that in 2-space, with $X = (x, y)$, we are led to the equation of the line in the ordinary sense. For example, the equation of the line passing through $(4, -3)$ and perpendicular to $(-5, 2)$ is

$$-5x + 2y = -20 - 6 = -26.$$

We are now in position to interpret the coefficients $(-5, 2)$ of x and y in this equation. They give rise to a vector perpendicular to the line. In any equation

$$ax + by = c$$

the vector (a, b) is perpendicular to the line determined by the equation. Similarly, in 3-space, the vector (a, b, c) is perpendicular to the plane determined by the equation

$$ax + by + cz = d.$$

Two vectors A, B are said to be parallel if there exists a number $c \neq 0$ such that $cA = B$. Two lines are said to be *parallel* if, given two distinct points P_1, Q_1 on the first line and P_2, Q_2 on the second, the vectors

$$P_1 - Q_1 \qquad \text{and} \qquad P_2 - Q_2$$

are parallel.

Two planes are said to be *parallel* (in 3-space) if their normal vectors are parallel. They are said to be *perpendicular* if their normal vectors are perpendicular. The *angle* between two planes is defined to be the angle between their normal vectors.

Example. Find the cosine of the angle between the planes

$$2x - y + z = 0$$
$$x + 2y - z = 1.$$

This cosine is the cosine of the angle between $(2, -1, 1)$ and $(1, 2, -1)$ and is therefore equal to $-\frac{1}{6}$.

EXERCISES

Find a parametric equation for the line passing through the following points
   1. $(1, 1, -1)$ and $(-2, 1, 3)$ 2. $(-1, 5, 2)$ and $(3, -4, 1)$

Find the equation of the line in 2-space, perpendicular to A and passing through P, for the following values of A and P.
   3. $A = (1, -1)$, $P = (-5, 3)$ 4. $A = (-5, 4)$, $P = (3, 2)$
   5. Show that the lines

$$3x - 5y = 1, \qquad 2x + 3y = 5$$

are not perpendicular.

6. Which of the following pairs of lines are perpendicular?

(a) $3x - 5y = 1$ and $2x + y = 2$.

(b) $2x + 7y = 1$ and $x - y = 5$.

(c) $3x - 5y = 1$ and $5x + 3y = 7$.

(d) $-x + y = 2$ and $x + y = 9$.

7. Find the equation of the plane perpendicular to the given vector N and passing through the given point P.

(a) $N = (1, -1, 3)$, $P = (4, 2, -1)$

(b) $N = (-3, -2, 4)$, $P = (2, \pi, -5)$

(c) $N = (-1, 0, 5)$, $P = (2, 3, 7)$.

8. Find the equation of the plane passing through the following three points.

(a) $(2, 1, 1)$, $(3, -1, 1)$, $(4, 1, -1)$

(b) $(-2, 3, -1)$, $(2, 2, 3)$, $(-4, -1, 1)$

(c) $(-5, -1, 2)$, $(1, 2, -1)$, $(3, -1, 2)$.

9. Find a vector perpendicular to $(1, 2, -3)$ and $(2, -1, 3)$, and another vector perpendicular to $(-1, 3, 2)$ and $(2, 1, 1)$.

10. Let P be the point $(1, 2, 3, 4)$ and Q the point $(4, 3, 2, 1)$. Let A be the vector $(1, 1, 1, 1)$. Let L be the line passing through P and parallel to A.

(a) Given a point X on the line L, compute the distance between Q and X (as a function of the parameter t).

(b) Show that there is precisely one point X_0 on the line such that this distance achieves a minimum, and that this minimum is $2\sqrt{5}$.

(c) Show that $X_0 - Q$ is perpendicular to the line.

11. Let P be the point $(1, -1, 3, 1)$ and Q the point $(1, 1, -1, 2)$. Let A be the vector $(1, -3, 2, 1)$. Solve the same questions as in the preceding problem, except that in this case the minimum distance is $\sqrt{146/15}$.

12. Find a vector parallel to the line of intersection of the two planes

$$2x - y + z = 1, \qquad 3x + y + z = 2.$$

13. Same question for the planes

$$2x + y + 5z = 2, \qquad 3x - 2y + z = 3.$$

14. Find a parametric equation for the line of intersection of the planes of Exercises 12 and 13.

15. Find the cosine of the angle between the following planes:

(a) $x + y + z = 1$

  $x - y - z = 5$

(b) $2x + 3y - z = 2$

  $x - y + z = 1$

(c) $x + 2y - z = 1$

  $-x + 3y + z = 2$

(d) $2x + y + z = 3$

  $-x - y + z = \pi$

16. Let $X \cdot N = P \cdot N$ be the equation of a plane in 3-space. Let Q be a point not lying in the plane. Show that there is a unique number t such that $Q + tN$ lies in the plane (i.e. satisfies the equation of the plane). What is this value in terms of P, Q, and N?

17. Let $Q = (1, -1, 2)$, $P = (1, 3, -2)$, and $N = (1, 2, 2)$. Find the point of intersection of the line through P in the direction of N, and the plane through Q perpendicular to N.

18. Let P, Q be two points and N a vector in 3-space. Let P' be the point of intersection of the line through P, in the direction of N, and the plane through Q, perpendicular to N. We define the *distance* from P to that plane to be the distance between P and P'. Find this distance when

$$P = (1, 3, 5), \qquad Q = (-1, 1, 7), \qquad N = (-1, 1, -1).$$

19. Let $P = (1, 3, 5)$ and $A = (-2, 1, 1)$. Find the intersection of the line through P in the direction of A, and the plane

$$2x + 3y - z = 1.$$

20. Find the distance between the point $(1, 1, 2)$ and the plane

$$3x + y - 5z = 2.$$

21. Let $P = (1, 3, -1)$ and $Q = (-4, 5, 2)$. Determine the coordinates of the following points: (a) The midpoint of the line segment between P and Q. (b) The two points on this line segment lying one-third and two-thirds of the way from P to Q.

22. If P, Q are two arbitrary points in n-space, give the general formula for the midpoint of the line segment between P and Q.

§6. *The cross product*

This section applies only in 3-space!

Let $A = (a_1, a_2, a_3)$ and $B = (b_1, b_2, b_3)$ be two vectors in 3-space. We define their *cross product*

$$A \times B = (a_2 b_3 - a_3 b_2, \ a_3 b_1 - a_1 b_3, \ a_1 b_2 - a_2 b_1).$$

We leave the following assertions as exercises:

1. $A \times B = -(B \times A)$.
2. $A \times (B + C) = (A \times B) + (A \times C)$.
3. For any number a, we have

$$(aA) \times B = a(A \times B) = A \times (aB).$$

4. $(A \times B) \times C = (A \cdot C)B - (B \cdot C)A$.
5. $A \times B$ is perpendicular to both A and B.
6. $(A \times B)^2 = (A \cdot A)(B \cdot B) - (A \cdot B)^2$.

From 6 and our interpretation of the dot product, we conclude that

$$\|A \times B\|^2 = \|A\|^2 \|B\|^2 - \|A\|^2 \|B\|^2 \cos^2 \theta,$$

where θ is the angle between A and B. Hence we obtain

$$\|A \times B\|^2 = \|A\|^2\|B\|^2 \sin^2 \theta$$

or

$$\|A \times B\| = \|A\| \|B\| |\sin \theta|.$$

This is analogous to the formula which gave us the absolute value of $A \cdot B$.

EXERCISES

Find $A \times B$ for the following vectors.

1. $A = (1, -1, 1)$ and $B = (-2, 3, 1)$

2. $A = (-1, 1, 2)$ and $B = (1, 0, -1)$

3. $A = (1, 1, -3)$ and $B = (-1, -2, -3)$

4. Find $A \times A$ and $B \times B$, in Exercises 1 through 3.

5. Let $E_1 = (1, 0, 0)$, $E_2 = (0, 1, 0)$, and $E_3 = (0, 0, 1)$. Find $E_1 \times E_2$, $E_2 \times E_3$, $E_3 \times E_1$.

To do the rest of the exercises, wait until you have read Chapter II, §1.

6. If $X(t)$ and $Y(t)$ are two differentiable curves (defined for the same values of t), show that

$$\frac{d[X(t) \times Y(t)]}{dt} = X(t) \times \frac{dY(t)}{dt} + \frac{dX(t)}{dt} \times Y(t).$$

7. Show that

$$\frac{d}{dt} [X(t) \times \dot{X}(t)] = X(t) \times \ddot{X}(t).$$

CHAPTER II

Differentiation of Vectors

We begin to acquire the flavour of the mixture of algebra, geometry, and differentiation. Each gains in appeal from being mixed with the other two.

The chain rule especially leads into the classical theory of curves. As you will see, the chain rule in its various aspects occurs very frequently in this book, and forms almost as basic a tool as the algebra of vectors, with which it will in fact be intimately mixed.

§1. Derivative

A vector X whose coordinates are given as functions of one variable t defined on some interval is said to represent a *curve*. We then write

$$X(t) = (x_1(t), \ldots, x_n(t)),$$

each $x_i(t)$ being a function of t. We say that this curve is *differentiable* if each function $x_i(t)$ is a differentiable function of t.

For instance, the curve

$$X(t) = (\cos t, \sin t, t)$$

is a spiral. Here we have

$$x(t) = \cos t, \qquad y(t) = \sin t, \qquad z(t) = t.$$

Remark. Unless otherwise specified in what follows, we shall assume that the intervals of definition for curves are open. Actually, this is slightly unnatural in some cases, as when we wish to join two points by a curve. It should therefore be remarked that most of what we prove holds also for closed or half-closed intervals, provided one makes the following conventions: We do not define the derivative if the interval consists only of one point. If the interval has more than one point, and contains an end point, say the left end point, define the derivative of a function at that point to be the right derivative, or alternatively, to be the usual limit

$$\lim_{h \to 0} \frac{f(a + h) - f(a)}{h}$$

19

taken only for those values of h such that $a + h$ lies in the interval. Then the usual rules for differentiation of functions are true in this greater generality, and thus Rules 1 through 4 below, and the chain rule of §2 remain true also. [An example of a statement which is not always true for curves defined over closed intervals is given by Exercise 11(b).]

Let us try to differentiate vectors using a Newton quotient. We consider

$$\frac{X(t + h) - X(t)}{h} = \left(\frac{x_1(t + h) - x_1(t)}{h}, \ldots, \frac{x_n(t + h) - x_n(t)}{h} \right)$$

and see that each component is a Newton quotient for the corresponding coordinate. If each $x_i(t)$ is differentiable, then each quotient

$$\frac{x_i(t + h) - x_i(t)}{h}$$

approaches the derivative dx_i/dt. For this reason, we define the *derivative* $\dfrac{dX}{dt}$ to be

$$\frac{dX}{dt} = \left(\frac{dx_1}{dt}, \ldots, \frac{dx_n}{dt} \right).$$

In fact, we could also say that the vector

$$\left(\frac{dx_1}{dt}, \ldots, \frac{dx_n}{dt} \right)$$

is the limit of the Newton quotient

$$\frac{X(t + h) - X(t)}{h}$$

as h approaches 0. Indeed, as h approaches 0, each component

$$\frac{x_i(t + h) - x_i(t)}{h}$$

approaches dx_i/dt. Hence the Newton quotient approaches the vector

$$\left(\frac{dx_1}{dt}, \ldots, \frac{dx_n}{dt} \right).$$

For example, if $X(t) = (\cos t, \sin t, t)$ then

$$\frac{dX}{dt} = (-\sin t, \cos t, 1).$$

It will also be convenient to denote dX/dt by $\dot{X}$. Thus in the previous example, we would also write

$$\dot{X}(t) = (-\sin t,\ \cos t,\ 1).$$

If we visualize geometrically the meaning of the difference quotient

$$\frac{X(t+h)-X(t)}{h},$$

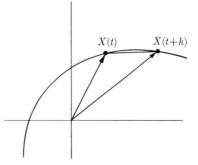

then it is reasonable to define a *tangent vector* to the curve (at time t) to be any vector which is equal to a constant multiple of $\dot{X}(t)$, provided $\dot{X}(t) \neq O$. If $\dot{X}(t) = O$, then we do not define the meaning of tangent vector.

We also define the *velocity* vector to be $\dot{X}$. Thus the velocity vector $\dot{X}(t)$ at a given value of t is tangent to the curve (provided it is not O).

In our previous example, when $t = \pi$, the velocity vector is

$$\dot{X}(\pi) = (0,\ -1,\ 1),$$

and for $t = \pi/4$, we get

$$\dot{X}\left(\frac{\pi}{4}\right) = \left(-\frac{1}{\sqrt{2}},\ \frac{1}{\sqrt{2}},\ 1\right).$$

We define the *acceleration* vector to be the derivative $\dfrac{d\dot{X}}{dt}$, provided of course that $\dot{X}$ is differentiable. We shall also denote the acceleration vector by $\ddot{X}$. In our example we see that

$$\ddot{X}(t) = (-\cos t,\ -\sin t,\ 0).$$

Since the derivative is defined componentwise, we have the following rules for differentiation.

Rule 1. Let $X(t)$ and $Y(t)$ be two differentiable curves (defined for the same values of t). Then the sum $X(t) + Y(t)$ is differentiable, and

$$\frac{d\big(X(t)+Y(t)\big)}{dt} = \frac{dX}{dt} + \frac{dY}{dt}.$$

Rule 2. Let c be a number, and let $X(t)$ be differentiable. Then $cX(t)$ is differentiable, and

$$\frac{d\big(cX(t)\big)}{dt} = c\,\frac{dX}{dt}.$$

Rule 3. Let $f(t)$ be a differentiable function, and $X(t)$ a differentiable curve (defined for the same values of t). Then $f(t)X(t)$ is differentiable, and

$$\frac{d(fX)}{dt} = f(t)\,\frac{dX}{dt} + \frac{df}{dt}\,X(t).$$

Rule 4. Let $X(t)$ and $Y(t)$ be two differentiable curves (defined for the same values of t). Then $X(t) \cdot Y(t)$ is a differentiable function whose derivative is

$$\frac{d}{dt}\,[X(t) \cdot Y(t)] = \dot{X}(t) \cdot Y(t) + X(t) \cdot \dot{Y}(t).$$

(This is formally analogous to the derivative of a product of functions, namely the first times the derivative of the second plus the second times the derivative of the first, except that the product is now a scalar product.)

As an example of the proofs we shall give the third one in detail, and leave the others to you as exercises.

To begin with, we make a remark concerning the product of a function by a vector. For each value of t, $f(t)$ is a number and $X(t)$ is a vector. Thus $f(t)X(t)$ is simply equal to a number times a vector, and we have already seen what this means. Thus if $X(t) = (x_1(t), \ldots, x_n(t))$, and $f = f(t)$ is a function, then by definition,

$$f(t)X(t) = (f(t)x_1(t), \ldots, f(t)x_n(t)).$$

We take the derivative of each component and can apply the rule for the derivative of a product of functions. We obtain:

$$\frac{d(fX)}{dt} = \left(f(t)\,\frac{dx_1}{dt} + \frac{df}{dt}\,x_1(t), \ldots, f(t)\,\frac{dx_n}{dt} + \frac{df}{dt}\,x_n(t) \right).$$

Using the rule for the sum of two vectors, we see that the expression on the right is equal to

$$\left(f(t)\,\frac{dx_1}{dt}, \ldots, f(t)\,\frac{dx_n}{dt} \right) + \left(\frac{df}{dt}\,x_1(t), \ldots, \frac{df}{dt}\,x_n(t) \right).$$

We can take f out of the vector on the left and df/dt out of the vector on the right to obtain

$$f(t)\,\frac{dX}{dt} + \frac{df}{dt}\,X(t),$$

as desired.

We define the *speed* of the curve $X(t)$ to be the length of the velocity vector. If we denote the speed by $v(t)$, then by definition we have

$$v(t) = \|\dot{X}(t)\|,$$

and thus

$$v(t)^2 = \dot{X}(t)^2 = \dot{X}(t) \cdot \dot{X}(t).$$

We can also omit the t from the notation, and write

$$v = \dot{X}^2.$$

The length of the acceleration vector is called the *acceleration scalar*, and will be denoted by $a(t)$. *Warning:* $a(t)$ is not necessarily the derivative of $v(t)$.

We define the *length* of a curve X between two values a, b of t ($a \le b$) in the interval of definition of the curve to be the integral

$$\int_a^b v(t)\, dt = \int_a^b \|\dot{X}(t)\|\, dt.$$

By definition, we can rewrite this integral in the form

$$\int_a^b \sqrt{\left(\frac{dx_1}{dt}\right)^2 + \cdots + \left(\frac{dx_n}{dt}\right)^2}\, dt.$$

When $n = 2$, then this is the same formula for the length which we gave in Volume I of this course. Thus the formula in dimension n is a very natural generalization of the formula in dimension 2.

Exercises

Find the velocity vector of the following curves.

1. $(e^t, \cos t, \sin t)$ 2. $(\sin 2t, \log (1 + t), t)$.

3. $(\cos t, \sin t)$ 4. $(\cos 3t, \sin 3t)$.

5. In Exercises 3 and 4, show that the velocity vector is perpendicular to the position vector.

6. In Exercises 3 and 4, show that the acceleration vector is in opposite direction from the position vector.

7. Let A, B be two constant vectors. What is the velocity vector of the curve $X = A + tB$?

8. Let $X(t)$ be a differentiable curve. A plane or line which is perpendicular to the velocity vector $\dot{X}(t)$ at the point $X(t)$ is said to be *normal* to the curve at the point t or also at the point $X(t)$. Find the equation of a line normal to the curves of Exercises 3 and 4 at the point $\pi/3$.

9. Find the equation of a plane normal to the curve

$$(e^t, t, t^2)$$

at the point $t = 1$.

10. Same question at the point $t = 0$.

11. Let $X(t)$ be a differentiable curve defined on an open interval. Let Q be a point which is not on the curve.

    (a) Write down the formula for the distance between Q and an arbitrary point on the curve.

(b) If t_0 is a value of t such that the distance between Q and $X(t_0)$ is at a minimum, show that the vector $Q - X(t_0)$ is normal to the curve, at the point $X(t_0)$. [*Hint:* Investigate the minimum of the square of the distance.]

(c) If $X(t)$ is the parametric equation of a straight line, show that there exists a unique value t_0 such that the distance between Q and $X(t_0)$ is a minimum.

12. Find the length of the spiral $(\cos t, \sin t, t)$ between $t = 0$ and $t = 1$.

13. Find the length of the spiral $(\cos 2t, \sin 2t, 3t)$ between $t = 1$ and $t = 3$.

14. Assume that the differentiable curve $X(t)$ lies on the sphere of radius 1. Show that the velocity vector is perpendicular to the position vector. [*Hint:* Start from the condition $X(t)^2 = 1$.]

15. Let A be a non-zero vector, c a number, and Q a point. Let P_0 be the point of intersection of the line passing through Q, in the direction of A, and the plane $X \cdot A = c$. Show that for all points P of the plane, we have

$$\|Q - P_0\| \le \|Q - P\|.$$

[*Hint:* If $P \ne P_0$, consider the straight line passing through P_0 and P, and use Exercise 11(c).]

§2. *The chain rule and applications*

Let X be a vector and c a number. As a matter of notation it will be convenient to define Xc to be cX, in other words, we allow ourselves to multiply vectors by numbers on the right. If we have a curve $X(t)$ defined for some interval, and a function $g(t)$ defined on the same interval, then we let

$$X(t)g(t) = g(t)X(t).$$

Let $X = X(t)$ be a differentiable curve.

Let f be a function defined on some interval, such that the values of f lie in the domain of definition of the curve $X(t)$. Then we may form the composite curve $X \circ f$. If f is given as a function of a variable s, then we can write $X(f(s))$, for the value of the composite at s.

For example, let $X(t) = (t^2, e^t)$ and let $f(s) = \sin s$. Then

$$X(f(s)) = (\sin^2 s, e^{\sin s}).$$

Each component of $X(f(s))$ becomes a function of s, just as when we studied the chain rule for functions.

It is customary to keep the notation $\dot X$ to denote derivative with respect to t. Since we shall deal with other variables than t, we agree to use the prime $'$ to denote derivative. Thus if we have a differentiable curve

$$Y = Y(s) = (y_1(s), \ldots, y_n(s)),$$

then we shall write

$$Y'(s) = (y'_1(s), \ldots, y'_n(s))$$

for its derivative.

The chain rule asserts: *If X is a differentiable curve and f is a differentiable function defined on some interval, whose values are contained in the interval of definition of the curve, then the composite curve X ∘ f is differentiable, and*

$$(X \circ f)'(s) = X'(f(s))f'(s).$$

The expression on the right can also be written $f'(s)X'(f(s))$. It is the product of the function f' times the vector X'.

In another notation, if we let $t = f(s)$, then we can write the above formula in the form

$$\frac{dX}{ds} = \frac{dX}{dt}\frac{dt}{ds}.$$

The proof of the chain rule is trivial, using the chain rule for functions. Indeed, let $Y(s) = X(f(s))$. Then

$$Y(s) = (x_1(f(s)), \ldots, x_n(f(s))).$$

Taking the derivative term by term, we find:

$$Y'(s) = (x'_1(f(s))f'(s), \ldots, x'_n(f(s))f'(s)).$$

We can take $f'(s)$ outside the vector, and get

$$Y'(s) = X'(f(s))f'(s),$$

which is precisely what we want.

Let us now assume that all the functions with which we dealt above have second derivatives. Using the chain rule, and the rule for the derivative of a product, we obtain the following two formulas:

(1) $$Y'(s) = f'(s)X'(f(s))$$
(2) $$Y''(s) = f''(s)X'(f(s)) + (f'(s))^2 X''(f(s)).$$

Since $t = f(s)$, we can also write these in the form:

(1) $$Y'(s) = f'(s)\dot{X}(t)$$
(2) $$Y''(s) = f''(s)\dot{X}(t) + (f'(s))^2\ddot{X}(t).$$

We shall consider an important special case of these formulas. We have defined

$$v(t) = \|\dot{X}(t)\|$$

to be the speed. Let us now assume that each coordinate function of $\dot{X}(t)$

is continuous. In that case, we say that $\dot{X}(t)$ is *continuous*. Then $v(t)$ is a continuous function of t. We shall assume throughout that $v(t) \neq 0$ for any value of t in the interval of definition of our curve. Then $v(t) > 0$ for all such values of t. We let

$$s(t) = \int v(t)\, dt$$

be a fixed indefinite integral of $v(t)$ over our interval. (For instance, if a is a point of the interval, we could let

$$s(t) = \int_a^t v(u)\, du.$$

We know that any two indefinite integrals of v over the interval differ by a constant.) Then

$$\frac{ds}{dt} = v(t) > 0$$

for all values of t, and hence s is a strictly increasing function. Consequently, the inverse function exists. Call it

$$t = f(s).$$

We can then write

$$X(t) = X(f(s)) = Y(s).$$

Thus we are in the situation described above.

We shall now give geometric interpretations for our formulas (1) and (2).

To begin with, we know from the theory of derivatives of inverse functions that

$$f'(s) = \frac{df}{ds} = \left(\frac{ds}{dt}\right)^{-1}.$$

Hence $f'(s)$ is always positive. This means that in the present case, Y' and $\dot{X}$ have the same direction.

Furthermore,

$$\|Y'(s)\| = |f'(s)|\,\|\dot{X}(t)\| = \frac{df}{ds}\frac{ds}{dt}.$$

By what we just saw above, this last expression is equal to 1. Thus $Y'(s)$ is a vector of length 1, a unit vector, in the same direction as $\dot{X}(t)$. Thus the velocity vector of the curve Y has constant length!

In particular, we have $Y'(s)^2 = 1$. Differentiating with respect to s, we get

$$2Y' \cdot Y'' = 0.$$

Hence $Y'(s)$ is perpendicular to $Y''(s)$ for each value of s.

From (2), we see that the acceleration $Y''(s)$ has two components. First a tangential component

$$f''(s)\dot{X}(t)$$

in the direction of $\dot{X}(t)$, which involves the naive notion of scalar acceleration, namely the second derivative $f''(s)$. Second, another component in the direction of $\ddot{X}(t)$, with a coefficient

$$(f'(s))^2$$

which is positive. [We assume of course that $\ddot{X}(t) \neq O$.]

For a given value of t, let us assume that $\dot{X}(t) \neq O$, $\ddot{X}(t) \neq O$, and also that $\dot{X}(t)$, $\ddot{X}(t)$ do not have the same direction. In the theory of curves, the plane spanned by $\dot{X}(t)$ and $\ddot{X}(t)$ is called the *osculating plane to the curve at point* $X(t)$.

Example. Let $X(t) = (\sin t, \cos t, t)$. Find the osculating plane to this curve at $t = \pi/2$.

We have $\dot{X}(\pi/2) = (0, 1, 1)$ and $\ddot{X}(\pi/2) = (-1, 0, 0)$. If we let $N = (0, 1, -1)$, then N is perpendicular to $\dot{X}(\pi/2)$ and $\ddot{X}(\pi/2)$. Furthermore, let $P = X(\pi/2) = (1, 0, \pi/2)$. Then the osculating plane at P is the plane passing through P, perpendicular to N, and its equation is therefore $y - z = -\pi/2$.

EXERCISES

1. Prove formula (2) from formula (1).

2. Write a parametric equation of the tangent line to the given curve at the given point in each of the following cases.
   - (a) $(\cos 4t, \sin 4t, t)$ at the point $\pi/8$.
   - (b) $(t, 2t, t^2)$ at the point $(1, 2, 1)$.
   - (c) $(e^{3t}, e^{-3t}, 3\sqrt{2}\,t)$ at $t = 1$.
   - (d) (t, t^3, t^4) at the point $(1, 1, 1)$.

3. Find the length of the curves of Exercise 2 for the following intervals.
   - (a) $t = 0$ to $t = \pi/8$.   (b) $t = 1$ to $t = 3$.   (c) $t = 0$ to $t = \frac{1}{3}$.

4. Show that the two curves $(e^t, e^{2t}, 1 - e^{-t})$ and $(1 - \theta, \cos\theta, \sin\theta)$ intersect at the point $(1, 1, 0)$. What is the angle between their tangents at that point?

5. At what points does the curve $(2t^2, 1 - t, 3 + t^2)$ intersect the plane $3x - 14y + z - 10 = 0$?

6. Find the equation of the osculating plane of each of the curves of Exercise 2, at the given point.

7. Let $X(t)$ be a differentiable curve and suppose that $\dot{X}(t) = O$ for all t throughout an interval. What can you say about $X(t)$? Suppose $\dot{X}(t) \neq O$ but $\ddot{X}(t) = O$ throughout the interval. What can you say about $X(t)$?

CHAPTER III

Functions of Several Variables

We view functions of several variables as functions of points in space. This appeals to our geometric intuition, and also relates such functions more easily with the theory of vectors. The gradient will appear as a natural generalization of derivative. In this chapter we are mainly concerned with basic definitions and notions. We postpone the important theorems to the next chapter.

§1. Graphs and level curves

In order to conform with usual terminology, and for the sake of brevity, a collection of objects will simply be called a *set*. In this chapter, we are mostly concerned with sets of points in space.

Let S be a set of points in n-space. A *function* (defined on S) is a rule which to each element of S associates a number.

In practice, we sometimes omit mentioning explicitly the set S, since the context usually makes it clear for which points the function is defined.

Example 1. In 2-space (the plane) we can define a function f by the rule $f(x, y) = x^2 + y^2$. It is defined for all points (x, y) and can be interpreted geometrically as the square of the distance between the origin and the point.

Example 2. Again in 2-space, let

$$f(x, y) = \frac{x^2 - y^2}{x^2 + y^2}$$

be defined for all $(x, y) \neq (0, 0)$. We do not define f at $(0, 0)$ (also written O).

Example 3. In 3-space, we can define a function f by the rule

$$f(x, y, z) = x^2 - \sin(xyz) + yz^3.$$

Since a point and a vector are the same thing (namely an n-tuple), we can think of a function above also as a function of vectors. When we do not want to write the coordinates, we write $f(X)$ instead of $f(x_1, \ldots, x_n)$. As with numbers, we call $f(X)$ the *value* of f at the point (or vector) X.

Just as with functions of one variable, one can define the graph of a function f of n variables $x_1, \ldots, x_n$ to be the set of points in $(n + 1)$-space of the form

$$(x_1, \ldots, x_n, f(x_1, \ldots, x_n)),$$

the $(x_1, \ldots, x_n)$ being in the domain of definition of f. Thus when $n = 1$, the graph of a function f is a set of points $(x, f(x))$. When $n = 2$, the graph of a function f is the set of points $(x, y, f(x, y))$. When $n = 2$, it is already difficult to draw the graph since it involves a figure in 3-space. However, we shall describe another means of visualizing the function.

For each number c, the equation $f(x, y) = c$ is the equation of a curve in the plane. We have considerable experience in drawing the graphs of such curves, and we may therefore assume that we know how to draw this graph in principle. This curve is called the *level curve* of f at c. It gives us the set of points (x, y) where f takes on the value c. By drawing a number of such level curves, we can get a good description of the function.

In Example 1 above, the level curves are described by equations

$$x^2 + y^2 = c.$$

These have a solution only when $c \geqq 0$. In that case, they are circles (unless $c = 0$ in which case the circle of radius 0 is simply the origin). On Fig. 1, we have drawn the level curves for $c = 1$ and 4.

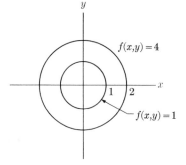

To find the level curves in Example 2, we have to determine the values (x, y) such that

$$x^2 - y^2 = c(x^2 + y^2)$$

for a given number c. This amounts to solving

$$x^2(1 - c) = y^2(1 + c).$$

FIGURE 1

If $x = 0$, then $f(0, y) = -1$. Thus on the vertical line passing through the origin, our function has the constant value -1. If $x \neq 0$, then we can divide by x in the above equality, and we obtain (for $c \neq -1$)

$$\frac{y^2}{x^2} = \frac{1 - c}{1 + c}.$$

Taking the square root, we obtain two level lines, namely

$$y = ax \quad \text{and} \quad y = -ax, \quad \text{where} \quad a = \sqrt{\frac{1 - c}{1 + c}}.$$

Thus the level curves are straight lines (excluding the origin). We have drawn some of them on Fig. 2. (The numbers indicate the value of the function on the corresponding line.)

It would of course be technically much more disagreeable to draw the level lines in Example 3, and we shall not do so.

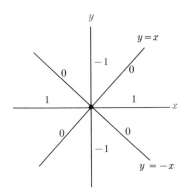

FIGURE 2

We see that the level lines are based on the same principle as the contour lines of a map. Each line describes so to speak the altitude of the function. If the graph is interpreted as a mountainous region, then each level curve gives the set of points of constant altitude. In Example 1, a person wanting to stay at a given altitude need but walk around in circles. In Example 2, such a person should walk on a straight line towards or away from the origin.

If we deal with a function of three variables, say $f(x, y, z)$, then $(x, y, z) = X$ is a point in 3-space. In that case, the set of points satisfying the equation

$$f(x, y, z) = c$$

for some constant c is a surface. The notion analogous to that of level curve is that of level surface.

In physics, a function f might be a potential function, giving the value of the potential energy at each point of space. The level surfaces are then sometimes called surfaces of *equipotential*. The function f might also give a temperature distribution (i.e. its value at a point X is the temperature at X). In that case, the level surfaces are called *isothermal* surfaces.

EXERCISES

Sketch the level lines for the following functions.

1. $x^2 + 2y^2$ 2. $y - x^2$ 3. $y - 3x^2$

4. $x - y^2$ 5. $3x^2 + 3y^2$ 6. xy

7. $(x - 1)(y - 2)$ 8. $(x + 1)(y + 3)$

9. $\dfrac{x^2}{4} + \dfrac{y^2}{16}$ 10. $2x - 3y$

11. $\dfrac{xy}{x^2 + y^2}$ 12. $\dfrac{xy^2}{x^2 + y^4}$

13. $\dfrac{4xy(x^2 - y^2)}{x^2 + y^2}$ (try polar coordinates)

14. $\dfrac{x + y}{x - y}$ 15. $\dfrac{x^2 + y^2}{x^2 - y^2}$

(In Exercises 11, 12, and 13, the function is not defined at $(0, 0)$. In 14, it is not defined for $y = x$, and in 15 it is not defined for $y = x$ or $y = -x$.)

16. $(x - 1)^2 + (y + 3)^2$ 17. $x^2 - y^2$

§2. *Partial derivatives*

In this section and the next, we discuss the notion of differentiability for functions of several variables. When we discussed the derivative of functions of one variable, we assumed that such a function was defined on an interval. We shall have to make a similar assumption in the case of several variables, and for this we need to introduce a new notion.

Let P be a point in n-space, and let a be a number > 0. The set of points X such that

$$\|X - P\| < a$$

will be called the *open ball* of radius a and center P. The set of points X such that

$$\|X - P\| \leqq a$$

will be called the *closed ball* of radius a and center P. The set of points X such that

$$\|X - P\| = a$$

will be called the *sphere* of radius a and center P.

Thus when $n = 1$, we are in 1-space, and the open ball of radius a is the open interval centered at P. The sphere of radius a and center P consists only of two points.

When $n = 2$, the open ball of radius a and center P is also called the open *disc*. The sphere is the *circle*.

When $n = 3$, then our terminology coincides with the obvious interpretation we might want to place on the words.

Let S_1 be the sphere of radius 1, centered at the origin. Let a be a number > 0. If X is a point of the sphere S_1, then aX is a point of the sphere of radius a, because

$$\|aX\| = a\|X\| = a.$$

In this manner, we get all points of the sphere of radius a. (Proof?) Thus the sphere of radius a is obtained by stretching the sphere of radius 1, through multiplication by a.

A similar remark applies to the open and closed balls of radius a, they being obtained from the open and closed balls of radius 1 through multiplication by a. (Prove this as an exercise.)

Let U be a set of points in n-space. We shall say that U is an *open set* in n-space if the following condition is satisfied: Given any point P in U, there exists an open ball B of radius $a > 0$ which is centered at P and such that B is contained in U.

Example 1. In the plane, the set consisting of the first quadrant, excluding the x- and y-axes, is an open set.

The x-axis is not open in the plane (i.e. in 2-space). Given a point on the x-axis, we cannot find an open disc centered at the point and contained in the x-axis.

On the other hand, if we view the x-axis as the set of points in 1-space, then it is open in 1-space. Similarly, the interval

$$-1 < x < 1$$

is open in 1-space, but not open in 2-space, or n-space for $n > 1$.

When we defined the derivative as a limit of

$$\frac{f(x + h) - f(x)}{h},$$

we needed the function f to be defined in some open interval around the point x.

Let now f be a function of n variables, defined on an open set U. Then for any point X in U, the function f is also defined at all points which are close to X, namely all points which are contained in an open ball centered at X and contained in U.

For small values of h, the point

$$(x_1 + h, x_2, \ldots, x_n)$$

is contained in such an open ball. Hence the function is defined at that point, and we may form the quotient

$$\frac{f(x_1 + h, x_2, \ldots, x_n) - f(x_1, \ldots, x_n)}{h}.$$

If the limit exists as h tends to 0, then we call it the *first partial derivative* of f and denote it by $D_1f(x_1, \ldots, x_n)$, or $D_1f(X)$, or also by

$$\frac{\partial f}{\partial x_1}.$$

Similarly, we let

$$D_i f(X) = \frac{\partial f}{\partial x_i} = \lim_{h \to 0} \frac{f(x_1, \ldots, x_i + h, \ldots, x_n) - f(x_1, \ldots, x_n)}{h}$$

if it exists, and call it the i-th partial derivative.

When $n = 2$ and we work with variables (x, y), then the first and second partials are also noted

$$\frac{\partial f}{\partial x} \quad \text{and} \quad \frac{\partial f}{\partial y}.$$

A partial derivative is therefore obtained by keeping all but one variable fixed, and taking the ordinary derivative with respect to this one variable.

Example 2. Let $f(x, y) = x^2 y^3$. Then

$$\frac{\partial f}{\partial x} = 2xy^3 \quad \text{and} \quad \frac{\partial f}{\partial y} = 3x^2 y^2.$$

We observe that when the partial derivatives are defined at all points where the function is defined, then they are themselves functions. This is the reason why the notation $D_i f$ is sometimes more useful than the notation $\partial f / \partial x_i$. It allows us to write $D_i f(P)$ for any point P in the set where the partial is defined. There cannot be any ambiguity or confusion with a (meaningless) symbol $D_i(f(P))$, since $f(P)$ is a number. Thus $D_i f(P)$ means $(D_i f)(P)$. It is the value of the function $D_i f$ at P.

Let f be defined in an open set U and assume that the partial derivatives of f exist at each point X of U. The *vector*

$$\left(\frac{\partial f}{\partial x_1}, \ldots, \frac{\partial f}{\partial x_n} \right) = (D_1 f(X), \ldots, D_n f(X)),$$

whose components are the partial derivatives, will be called the *gradient* of f at X and will be denoted by $\operatorname{grad} f(X)$. One must read this

$$(\operatorname{grad} f)(X),$$

but we shall usually omit the parentheses around $\operatorname{grad} f$.

In Example 2, we see that

$$\operatorname{grad} f(X) = \operatorname{grad} f(x, y) = (2xy^3, 3x^2 y^2).$$

Thus the gradient is a rule which to each point X associates a *vector*. This is a different kind of thing from a function, which is a rule associating a *number* to a point.

Using the formula for the derivative of a sum of two functions, and the derivative of a constant times a function, we conclude at once that the gradient satisfies the following properties:

THEOREM 1. *Let f, g be two functions defined on an open set U, and assume that their partial derivatives exist at every point of U. Let c be a number. Then*

$$\text{grad } (f + g) = \text{grad } f + \text{grad } g$$
$$\text{grad } (cf) = c \text{ grad } f.$$

You should carry out the details of the proof as an exercise.

We shall give later several geometric and physical interpretations for the gradient.

EXERCISES

Find the partial derivatives

$$\frac{\partial f}{\partial x}, \quad \frac{\partial f}{\partial y}, \quad \text{and} \quad \frac{\partial f}{\partial z},$$

for the following functions $f(x, y)$ or $f(x, y, z)$.

1. $xy + z$
2. $x^2 y^5 + 1$
3. $\sin (xy) + \cos z$
4. $\cos (xy)$
5. $\sin (xyz)$
6. e^{xyz}
7. $x^2 \sin (yz)$
8. xyz
9. $xz + yz + xy$
10. $x \cos (y - 3z) + \arcsin (xy)$
11. Find grad $f (P)$ if P is the point $(1, 2, 3)$ in Exercises 1, 2, 6, 8, and 9.
12. Find grad $f (P)$ if P is the point $(1, \pi, \pi)$ in Exercises 4, 5, 7.
13. Find grad $f (P)$ if $f(x, y, z) = \log (z + \sin (y^2 - x))$ and $P = (1, -1, 1)$.
14. Find the partial derivatives of x^y.

§3. *Differentiability and gradient*

Let f be a function defined on an open set U. Let X be a point of U. For all vectors H such that $\|H\|$ is small (and $H \neq O$), the point $X + H$ also lies in the open set. However we cannot form a quotient

$$\frac{f(X + H) - f(X)}{H}$$

because it is meaningless to divide by a vector. In order to define what we mean for a function f to be differentiable, we must therefore find a way which does not involve dividing by H.

We reconsider the case of functions of one variable. We had defined the derivative to be

$$f'(x) = \lim_{h \to 0} \frac{f(x + h) - f(x)}{h}.$$

Let

$$g(x, h) = \frac{f(x + h) - f(x)}{h} - f'(x).$$

Then $g(x, h)$ is not defined when $h = 0$, but for each value of x,

$$\lim_{h \to 0} g(x, h) = 0.$$

We can write

$$f(x + h) - f(x) = f'(x)h + hg(x, h).$$

This relation has meaning so far only when $h \neq 0$. However, we observe that if we define $g(x, 0)$ to be 0, then the preceding relation is obviously true when $h = 0$ (because we just get $0 = 0$).

Furthermore, we can replace h by $-h$ if we replace g by $-g$. Thus we have shown that if f is differentiable, there exists a function $g(x, h)$ such that

(1) $$f(x + h) - f(x) = f'(x)h + |h| \, g(x, h)$$

and such that

$$\lim_{h \to 0} g(x, h) = 0.$$

Conversely, suppose that there exists a function $\varphi(x)$ and a function $g(x, h)$ such that

(1a) $$\lim_{h \to 0} g(x, h) = 0,$$

and

$$f(x + h) - f(x) = \varphi(x)h + |h| \, g(x, h).$$

We find for $h \neq 0$,

$$\frac{f(x + h) - f(x)}{h} = \varphi(x) + \frac{|h|}{h} \, g(x, h).$$

Taking the limit as h approaches 0, we observe that

$$\lim_{h \to 0} \frac{|h|}{h} \, g(x, h) = 0.$$

Hence the limit of the Newton quotient exists and is equal to $\varphi(x)$. Hence f is differentiable, and its derivative $f'(x)$ is equal to $\varphi(x)$.

Therefore, the existence of functions $\varphi(x)$ and $g(x, h)$ satisfying (1a) above could have been used as the definition of differentiability in the case of functions of one variable. The great advantage of (1) is that no h appears in the denominator. It is this relation which will suggest to us how to define differentiability for functions of several variables, and how to prove the chain rule for them.

We now consider a function of n variables.

Let f be a function defined on an open set U. Let X be a point of U. If $H = (h_1, \ldots, h_n)$ is a vector such that $\|H\|$ is small enough, then

$X + H$ will also be a point of U and so $f(X + H)$ is defined. Note that

$$X + H = (x_1 + h_1, \ldots, x_n + h_n).$$

This is the generalization of the $x + h$ with which we dealt previously.

The point $X + H$ is close to X and we are interested in the difference $f(X + H) - f(X)$, which is the difference of the value of the function at $X + H$ and the value of the function at X.

We say that f is *differentiable* at X if the partial derivatives $D_1 f(X), \ldots, D_n f(X)$ exist, and if there exists a function $g(X, H)$ (defined for small H) such that

$$\lim_{H \to 0} g(X, H) = 0 \qquad (\text{also written } \lim_{\|H\| \to 0} g(X, H) = 0)$$

and

$$f(X + H) - f(X) = D_1 f(X) h_1 + \cdots + D_n f(X) h_n + \|H\| g(X, H).$$

With the other notation for partial derivatives, this last relation reads:

$$f(X + H) - f(X) = \frac{\partial f}{\partial x_1} h_1 + \cdots + \frac{\partial f}{\partial x_n} h_n + \|H\| g(X, H).$$

We say that f is *differentiable* in the open set U if it is differentiable at every point of U, so that the above relation holds for every point X in U.

In view of the definition of the gradient in §2, we can rewrite our fundamental relation in the form

$$(2) \qquad f(X + H) - f(X) = (\operatorname{grad} f(X)) \cdot H + \|H\| g(X, H).$$

The term $\|H\| g(X, H)$ has an order of magnitude smaller than the previous term involving the dot product. This is one advantage of the present notation. We know how to handle the formalism of dot products and are accustomed to it, and its geometric interpretation. This will help us later in interpreting the gradient geometrically.

For the moment, we observe that the gradient is the only vector which will make formula (2) valid (cf. Exercise 7).

Formula (2) is the one which is used throughout the applications of differentiability. It is therefore important to know when a function is differentiable. The next theorem will give us a criterion which can be used in practice.

Let g be a function. We shall say that g is *continuous* if for every point X such that $g(X)$ is defined, we have

$$\lim_{Q \to X} g(Q) = g(X).$$

In other words, as Q approaches X, $g(Q)$ must approach $g(X)$.

THEOREM 2. *Let f be a function defined on some open set U. Assume that its partial derivatives exist for every point in this open set, and that they are continuous. Then f is differentiable.*

Proof. For simplicity of notation, we shall use two variables. Thus we deal with a function $f(x, y)$. We let $H = (h, k)$. Let (x, y) be a point in U, and take H small, $H \neq (0, 0)$. We have to consider the difference $f(X + H) - f(X)$, which is simply

$$f(x + h, y + k) - f(x, y).$$

This is equal to

$$f(x + h, y + k) - f(x, y + k) + f(x, y + k) - f(x, y).$$

Applying the mean value theorem for functions of *one* variable, and applying the definition of partial derivatives, we see that there is a number s between x and $x + h$ such that

$$(3) \qquad f(x + h, y + k) - f(x, y + k) = D_1f(s, y + k)h.$$

Similarly, there is a number t between y and $y + k$ such that

$$(4) \qquad f(x, y + k) - f(x, y) = D_2f(x, t)k.$$

We shall now analyse the expressions on the right-hand side of equations (3) and (4).
　　Let

$$g_1(X, H) = D_1f(s, y + k) - D_1f(x, y).$$

As H approaches O, $(s, y + k)$ approaches (x, y) because s is between x and $x + h$. Since D_1f is continuous, it follows that

$$\lim_{H \to O} g_1(X, H) = 0.$$

But

$$D_1f(s, y + k) = D_1f(x, y) + g_1(X, H).$$

Hence equation (3) can be rewritten as

$$(5) \qquad f(x + h, y + k) - f(x, y + k) = D_1f(x, y)h + hg_1(X, H).$$

By a similar argument, we can rewrite equation (4) in the form

$$(6) \qquad f(x, y + k) - f(x, y) = D_2f(x, y)k + kg_2(X, H)$$

with some function $g_2(X, H)$ such that

$$\lim_{H \to O} g_2(X, H) = 0.$$

If we add (5) and (6), we obtain

$$(7) \quad f(X + H) - f(X) = D_1 f(X)h + D_2 f(X)k + hg_1(X, H) + kg_2(X, H).$$

To prove our theorem it will therefore suffice to prove that these last two terms can be put in the form indicated in the statement of the theorem.

We observe that

$$\frac{h}{\sqrt{h^2 + k^2}} = \frac{h}{\|H\|} \quad \text{and} \quad \frac{k}{\sqrt{h^2 + k^2}} = \frac{k}{\|H\|}$$

have absolute value ≤ 1. We therefore multiply and divide the last two terms by $\|H\|$ and bring them in the form:

$$\|H\| \left[\frac{h}{\|H\|} g_1(X, H) + \frac{k}{\|H\|} g_2(X, H) \right].$$

We let

$$g(X, H) = \frac{h}{\|H\|} g_1(X, H) + \frac{k}{\|H\|} g_2(X, H).$$

Then

$$\lim_{H \to O} g(X, H) = 0,$$

and we see that the right-hand side of (7) is now in the form

$$D_1 f(X)h + D_2 f(X)k + \|H\|g(X, H),$$

which proves our theorem.

Remark. If we dealt with n variables, then we would consider the expression for $f(X + H) - f(X)$ given by

$$f(x_1 + h_1, \ldots, x_n + h_n) - f(x_1, x_2 + h_2, \ldots, x_n + h_n)$$
$$+ f(x_1, x_2 + h_2, \ldots, x_n + h_n) - f(x_1, x_2, \ldots, x_n + h_n)$$
$$\vdots$$
$$+ f(x_1, \ldots, x_{n-1}, x_n + h_n) - f(x_1, \ldots, x_n).$$

We would then apply the mean value theorem at each step, take the sum, and argue in essentially the same way as with two variables.

EXERCISES

1. Show that $h^2 + k^2 \leq 2\|H\|^2$ if $H = (h, k)$.
2. Show that
$$|h^2 + 3hk| \leq 4\|H\|^2.$$
3. Show that
$$|h^3 + h^2k + k^3| \leq 3\|H\|^3.$$

4. If $\|H\| \leq 1$, show that

$$|h^2 + k^3 + k^2| \leq 3\|H\|^2.$$

5. Show that

$$|(h + k)^4| \leq 16\|H\|^4.$$

6. Let

$$g(h, k) = \frac{h^2 - k^2}{h^2 + k^2}$$

be defined for $(h, k) \neq (0, 0)$. Find

$$\lim_{h \to 0} g(h, k), \qquad \lim_{k \to 0} \left[\lim_{h \to 0} g(h, k) \right]$$

$$\lim_{k \to 0} g(h, k), \qquad \lim_{h \to 0} \left[\lim_{k \to 0} g(h, k) \right].$$

7. Let f be defined on an open set U. Let P be a point of U. Assume that there are two vectors A, B and two functions $g_1(H)$, $g_2(H)$ such that

$$\lim_{H \to O} g_1(H) = 0 \qquad \text{and} \qquad \lim_{H \to O} g_2(H) = 0,$$

and such that

$$f(P + H) - f(P) = A \cdot H + \|H\|g_1(H)$$
$$= B \cdot H + \|H\|g_2(H).$$

Show that $A = B$. [*Hint:* Subtract, and let $H = tK$ for any K, $t \to 0$.]

8. Let the assumptions be as in Exercise 7. Show that all partial derivatives of f exist at P, and that $A = \text{grad } f(P)$. [*Hint:* Take H to be hE_i, with a unit vector E_i.]

9. Let $g(H) = g(h_1, \ldots, h_n)$ be a polynomial, i.e. an expression of the form

$$g(H) = \sum c_{i_1 \ldots i_n} h_1^{i_1} \cdots h_n^{i_n},$$

where $c_{i_1 \ldots i_n}$ are numbers, and the sum is taken over a finite number of n-tuples $(i_1, \ldots, i_n)$ of integers ≥ 0. We call $c_{i_1 \ldots i_n}$ the *coefficients* of g, and abbreviate them by $c_{(i)}$. Assume that $g(O) = 0$, and that s is an integer > 0 such that $i_1 + \cdots + i_n \geq s$ for all (i). Show that for any H with $\|H\| \leq 1$ we have

$$|g(H)| \leq NM\|H\|^s,$$

if N is the number of terms in the sum expressing g, and M is a number such that $|c_{(i)}| \leq M$ for all (i).

10. Read the part of Appendix 2 concerning $o(H)$, and do the suggested exercises.

CHAPTER IV

The Chain Rule and the Gradient

In this chapter, we prove the chain rule for functions of several variables and give a number of applications. Among them will be several interpretations for the gradient. These form one of the central points of our theory. They show how powerful the tools we have accumulated turn out to be.

§1. The chain rule

Let f be a function defined on some open set U. Let $X(t)$ be a curve such that the values $X(t)$ are contained in U. Then we can form $f(X(t))$, which is a function of t.

As an example, take $f(x, y) = e^x \sin (xy)$. Let $X(t) = (t^2, t^3)$. Then

$$f(X(t)) = e^{t^2} \sin (t^5).$$

This is a function of t in the old sense of functions of one variable.

The chain rule tells us how to find the derivative of this function, provided we know the gradient of f and the derivative $\dot{X}$. Its statement is as follows.

Let f be a function which is defined and differentiable on an open set U. Let $X(t)$ be a differentiable curve (defined for some interval of numbers t) such that the values $X(t)$ lie in the open set U. Then the function

$$f(X(t))$$

is differentiable (as a function of t), and

$$\frac{df(X(t))}{dt} = (\operatorname{grad} f\,(X(t)) \cdot \dot{X}(t).$$

In the notation dX/dt, this also reads

$$\frac{df(X(t))}{dt} = \operatorname{grad} f\,(X(t)) \cdot \frac{dX}{dt}.$$

Proof. By definition, we must investigate the quotient

$$\frac{f(X(t + h)) - f(X(t))}{h}.$$

Let

$$K = K(t, h) = X(t + h) - X(t).$$

40

Then our quotient can be rewritten in the form

$$\frac{f(X(t) + K) - f(X(t))}{h}.$$

Using the definition of differentiability for f, we have

$$f(X + K) - f(X) = \operatorname{grad} f(X) \cdot K + \|K\| g(X, K)$$

and

$$\lim_{\|K\| \to 0} g(X, K) = 0.$$

Replacing K by what it stands for, namely $X(t + h) - X(t)$, and dividing by h, we obtain:

$$\frac{f(X(t + h)) - f(X(t))}{h} = \operatorname{grad} f(X(t)) \cdot \frac{X(t + h) - X(t)}{h}$$
$$\pm \left\| \frac{X(t + h) - X(t)}{h} \right\| g(X, K).$$

As h approaches 0, the first term of the sum approaches what we want, namely

$$\operatorname{grad} f(X(t)) \cdot \dot{X}(t).$$

The second term approaches

$$\pm \|\dot{X}(t)\| \lim_{h \to 0} g(X, K),$$

and when h approaches 0, so does $K = X(t + h) - X(t)$. Hence the second term of the sum approaches 0. This proves our chain rule.

Let us write out in full the chain rule in terms of components. For simplicity, we do it in two variables (x, y). Then

$$\frac{df(X(t))}{dt} = \frac{\partial f}{\partial x} \frac{dx}{dt} + \frac{\partial f}{\partial y} \frac{dy}{dt}.$$

This can be applied to the seemingly more general situation when x, y are functions of more than one variable t. Suppose for instance that

$$x = \varphi(t, u) \qquad \text{and} \qquad y = \psi(t, u)$$

are differentiable functions of two variables. Let

$$g(t, u) = f(\varphi(t, u), \psi(t, u)).$$

If we keep u fixed and take the partial derivative of g with respect to t, then we can apply our chain rule, and obtain

$$\frac{\partial g}{\partial t} = \frac{\partial f}{\partial x} \frac{\partial x}{\partial t} + \frac{\partial f}{\partial y} \frac{\partial y}{\partial t}.$$

Example 1. Let $f(x, y) = x^2 + 2xy$. Let $x = r \cos \theta$ and $y = r \sin \theta$. Let $g(r, \theta)$ be the composite function. Find $\partial g/\partial \theta$.

We have

$$\frac{\partial x}{\partial \theta} = -r \sin \theta \quad \text{and} \quad \frac{\partial y}{\partial \theta} = r \cos \theta.$$

Hence

$$\frac{\partial g}{\partial \theta} = (2x + 2y)(-r \sin \theta) + 2x(r \cos \theta).$$

If you want the answer completely in terms of r, θ, you can substitute $r \cos \theta$ and $r \sin \theta$ for x and y respectively in this expression.

EXERCISES

(All functions are assumed to be differentiable as needed.)

1. If $x = u(r, s, t)$ and $y = v(r, s, t)$ and $z = f(x, y)$, write out the formula for

$$\frac{\partial z}{\partial r} \quad \text{and} \quad \frac{\partial z}{\partial t}.$$

2. Find the partial derivatives with respect to x, y, s, and t for the following functions.

(a) $f(x, y, z) = x^3 + 3xyz - y^2z$, $x = 2t + s$, $y = -t - s$, $z = t^2 + s^2$
(b) $f(x, y) = (x + y)/(1 - xy)$, $x = \sin 2t$, $y = \cos (3t - s)$.

3. Let $f(x, y, z) = (x^2 + y^2 + z^2)^{1/2}$. Find $\partial f/\partial x$ and $\partial f/\partial y$.

4. Let $r = (x_1^2 + \cdots + x_n^2)^{1/2}$. What is $\partial r/\partial x_i$?

5. If $u = f(x - y, y - x)$, show that

$$\frac{\partial u}{\partial x} + \frac{\partial u}{\partial y} = 0.$$

6. If $u = x^3 f(y/x, z/x)$, show that

$$x \frac{\partial u}{\partial x} + y \frac{\partial u}{\partial y} + z \frac{\partial u}{\partial z} = 3u.$$

7. Let $x = r \cos \theta$ and $y = r \sin \theta$. Let $f(x, y) = g(r, \theta)$. Show that

$$\left(\frac{\partial g}{\partial r}\right)^2 + \frac{1}{r^2} \left(\frac{\partial g}{\partial \theta}\right)^2 = \left(\frac{\partial f}{\partial x}\right)^2 + \left(\frac{\partial f}{\partial y}\right)^2.$$

8. Let g be a function of r, let $r = \|X\|$, and $X = (x, y, z)$. Let $f(X) = g(r)$. Show that

$$\left(\frac{dg}{dr}\right)^2 = \left(\frac{\partial f}{\partial x}\right)^2 + \left(\frac{\partial f}{\partial y}\right)^2 + \left(\frac{\partial f}{\partial z}\right)^2.$$

9. Let g be a function of r, and $r = \|X\|$. Let $f(X) = g(r)$. Find $\operatorname{grad} f(X)$ for the following functions.

(a) $g(r) = 1/r$

(b) $g(r) = r^2$

(c) $g(r) = 1/r^3$

(d) $g(r) = e^{-r^2}$

(e) $g(r) = \log \dfrac{1}{r}$

(f) $g(r) = 4/r^m$ (m integer $\neq 1$.)

10. Let $x = u \cos \theta - v \sin \theta$, and $y = u \sin \theta + v \cos \theta$, with θ equal to a constant. Let $f(x, y) = g(u, v)$. Show that

$$\left(\frac{\partial g}{\partial u}\right)^2 + \left(\frac{\partial g}{\partial v}\right)^2 = \left(\frac{\partial f}{\partial x}\right)^2 + \left(\frac{\partial f}{\partial y}\right)^2.$$

11. Let f be a differentiable function (in two variables) such that $\operatorname{grad} f(X) = cX$ for some constant c and all X in 2-space. Show that f is constant on any circle of radius $a > 0$. [*Hint:* Put $x = a \cos t$ and $y = a \sin t$ and find df/dt.]

12. Generalize to the case of n variables. [You may a sume that any two points on the sphere of radius a are connected by a differentiable curve $X(t)$.]

13. Let $r = \|X\|$. Let g be a differentiable function of one variable whose derivative is never equal to 0. Let $f(X) = g(r)$. Show that $\operatorname{grad} f(X)$ is parallel to X for $X \neq O$.

14. Let f be a function which is differentiable at all points $X \neq O$ in n-space. Assume that there exists an integer $m \geq 1$ such that $f(tX) = t^m f(X)$ for all numbers $t \neq 0$ and all points $X \neq O$. Prove Euler's relation:

$$x_1 \frac{\partial f}{\partial x_1} + \cdots + x_n \frac{\partial f}{\partial x_n} = mf(X),$$

which can also be written $X \cdot \operatorname{grad} f(X) = mf(X)$.

15. Reconsider Exercise 6 in the light of Exercise 14. Generalize.

§2. *Tangent plane*

Let f be a differentiable function and c a number. The set of points X such that $f(X) = c$ and $\operatorname{grad} f(X) \neq O$ is called a *surface*.

Let $X(t)$ be a differentiable curve. We shall say that the curve *lies on* the surface if, for all t, we have

$$f(X(t)) = c.$$

This simply means that all the points of the curve satisfy the equation of the surface. If we differentiate this relation, we get from the chain rule:

$$\operatorname{grad} f(X(t)) \cdot \dot{X}(t) = 0.$$

Let P be a point of the surface, and let $X(t)$ be a curve on the surface passing through P. This means that there is a number t_0 such that

$X(t_0) = P$. For this value t_0, we obtain

$$\text{grad} f (P) \cdot \dot{X}(t_0) = 0.$$

Thus the gradient of f at P is perpendicular to the tangent vector of the curve at P. [We assume that $\dot{X}(t_0) \neq 0$.] This is true for *any* differentiable curve passing through P. It is therefore very reasonable to *define* the *plane* (or hyperplane) *tangent* to the surface at P to be the plane passing through P and perpendicular to the vector grad f (P). (We know from Chapter I how to find such planes.) This definition applies only when grad f $(P) \neq 0$. If grad f $(P) = 0$, then we do not define the notion of tangent plane.

The fact that grad f (P) is perpendicular to every curve passing through P on the surface also gives us an interpretation of the gradient as being perpendicular to the surface

$$f(X) = c$$

(which is one of the level surfaces for the function f).

Example 1. Find the tangent plane to the surface

$$x^2 + y^2 + z^2 = 3$$

at the point $(1, 1, 1)$.

Let $f(X) = x^2 + y^2 + z^2$. Then at the point $P = (1, 1, 1)$,

$$\text{grad} f (P) = (2, 2, 2).$$

The equation of a plane passing through P and perpendicular to a vector N is

$$X \cdot N = P \cdot N.$$

In the present case, this yields

$$2x + 2y + 2z = 2 + 2 + 2 = 6.$$

Observe that our arguments also give us a means of finding a vector perpendicular to a curve in 2-space at a given point, simply by applying the preceding discussion to the plane instead of 3-space.

Example 2. Find the tangent line to the curve

$$x^2 y + y^3 = 10$$

at the point $(1, 2)$, and find a vector perpendicular to the curve at that point.

Let $f(x, y) = x^2 y + y^3$. The gradient at the given point P is easily computed, and we find

$$\text{grad} f (P) = (4, 13).$$

This is a vector perpendicular to the curve at the given point. The tangent line is also given by $X \cdot N = P \cdot N$, and thus is

$$4x + 13y = 4 + 26 = 30.$$

EXERCISES

1. Find the equation of the tangent plane and normal line to each of the following surfaces at the specific point.

(a) $x^2 + y^2 + z^2 = 49$ at $(6, 2, 3)$
(b) $xy + yz + zx - 1 = 0$ at $(1, 1, 0)$
(c) $x^2 + xy^2 + y^3 + z + 1 = 0$ at $(2, -3, 4)$
(d) $2y - z^3 - 3xz = 0$ at $(1, 7, 2)$
(e) $x^2y^2 + xz - 2y^3 = 10$ at $(2, 1, 4)$
(f) $\sin xy + \sin yz + \sin xz = 1$ at $(1, \pi/2, 0)$

2. Let $f(x, y, z) = z - e^x \sin y$, and $P = (\log 3, 3\pi/2, -3)$. Find:

(a) $\operatorname{grad} f(P)$,
(b) the normal line at P to the level surface for f which passes through P,
(c) the tangent plane to this surface at P.

3. Find the parametric equation of the tangent line to the curve of intersection of the following surfaces at the indicated point.

(a) $x^2 + y^2 + z^2 = 49$ and $x^2 + y^2 = 13$ at $(3, 2, -6)$
(b) $xy + z = 0$ and $x^2 + y^2 + z^2 = 9$ at $(2, 1, -2)$
(c) $x^2 - y^2 - z^2 = 1$ and $x^2 - y^2 + z^2 = 9$ at $(3, 2, 2)$

[*Note.* The tangent line above may be defined to be the line of intersection of the tangent planes of the given point.]

4. Let $f(X) = 0$ be a differentiable surface. Let Q be a point which does not lie on the surface. Given a differentiable curve $X(t)$ on the surface, defined on an open interval, give the formula for the distance between Q and a point $X(t)$. Assume that this distance reaches a minimum for $t = t_0$. Let $P = X(t_0)$. Show that the line joining Q to P is perpendicular to the curve at P.

§3. *Directional derivative*

Let f be defined on an open set and assume that f is differentiable. Let P be a point of the open set, and let A be a unit vector (i.e. $\|A\| = 1$). Then $P + tA$ is the parametric equation of a straight line in the direction of A and passing through P. We observe that

$$\frac{d(P + tA)}{dt} = A.$$

Hence by the chain rule, if we take the derivative of the function

$f(P + tA)$, which is defined for small values of t, we obtain

$$\frac{df(P + tA)}{dt} = \operatorname{grad} f\,(P + tA) \cdot A.$$

When t is equal to 0, this derivative is equal to

$$\operatorname{grad} f\,(P) \cdot A.$$

For obvious geometrical reasons, we call it the *directional derivative* of f in the direction of A. We interpret it as the rate of change of f along the straight line in the direction of A, at the point P.

Example. Let $f(x, y) = x^2 + y^3$ and let $B = (1, 2)$. Find the directional derivative of f in the direction of B, at the point $(-1, 3)$.

We note that B is not a unit vector. Its length is $\sqrt{5}$. Let

$$A = \frac{1}{\sqrt{5}}\,B.$$

Then A is a unit vector having the same direction as B. Let $P = (-1, 3)$. Then $\operatorname{grad} f\,(P) = (-2, 27)$. Hence by our formula, the directional derivative is equal to:

$$\operatorname{grad} f\,(P) \cdot A = \frac{1}{\sqrt{5}}\,(-2 + 54) = \frac{52}{\sqrt{5}}.$$

Consider again a differentiable function f on an open set U.

Let P be a point of U. *Let us assume that* $\operatorname{grad} f\,(P) \neq O$, and let A be a unit vector. We know that

$$\operatorname{grad} f\,(P) \cdot A = \|\operatorname{grad} f\,(P)\|\,\|A\|\,\cos\theta,$$

where θ is the angle between $\operatorname{grad} f\,(P)$ and A. Since $\|A\| = 1$, we see that the directional derivative is equal to

$$\|\operatorname{grad} f\,(P)\|\,\cos\theta.$$

The value of $\cos\theta$ varies between -1 and $+1$ when we select all possible unit vectors A.

The maximal value of $\cos\theta$ is obtained when we select A such that $\theta = 0$, i.e. when we select A to have the same direction as $\operatorname{grad} f\,(P)$. In that case, the directional derivative is equal to the length of the gradient [cf. Exercise 10 of Chapter I, §4].

Thus we have obtained another interpretation for the gradient: *Its direction is that of maximal increase of the function, and its length is the rate of increase of the function in that direction.*

The directional derivative in the direction of A is a minimum when $\cos \theta = -1$. This is the case when we select A to have opposite direction to grad $f(P)$. That direction is therefore the direction of maximal decrease of the function.

For example, f might represent a temperature distribution in space. At any point P, a particle which feels cold and wants to become warmer fastest should move in the direction of grad $f(P)$. Another particle which is warm and wants to cool down fastest should move in the direction of $-$grad $f(P)$.

EXERCISES

1. In Exercise 2 of the preceding section, find:
   (a) The directional derivative of f at P in the direction of $(1, 2, 2)$.
   (b) The maximum and minimum values for the directional derivatives of f at P.

2. Find the directional derivatives of the following functions at the specified points in the specified directions.
   (a) $\log (x^2 + y^2)^{1/2}$ at $(1, 1)$, direction $(2, 1)$.
   (b) $xy + yz + zx$ at $(-1, 1, 7)$, direction $(3, 4, -12)$.
   (c) $4x^2 + 9y^2$ at $(2, 1)$ in the direction of maximum directional derivative.

3. A temperature distribution in space is given by the function $f(x, y) = 10 + 6 \cos x \cos y + 3 \cos 2x + 4 \cos 3y$. At the point $(\pi/3, \pi/3)$, find the direction of greatest increase of temperature, and the direction of greatest decrease of temperature.

4. In what direction are the following functions of X increasing most rapidly at the given point?
   (a) $x/\|X\|^{3/2}$ at $(1, -1, 2)$ $(X = (x, y, z))$
   (b) $\|X\|^5$ at $(1, 2, -1, 1)$ $(X = (x, y, z, w))$

§4. *Conservation law*

As a final application of the chain rule, we derive the conservation law of physics.

Let U be an open set. By a *vector field* on U we mean a rule which to every point of U associates a vector of the same dimension.

If f is a differentiable function on U, then we observe that grad f is a vector field, which associates the vector grad $f(P)$ to the point P of U.

A vector field in physics is often interpreted as a field of forces.

If F is a vector field on U, and X a point of U, then we denote by $F(X)$ the vector associated to X by F and call it the value of F at X, as usual.

If F is a vector field, and if there exists a differentiable function f such that $F = \text{grad } f$, then the vector field is called *conservative*. Since

$-\operatorname{grad} f = \operatorname{grad} (-f)$, it does not matter whether we use f or $-f$ in the definition of conservative.

Let us assume that F is a conservative field on u, and let Φ be a differentiable function such that for all points X in u we have

$$F(X) = -\operatorname{grad} \Phi.$$

In physics, one interprets Φ as a potential function. Suppose that a particle of mass m moves along a differentiable curve $X(t)$ in u, and let us assume that this particle obeys Newton's law:

$$F(X) = m\ddot{X}, \quad \text{i.e.} \quad F\big(x(t)\big) = m\ddot{X}(t)$$

for all t where $X(t)$ is defined. Then according to our hypotheses,

$$m\ddot{X} + \operatorname{grad} \Phi (X) = 0.$$

Take the dot product of both sides with $\dot{X}$. We obtain

$$m\dot{X} \cdot \ddot{X} + \operatorname{grad} \Phi (X) \cdot \dot{X} = 0.$$

But the derivative (with respect to t) of $\dot{X}^2$ is $2\dot{X} \cdot \ddot{X}$. The derivative with respect to t of $\Phi\big(X(t)\big)$ is equal to

$$\operatorname{grad} \Phi (X) \cdot \dot{X}$$

by the chain rule. Hence the expression on the left of our last equation is the derivative of the *function*

$$\tfrac{1}{2}m\dot{X}^2 + \Phi(X),$$

and that derivative is 0. Hence this function is equal to a constant. This is what one means by the conservation law.

The function $\tfrac{1}{2}m\dot{X}^2$ is called the *kinetic energy*, and the conservation law states that the sum of the kinetic and potential energies is constant.

It is not true that all vector fields are conservative. We shall discuss the problem of determining which ones are conservative in the next section.

The fields of classical physics are for the most part conservative. For instance, consider a force which is inversely proportional to the square of the distance from the point to the origin, and in the direction of the position vector. Then there is a constant C such that for $X \neq O$ we have

$$F(X) = C \, \frac{1}{\|X\|^2} \, \frac{X}{\|X\|},$$

because $\dfrac{X}{\|X\|}$ is a unit vector in the direction of X. Thus

$$F(X) = C \frac{1}{r^3} X,$$

where $r = \|X\|$. A potential function for F is given by

$$-\frac{C}{r}.$$

Exercises

1. Find a potential function for a force field which is inversely proportional to the distance from the point to the origin, and is in the direction of the position vector.

2. Same question, replacing "distance" with "cube of the distance".

CHAPTER V

Potential Functions and Line Integrals

We are going to deal systematically with the possibility of finding a potential function for a vector field. The discussion of the existence of such a function will be limited to the case of two variables. Actually, there is no essential difficulty in extending the results to arbitrary n-space but we leave this to the reader.

The problem is one of integration, and the line integrals are a natural continuation of the integrals at the end of §1 (taken on vertical and horizontal lines).

§1. Potential functions

Let F be a vector field on an open set U. If φ is a differentiable function on U such that $F = \operatorname{grad} \varphi$, then we say that φ is a *potential function* for F.

One can raise two questions about potential functions. Are they unique, and do they exist?

We consider the first question, and we shall be able to give a satisfactory answer to it. The problem is analogous to determining an integral for a function of one variable, up to a constant, and we shall formulate and prove the analogous statement in the present situation.

We recall that even in the case of functions of one variable, it is *not* true that whenever two functions f, g are such that

$$\frac{df}{dx} = \frac{dg}{dx},$$

then f and g differ by a constant, unless we assume that f, g are defined on some interval. As we emphasized in the *First Course*, we could for instance take

$$f(x) = \begin{cases} \dfrac{1}{x} + 5 & \text{if } x < 0, \\[2mm] \dfrac{1}{x} - \pi & \text{if } x > 0, \end{cases}$$

$$g(x) = \frac{1}{x} \quad \text{if } x \neq 0.$$

50

Then f, g have the same derivative, but there is no constant C such that for all $x \neq 0$ we have $f(x) = g(x) + C$.

In the case of functions of several variables, we shall have to make a similar restriction on the domain of definition of the functions.

Let U be an open set and let P, Q be two points of U. We shall say that P, Q can be joined by a *differentiable curve* if there exists a differentiable curve $X(t)$ (with t ranging over some interval of numbers) which is contained in U, and two values of t, say t_1 and t_2 in that interval, such that

$$X(t_1) = P \quad \text{and} \quad X(t_2) = Q.$$

For example, if U is the entire plane, then any two points can be joined by a straight line. In fact, if P, Q are two points, then we take

$$X(t) = P + t(Q - P).$$

When $t = 0$, then $X(0) = P$. When $t = 1$, then $X(1) = Q$.

It is not always the case that two points of an open set can be joined by a straight line. We have drawn a picture of two points P, Q in an open set U which cannot be so joined.

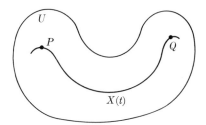

We are now in position to state the theorem we had in mind.

THEOREM 1. *Let U be an open set, and assume that any two points in U can be joined by a differentiable curve. Let f, g be two differentiable functions on U. If* grad $f(X)$ = grad $g(X)$ *for every point X of U, then there exists a constant C such that*

$$f(X) = g(X) + C$$

for all points X of U.

Proof. We note that grad $(f - g)$ = grad f − grad g = O, and we must prove that $f - g$ is constant. Letting $\varphi = f - g$, we see that it suffices to prove: If grad $\varphi(X) = O$ for every point X of U, then φ is constant.

Let P be a fixed point of U and let Q be any other point. Let $X(t)$ be a differentiable curve joining P to Q, which is contained in U, and defined over an interval. The derivative of the function $\varphi(X(t))$ is, by the chain rule,

$$\text{grad } \varphi \, (X(t)) \cdot \dot{X}(t).$$

But $X(t)$ is a point of U for all values of t in the interval. Hence by our assumption, the derivative of $\varphi(X(t))$ is 0 for all t in the interval. Hence there is a constant C such that

$$\varphi(X(t)) = C$$

for all t in the interval. In other words, the function φ is constant on the curve. Hence $\varphi(P) = \varphi(Q)$.

This result is true for any point Q of U. Hence φ is constant on U, as was to be shown.

Our theorem proves the uniqueness of potential functions (within the restrictions placed by our extra hypothesis on the open set U).

We still have the problem of determining when a vector field F admits a potential function.

A complete discussion of this problem would lead us too far afield. We shall limit ourselves to some useful practical remarks in the case of functions of two variables.

Let F be a vector field (in 2-space), so that we can write

$$F(x, y) = (f(x, y), g(x, y))$$

with functions f and g, defined over a suitable open set. We want to know when there exists a function $\varphi(x, y)$ such that

$$\frac{\partial \varphi}{\partial x} = f \quad \text{and} \quad \frac{\partial \varphi}{\partial y} = g.$$

Such a function would be a potential function for F, by definition. (We assume throughout that all hypotheses of differentiability are satisfied as needed.)

Suppose that such a function φ exists. Then

$$\frac{\partial f}{\partial y} = \frac{\partial}{\partial y}\left(\frac{\partial \varphi}{\partial x}\right) \quad \text{and} \quad \frac{\partial g}{\partial x} = \frac{\partial}{\partial x}\left(\frac{\partial \varphi}{\partial y}\right).$$

We shall show in the next chapter that under suitable hypotheses, the two partial derivatives on the right are equal. This means that if there exists a potential function for F, then

$$\frac{\partial f}{\partial y} = \frac{\partial g}{\partial x}.$$

This gives us a simple test in practice to tell whether a potential function may exist.

THEOREM 2. *Let f, g be differentiable functions having continuous partial derivatives on an open set U in 2-space. If*

$$\frac{\partial f}{\partial y} \neq \frac{\partial g}{\partial x}$$

then the vector field $F(x, y) = (f(x, y), g(x, y))$ does not have a potential function.

It can be shown that the converse is true in some very important cases. We shall state a theorem which will give us conditions under which the converse is true.

THEOREM 3. *Let f, g be differentiable functions on an open set of the plane. If this open set is the entire plane, or if it is an open disc, or the inside of a rectangle, if the partial derivatives of f, g exist and are continuous, and if*

$$\frac{\partial f}{\partial y} = \frac{\partial g}{\partial x},$$

then the vector field $F(x, y) = (f(x, y), g(x, y))$ has a potential function.

We shall indicate how a proof of Theorem 3 might go for a rectangle after we have discussed some examples.

Example 1. Determine whether the vector field

$$F(x, y) = (e^{xy}, e^{x+y})$$

has a potential function.

Here, $f(x, y) = e^{xy}$ and $g(x, y) = e^{x+y}$. We have:

$$\frac{\partial f}{\partial y} = xe^{xy} \qquad \text{and} \qquad \frac{\partial g}{\partial x} = e^{x+y}.$$

Since these are not equal, we know that there cannot be a potential function.

If the partial derivatives $\partial f/\partial y$ and $\partial g/\partial x$ turn out to be equal, then one can try to find a potential function by integrating with respect to one of the variables. Thus we try to find

$$\int f(x, y) \, dx,$$

keeping y constant, and taking the ordinary integral of functions of one variable. If we can find such an integral, it will be a function $\psi(x, y)$, whose partial with respect to x will be equal to $f(x, y)$ (by definition).

Adding a function of y, we can then adjust it so that its partial with respect to y is equal to $g(x, y)$.

Example 2. Let $F(x, y) = (2xy,\ x^2 + 3y^2)$. Determine whether this vector field has a potential function, and if it does, find it.

Applying the test which we mentioned above, we find that a potential function may exist. To find it, we consider first the integral

$$\int 2xy\ dx,$$

viewing y as constant. We obtain x^2y for the indefinite integral. We must now find a function $u(y)$ such that

$$\frac{\partial}{\partial y}\left(x^2y + u(y)\right) = x^2 + 3y^2.$$

This means that we must find a function $u(y)$ such that

$$x^2 + \frac{du}{dy} = x^2 + 3y^2,$$

or in other words,

$$\frac{du}{dy} = 3y^2.$$

This is a simple integration problem in one variable, and we find $u(y) = y^3$. Thus finally, if we let

$$\varphi(x, y) = x^2y + y^3,$$

then we see that φ is a potential function for F.

The procedure we have just applied works when the open set U is a rectangle. For simplicity, let a, b be numbers > 0 and consider the rectangle $-a < x < a$ and $-b < y < b$. We are given two continuous functions $f(x, y)$ and $g(x, y)$ in this rectangle. We assume that their partial derivatives exist, are continuous, and that

$$\frac{\partial f}{\partial y} = \frac{\partial g}{\partial x}.$$

It will be convenient to use also the D notation, so that this relation reads

$$D_2 f = D_1 g.$$

We wish to find a potential function for F. Let

$$\psi(x, y) = \int_0^x f(t, y)\ dt.$$

In this integral, we regard y as constant. By definition, we obtain

$$D_1 \psi(x, y) = f(x, y).$$

What is $D_2\psi$? It can be shown that D_2 can be moved inside the integral sign. (We do not do it here because the proof has too many ϵ and δ in it.) Thus we obtain

$$D_2\psi(x, y) = \int_0^x D_2f(t, y)\, dt = \int_0^x D_1g(t, y)\, dt.$$

Since the integral of the derivative is equal to the function, this last expression gives

$$D_2\psi(x, y) = g(t, y)\Big|_0^x = g(x, y) - g(0, y).$$

Now let

$$u(y) = \int_0^y g(0, t)\, dt,$$

so that the derivative of $u(y)$ is $g(0, y)$. Finally, let

$$\varphi(x, y) = \psi(x, y) + u(y).$$

We contend that φ is the desired potential function.

Taking the partial with respect to x kills the term $u(y)$. Hence

$$D_1\varphi(x, y) = D_1\psi(x, y) = f(x, y).$$

As for the second partial,

$$\begin{aligned} D_2\varphi(x, y) &= D_2\psi(x, y) + D_2u(y) \\ &= g(x, y) - g(0, y) + g(0, y) \\ &= g(x, y). \end{aligned}$$

This concludes our arguments that φ is a potential function.

EXERCISES

Determine which of the following vector fields admit potential functions.

1. $(e^x, \sin xy)$ 2. $(2x^2y, y^3)$
3. $(2xy, y^2)$ 4. $(y^2x^2, x + y^4)$

Find potential functions for the following vector fields.

5. (a) $F(X) = \dfrac{1}{r}X$ (b) $F(X) = \dfrac{1}{r^2}X$
 (c) $F(X) = r^nX$ (if n is an integer $\neq -2$). (In this Exercise, $r = \|X\|$, and $X \neq O$.)

6. $(4xy, 2x^2)$ 7. $(xy \cos xy + \sin xy, x^2 \cos xy)$
8. $(3x^2y^2, 2x^3y)$ 9. $(2x, 4y^3)$
10. (ye^{xy}, xe^{xy})

11. Let $r = \|X\|$. Let g be a differentiable function of one variable. Show that the vector field defined by

$$F(X) = \frac{g'(r)}{r} X$$

in the domain $X \neq O$ always admits a potential function. What is this potential function?

12. Generalize Theorem 3 to functions of three variables, indicating how a proof might go along the same lines as the proof we sketched for two variables.

§2. *Line integrals*

Let U be an open set (of n-space), and let F be a vector field on U. We can represent F by components:

$$F(X) = (f_1(X), \ldots, f_n(X)),$$

each f_i being a function. When $n = 2$,

$$F(X) = (f(x, y), g(x, y)).$$

If each function $f_1(X), \ldots, f_n(X)$ is continuous, then we shall say that F is a *continuous* vector field. If each function $f_1(X), \ldots, f_n(X)$ is differentiable, then we shall say that F is a *differentiable* vector field.

We shall also deal with curves. Rather than use the letter X to denote a curve, we shall use another letter, for instance C, to avoid certain confusions which might arise in the present context. Furthermore, it is now convenient to assume that our curve C is defined on a *closed* interval $I = [a, b]$, with $a < b$. For each number t in I, the value $C(t)$ is a point in n-space. We shall say that the curve C lies in U if $C(t)$ is a point of U for all t in I. We say that C is *continuously differentiable* if its derivative $\dot{C}(t) = dC/dt$ exists and is continuous.

Let F be a continuous vector field on U, and let C be a continuously differentiable curve in U. The dot product

$$F(C(t)) \cdot \frac{dC}{dt}$$

is a *function* of t, and it can be shown easily that this function is continuous (by ϵ and δ techniques which we always omit). We suppose that C is defined on the interval $[a, b]$. We define the *integral of F along C* to be

$$\int_C F = \int_a^b F(C(t)) \cdot \frac{dC}{dt} \, dt.$$

This integral is a direct generalization of the familiar notion of integral of functions of one variable. If we are given a function $f(u)$, and u is a function of t, then

$$\int_{u(a)}^{u(b)} f(u)\, du = \int_a^b f(u(t))\, \frac{du}{dt}\, dt.$$

(This is the formula describing the substitution method for evaluating integrals.)

In n-space, $C(a)$ and $C(b)$ are points, and our curve passes through these two points. Thus the integral we have written down can be interpreted as an integral of the vector field, along the curve, between the two points. It will be convenient to write the integral in the form

$$\int_{P,C}^{Q} F = \int_{C(a)}^{C(b)} F(C) \cdot dC$$

to denote the integral along the curve C, from P to Q.

Example. Let $F(x, y) = (x^2 y, y^3)$. Find the integral of F along the straight line from the origin to the point $(1, 1)$.

We can parametrize the line in the form

$$C(t) = (t, t).$$

Thus

$$F(C(t)) = (t^3, t^3).$$

Furthermore,

$$\frac{dC}{dt} = (1, 1).$$

Hence

$$F(C(t)) \cdot \frac{dC}{dt} = 2t^3.$$

The integral we must find is therefore equal to:

$$\int_C F = \int_0^1 2t^3\, dt = \frac{2t^4}{4}\Big|_0^1 = \frac{1}{2}.$$

Remark. If we are given a finite number of continuously differentiable curves forming a path as indicated on the following figure:

then the integral over the path is simply the sum of the integrals over each segment. Such a path is called *piecewise continuously differentiable.*

Thus a piecewise continuously differentiable curve C consists of a sequence $\{C_1, \ldots, C_m\}$, where each C_i is a continuously differentiable curve, defined on an interval $[a_i, b_i]$, such that the end point of C_i is the beginning point of C_{i+1}, in other words

$$C_i(b_i) = C_{i+1}(a_{i+1}).$$

We define the integral of F along such a curve C to be the sum

$$\int_{C_1} F + \int_{C_2} F + \cdots + \int_{C_m} F.$$

We say that our curve C is a *closed curve* if the end point of C_m is the beginning point of C_1.

In the following picture, we have drawn a closed curve such that the beginning point of C_1, namely P_1, is the end point of the curve C_4, which joins P_4 to P_1.

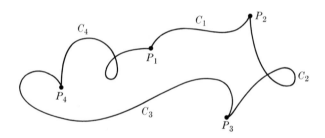

Finally, we observe that in physics, one may interpret a vector field $F(X)$ as describing a force. Then the integral of this vector field along a curve C describes the *work* done by the force along this curve.

EXERCISES

Compute the line integrals of the vector field over the indicated curves.

1. $F(x, y) = (x^2 - 2xy, y^2 - 2xy)$ along the parabola $y = x^2$ from $(-2, 4)$ to $(1, 1)$.

2. $(x, y, xz - y)$ over the line segment from $(0, 0, 0)$ to $(1, 2, 4)$.

3. Let $r = (x^2 + y^2)^{1/2}$. Let $F(X) = r^{-1}X$. Find the integral of $F(X)$ over the circle of radius 2, taken in counterclockwise direction.

4. Let C be a circle of radius 20 with center at the origin. Let $F(X)$ be a vector field such that $F(X)$ has the same direction as X. What is the integral of F around C?

5. What is the work done by the force $F(x, y) = (x^2 - y^2, 2xy)$ by moving a particle of mass m along the square bounded by the coordinate axes and the lines $x = 3$, $y = 3$ in counterclockwise direction?

6. Let $F(x, y) = (cxy, x^6 y^2)$, where c is a positive constant. Let a, b be numbers > 0. Find a value of a in terms of c such that the line integral of F along the curve $y = ax^b$ from $(0, 0)$ to the line $x = 1$ is independent of b.

Find the values of the indicated integrals of vector fields along the given curves.

7. $(y^2, -x)$ along the parabola $x = y^2/4$ from $(0, 0)$ to $(1, 2)$.

8. $(x^2 - y^2, x)$ along the arc in the first quadrant of the circle $x^2 + y^2 = 4$ from $(0, 2)$ to $(2, 0)$.

9. $(x^2 y^2, xy^2)$ along the closed curve formed by parts of the line $x = 1$ and the parabola $y^2 = x$, counterclockwise.

10. $(x^2 - y^2, x)$ counterclockwise around the circle $x^2 + y^2 = 4$.

11. The vector field
$$\left(\frac{-y}{x^2 + y^2}, \frac{x}{x^2 + y^2} \right)$$
counterclockwise along the circle $x^2 + y^2 = 2$ from $(1, 1)$ to $(-\sqrt{2}, 0)$.

12. The same vector field along the line $x + y = 1$ from $(0, 1)$ to $(1, 0)$.

13. $(2xy, -3xy)$ clockwise around the square bounded by the lines $x = 3$, $x = 5$, $y = 1$, $y = 3$.

14. Let F be a continuous vector field on an open set U. Suppose that $F = \text{grad } \varphi$ for some differentiable function φ on U. Prove that the line integral of F around any closed continuously differentiable curve in U is equal to 0. Prove the same conclusion if the curve is assumed to be only piecewise continuously differentiable.

15. Conversely, let F be a continuous vector field on an open set U. Assume that any two points of U can be joined by a piecewise continuously differentiable curve, and assume that the integral of F along any closed piecewise continuously differentiable curve in U is equal to 0. Prove that F is the gradient of some function on U. [*Hint:* Let P_0 be a fixed point of U, and for any point P of U define $\varphi(P)$ to be the value of the integral
$$\int_{P_0}^{P} F$$
taken along any piecewise continuously differentiable curve between P_0 and P. Show that φ has partial derivatives, and that its gradient is F.]

CHAPTER VI

Taylor's Formula

In this chapter, we discuss two things which are of independent interest. First, we define partial differential operators (with constant coefficients). It is very useful to have facility in working with these formally.

Secondly, we apply them to the derivation of Taylor's formula for functions of several variables, which will be very similar to the formula for one variable. The formula, as before, tells us how to approximate a function by means of polynomials. In the present theory, these polynomials involve several variables, of course. We shall see that they are hardly more difficult to handle than polynomials in one variable in the matters under consideration.

The proof that the partial derivatives commute is tricky. It can be omitted without harm in a class allergic to theory, because the technique involved never reappears in the rest of this book.

§1. Repeated partial derivatives

Let f be a function of two variables, defined on an open set U in 2-space. Assume that its first partial derivative exists. Then $D_1 f$ (which we also write $\partial f / \partial x$ if x is the first variable) is a function defined on U. We may then ask for its first or second partial derivative, i.e. we may form $D_2 D_1 f$ or $D_1 D_1 f$ if these exist. Similarly, if $D_2 f$ exists, and if the first partial derivative of $D_2 f$ exists, we may form $D_1 D_2 f$.

Suppose that we write f in terms of the two variables (x, y). Then we can write

$$D_1 D_2 f(x, y) = \frac{\partial}{\partial x} \left(\frac{\partial f}{\partial y} \right) = (D_1(D_2 f))(x, y),$$

and

$$D_2 D_1 f(x, y) = \frac{\partial}{\partial y} \left(\frac{\partial f}{\partial x} \right) = (D_2(D_1 f))(x, y).$$

For example, let $f(x, y) = \sin(xy)$. Then

$$\frac{\partial f}{\partial x} = y \cos(xy) \qquad \text{and} \qquad \frac{\partial f}{\partial y} = x \cos(xy).$$

Hence

$$D_2 D_1 f(x, y) = -xy \sin(xy) + \cos(xy).$$

60

But differentiating $\partial f/\partial y$ with respect to x, we see that

$$D_1 D_2 f(x, y) = -xy \sin (xy) + \cos (xy).$$

These two repeated partial derivatives are equal!

The next theorem tells us that in practice, this will always happen.

THEOREM 1. *Let f be a function of two variables, defined on an open set U of 2-space. Assume that the partial derivatives $D_1 f$, $D_2 f$, $D_1 D_2 f$, and $D_2 D_1 f$ exist and are continuous. Then*

$$D_1 D_2 f = D_2 D_1 f.$$

Proof. A direct use of the definition of these partial and repeated partial derivatives would lead to a blind alley. Hence we shall have to use a special trick to pull through.

Let (x, y) be a point in U, and let $H = (h, k)$ be small, $h \neq 0$, $k \neq 0$. We consider the expression

$$g(x) = f(x, y + k) - f(x, y).$$

If we apply the mean value theorem to g, then we conclude that there exists a number s_1 between x and $x + h$ such that

$$g(x + h) - g(x) = g'(s_1)h,$$

or in other words, using the definition of partial derivative:

(1) $g(x + h) - g(x) = [D_1 f(s_1, y + k) - D_1 f(s_1, y)]h.$

But the difference on the left of this equation is

(2) $f(x + h, y + k) - f(x + h, y) - f(x, y + k) + f(x, y).$

On the other hand, we can now apply the mean value theorem to the expression in brackets in (1) *with respect to the second variable.* If we do this, we see that the long expression in (2) is equal to

(3) $D_2 D_1 f(s_1, s_2)kh$

for some number s_2 lying between y and $y + k$.

We now start all over again, and consider the expression

$$g_2(y) = f(x + h, y) - f(x, y).$$

We apply the mean value theorem to g_2, and conclude that there is a number t_2 between y and $y + k$ such that

$$g_2(y + k) - g_2(y) = g'_2(t_2)k,$$

or in other words, is equal to

(4) $$[D_2f(x + h, t_2) - D_2f(x, t_2)]k.$$

If you work out $g_2(y + k) - g_2(y)$, you will see that it is equal to the long expression of (2). Furthermore, proceeding as before, and applying the mean value theorem to the first variable in (4), we see that (4) becomes

(5) $$D_1D_2f(t_1, t_2)hk$$

for some number t_1 between x and $x + h$. Since (5) and (3) are both equal to the long expression in (2), they are equal to each other. Thus finally we obtain

$$D_2D_1f(s_1, s_2)kh = D_1D_2f(t_1, t_2)hk.$$

Since we assume from the beginning that $h \neq 0$ and $k \neq 0$, we can cancel hk, and get

$$D_2D_1f(s_1, s_2) = D_1D_2f(t_1, t_2).$$

Now as h, k approach 0, the left side of this equation approaches $D_2D_1f(x,y)$ because D_2D_1f is assumed to be continuous. Similarly, the right-hand side approaches $D_1D_2f(x, y)$. We can therefore conclude that

$$D_1D_2f(x, y) = D_2D_1f(x, y),$$

as desired.

Consider now a function of three variables $f(x, y, z)$. We can then take three kinds of partial derivatives: D_1, D_2, or D_3 (in other notation, $\partial/\partial x$, $\partial/\partial y$, and $\partial/\partial z$). Let us assume throughout that all the partial derivatives which we shall consider exist and are continuous, so that we may form as many repeated partial derivatives as we please. Then using Theorem 1, we can show that it does not matter in which order we take these partials.

For instance, we see that

$$D_3D_1f = D_1D_3f.$$

This is simply an application of Theorem 1, keeping the second variable fixed. We may take a further partial derivative, for instance

$$D_1D_3D_1f.$$

Here D_1 occurs twice and D_3 once. Then this expression will be equal to any other repeated partial derivative of f in which D_1 occurs twice and D_3 once. For example, we apply the theorem to the function (D_1f).

Then the theorem allows us to interchange D_1 and D_3 in front of (D_1f) (always assuming that all partials we want to take exist and are continuous). We obtain

$$D_1D_3(D_1f) = D_3D_1(D_1f).$$

As another example, consider

(6) $$D_2D_1D_3D_2f.$$

We wish to show that it is equal to $D_1D_2D_2D_3f$. By Theorem 1, we have $D_3D_2f = D_2D_3f$. Hence:

(7) $$D_2D_1(D_3D_2f) = D_2D_1(D_2D_3f).$$

We then apply Theorem 1 again, and interchange D_2 and D_1 to obtain the desired expression.

In general, suppose that we are given three positive integers m_1, m_2, and m_3. We wish to take the repeated partial derivatives of f by using m_1 times the first partial D_1, using m_2 times the second partial D_2, and using m_3 times the third partial D_3. Then it does not matter in which order we take these partial derivatives, we shall always get the same answer.

To see this, note that by repeated application of Theorem 1, we can always interchange any occurrence of D_3 with D_2 or D_1 so as to push D_3 towards the right. We can perform such interchanges until all occurrences of D_3 occur furthest to the right, in the same way as we pushed D_3 towards the right going from expression (6) to expression (7). Once this is done, we start interchanging D_2 with D_1 until all occurrences of D_2 pile up just behind D_3. Once this is done, we are left with D_1 repeated a certain number of times on the left.

No matter with what arrangement of D_1, D_2, D_3 we started, we end up with the *same* arrangement, namely

$$\underbrace{D_1 \cdots D_1}_{m_1} \underbrace{D_2 \cdots D_2}_{m_2} \underbrace{D_3 \cdots D_3}_{m_3} f,$$

with D_1 occurring m_1 times, D_2 occurring m_2 times, and D_3 occurring m_3 times.

Exactly the same argument works for functions of more variables.

EXERCISES

Find the partial derivatives of order 2 for the following functions and verify explicitly in each case that $D_1D_2f = D_2D_1f$.

1. e^{xy} 2. $\sin(xy)$

3. $x^2y^3 + 3xy$ 4. $2xy + y^2$

5. $e^{x^2+y^2}$ 6. $\sin (x^2 + y)$

7. $\cos (x^3 + xy)$ 8. $\arctan (x^2 - 2xy)$

9. e^{x+y} 10. $\sin (x + y)$.

Find $D_1 D_2 D_3 f$ and $D_3 D_2 D_1 f$ in the following cases.

11. xyz 12. $x^2 yz$

13. e^{xyz} 14. $\sin (xyz)$

15. $\cos (x + y + z)$ 16. $\sin (x + y + z)$

17. $(x^2 + y^2 + z^2)^{-1}$ 18. $x^3 y^2 z + 2(x + y + z)$.

19. Let $x = r \cos \theta$ and $y = r \sin \theta$. Let $f(x, y) = g(r, \theta)$. Show that

$$\frac{\partial}{\partial x} = \cos \theta \, \frac{\partial}{\partial r} - \frac{\sin \theta}{r} \frac{\partial}{\partial \theta}$$

$$\frac{\partial}{\partial y} = \sin \theta \, \frac{\partial}{\partial r} + \frac{\cos \theta}{r} \frac{\partial}{\partial \theta},$$

the partials on the left being viewed as acting on f, and those on the right as acting on g.

20. Let $x = r \cos \theta$ and $y = r \sin \theta$. Let $f(x, y) = g(r, \theta)$. Show that

$$\frac{\partial^2 g}{\partial r^2} + \frac{1}{r} \frac{\partial g}{\partial r} + \frac{1}{r^2} \frac{\partial^2 g}{\partial \theta^2} = \frac{\partial^2 f}{\partial x^2} + \frac{\partial^2 f}{\partial y^2}.$$

21. Let $f(X) = g(r)$ (with $r = \|X\|$), and assume $X = (x, y, z)$. Show that

$$\frac{d^2 g}{dr^2} + \frac{2}{r} \frac{dg}{dr} = \frac{\partial^2 f}{\partial x^2} + \frac{\partial^2 f}{\partial y^2} + \frac{\partial^2 f}{\partial z^2}.$$

22. Let $f(x, y)$ satisfy $f(tx, ty) = t^n f(x, y)$ for all t (n being some integer ≥ 1). Show that

$$x \frac{\partial f}{\partial x} + y \frac{\partial f}{\partial y} = nf(x, y).$$

23. Let f be as in Exercise 22. Show that

$$x^2 \frac{\partial^2 f}{\partial x^2} + 2xy \frac{\partial^2 f}{\partial x \, \partial y} + y^2 \frac{\partial^2 f}{\partial y^2} = n(n - 1)f(x, y).$$

(It is understood throughout that all functions are as many times differentiable as is necessary.)

§2. Partial differential operators

We shall continue the discussion at the end of the last section, but we shall build up a convenient system to talk about iterated partial derivatives.

For simplicity, let us begin with functions of one variable x. We can then take only one type of derivative,

$$D = \frac{d}{dx}.$$

Let f be a function of one variable, and let us assume that all the iterated derivatives of f exist. Let m be a positive integer. Then we can take the m-th derivative of f, which we once denoted by $f^{(m)}$. We now write it

$$DD \cdots Df \quad \text{or} \quad \frac{d}{dx}\left(\frac{d}{dx}\cdots\left(\frac{df}{dx}\right)\cdots\right),$$

the derivative D (or d/dx) being iterated m times. What matters here is the number of times D occurs. We shall use the notation D^m or $(d/dx)^m$ to mean the iteration of D, m times. Thus we write

$$D^m f \quad \text{or} \quad \left(\frac{d}{dx}\right)^m f$$

instead of the above expressions. This is shorter. But even better, we have the rule

$$D^m D^n f = D^{m+n} f$$

for any positive integers m, n. So this iteration of derivatives begins to look like a multiplication. Furthermore, if we define $D^0 f$ to be simply f, then the rule above also holds if m, n are ≥ 0.

The expression D^m will be called a *simple differential operator of order m* (in one variable, so far).

Let us now look at the case of two variables, say (x, y). We can then take two partials D_1 and D_2 (or $\partial/\partial x$ and $\partial/\partial y$). Let m_1, m_2 be two integers ≥ 0. Instead of writing

$$\underbrace{D_1 \cdots D_1}_{m_1}\underbrace{D_2 \cdots D_2}_{m_2} f \quad \text{or} \quad \underbrace{\frac{\partial}{\partial x}\cdots\left(\frac{\partial}{\partial x}\right.}_{m_1}\underbrace{\left(\frac{\partial}{\partial y}\cdots\left(\frac{\partial f}{\partial y}\right)\right.}_{m_2}\cdots\bigg)\bigg),$$

we shall write

$$D_1^{m_1} D_2^{m_2} f \quad \text{or} \quad \left(\frac{\partial}{\partial x}\right)^{m_1}\left(\frac{\partial}{\partial y}\right)^{m_2} f.$$

For instance, taking $m_1 = 2$ and $m_2 = 5$ we would write

$$D_1^2 D_2^5 f.$$

This means: take the first partial twice and the second partial five times (in any order). (We assume throughout that all repeated partials exist and are continuous.)

An expression of type

$$D_1^{m_1} D_2^{m_2}$$

will be called a simple differential operator, and we shall say that its *order* is $m_1 + m_2$. In the example we just gave, the order is $5 + 2 = 7$.

It is now clear how to proceed with three or more variables, and it is no harder to express our thoughts in terms of n variables than in terms of three. Consequently, if we deal with functions of n variables, all of whose repeated partial derivatives exist and are continuous in some open set U, and if $D_1, \ldots, D_n$ denote the partial derivatives with respect to these variables, then we call an expression

$$D_1^{m_1} \cdots D_n^{m_n} \qquad \text{or} \qquad \left(\frac{\partial}{\partial x_1}\right)^{m_1} \cdots \left(\frac{\partial}{\partial x_n}\right)^{m_n}$$

a *simple differential operator*, $m_1, \ldots, m_n$ being integers $\geqq 0$. We say that its *order* is $m_1 + \cdots + m_n$.

Given a function f (satisfying the above stated conditions), and a simple differential operator D, we write Df to mean the function obtained from f by applying repeatedly the partial derivatives $D_1, \ldots, D_n$, the number of times being the number of times each D_i occurs in D.

Example 1. Consider functions of three variables (x, y, z). Then

$$D = \left(\frac{\partial}{\partial x}\right)^3 \left(\frac{\partial}{\partial y}\right)^5 \left(\frac{\partial}{\partial z}\right)^2$$

is a simple differential operator of order $3 + 5 + 2 = 10$. Let f be a function of three variables satisfying the usual hypotheses. To take Df means that we take the partial derivative with respect to z twice, the partial with respect to y five times, and the partial with respect to x three times.

We observe that a simple differential operator gives us a rule which to each function f associates another function Df.

As a matter of notation, referring to Example 1, one would also write the differential operator D in the form

$$D = \frac{\partial^{10}}{\partial x^3 \, \partial y^5 \, \partial z^2} .$$

In this notation, one would thus have

$$\left(\frac{\partial}{\partial x}\right)^2 f = \frac{\partial^2 f}{\partial x^2}$$

and

$$\frac{\partial}{\partial x}\left(\frac{\partial f}{\partial y}\right) = \frac{\partial^2 f}{\partial x \, \partial y} .$$

All the above notations are used in the scientific literature, and this is the reason for including them here.

Warning. Do not confuse the two expressions

$$\left(\frac{\partial}{\partial x}\right)^2 f = \frac{\partial^2 f}{\partial x^2} \quad \text{and} \quad \left(\frac{\partial f}{\partial x}\right)^2,$$

which are usually **not** equal. For instance, if $f(x, y) = x^2 y$, then

$$\frac{\partial^2 f}{\partial x^2} = 2y \quad \text{and} \quad \left(\frac{\partial f}{\partial x}\right)^2 = 4x^2 y^2.$$

We shall now show how one can add simple differential operators and multiply them by constants.

Let D, D' be two simple differential operators. For any function f we define $(D + D')f$ to be $Df + D'f$. If c is a number, then we define $(cD)f$ to be $c(Df)$. In this manner, taking iterated sums, and products with constants, we obtain what we shall call *differential operators*. Thus a *differential operator* D is a sum of terms of type

$$cD_1^{m_1} \cdots D_n^{m_n},$$

where c is a number and $m_1, \ldots, m_n$ are integers ≥ 0.

Example 2. Dealing with two variables, we see that

$$D = 3\frac{\partial}{\partial x} + 5\left(\frac{\partial}{\partial x}\right)^2 - \pi \frac{\partial}{\partial x}\frac{\partial}{\partial y}$$

is a differential operator.

Let $f(x, y) = \sin(xy)$. We wish to find Df. By definition,

$$Df(x, y) = 3\frac{\partial f}{\partial x} + 5\left(\frac{\partial}{\partial x}\right)^2 f - \pi \frac{\partial}{\partial x}\frac{\partial f}{\partial y}$$

$$= 3y\cos(xy) + 5(-y^2 \sin(xy)) - \pi[y(-\sin(xy))x + \cos(xy)].$$

We see that a differential operator gives rise to a rule which allows us to associate with each function f (satisfying the usual conditions) another function Df.

Let c be a number and f a function. Let D_i be any partial derivative. Then

$$D_i(cf) = cD_i f.$$

This is simply the old property that the derivative of a constant times a function is equal to the constant times the derivative of the function. Iterating partial derivatives, we see that this same property applies to differential operators. For any differential operator D, and any number c, we have

$$D(cf) = cDf.$$

Furthermore, if f, g are two functions (defined on the same open set, and having continuous partial derivatives of all order), then for any partial derivative D_i, we have

$$D_i(f + g) = D_i f + D_i g.$$

Iterating the partial derivatives, we find that for any differential operator D, we have

$$D(f + g) = Df + Dg.$$

Having learned how to add differential operators, we now learn how to multiply them.

Let D, D' be two differential operators. Then we define the differential operator DD' to be the one obtained by taking first D' and then D. In other words, if f is a function, then

$$(DD')f = D(D'f).$$

Example 3. Let

$$D = 3\frac{\partial}{\partial x} + 2\frac{\partial}{\partial y} \qquad \text{and} \qquad D' = \frac{\partial}{\partial x} + 4\frac{\partial}{\partial y}.$$

Then

$$DD' = 3\left(\frac{\partial}{\partial x}\right)^2 + 14\frac{\partial}{\partial x}\frac{\partial}{\partial y} + 8\left(\frac{\partial}{\partial y}\right)^2.$$

Differential operators multiply just like polynomials and numbers, and their addition and multiplication satisfy all the rules of addition and multiplication of polynomials. For instance:

If D, D' are two differential operators, then

$$DD' = D'D.$$

If D, D', D'' are three differential operators, then

$$D(D' + D'') = DD' + DD''.$$

It would be tedious to list all the properties here and to give in detail all the proofs (even though these are quite simple). We shall therefore omit these proofs. The main purpose of this section is to insure that you develop as great a facility in adding and multiplying differential operators as you have in adding and multiplying numbers or polynomials.

When a differential operator is written as a sum of terms of type

$$cD_1^{m_1} \cdots D_n^{m_n},$$

then we shall say that it is in *standard form*.

For example,

$$3\left(\frac{\partial}{\partial x}\right)^2 + 14\,\frac{\partial}{\partial x}\,\frac{\partial}{\partial y} + 8\left(\frac{\partial}{\partial y}\right)^2$$

is in standard form, but

$$\left(3\,\frac{\partial}{\partial x} + 2\,\frac{\partial}{\partial y}\right)\left(\frac{\partial}{\partial x} + 4\,\frac{\partial}{\partial y}\right)$$

is not.

Each term

$$cD_1^{m_1} \cdots D_n^{m_n}$$

is said to have degree $m_1 + \cdots + m_n$. If a differential operator is expressed as a sum of simple differential operators which all have the same degree, say m, then we say that it is *homogeneous* of degree m.

The differential operator of Example 2 is not homogeneous. The differential operator DD' of Example 3 is homogeneous of degree 2.

EXERCISES

Put the following differential operators in standard form.

1. $(3D_1 + 2D_2)^2$
2. $(D_1 + D_2 + D_3)^2$
3. $(D_1 - D_2)(D_1 + D_2)$
4. $(D_1 + D_2)^2$
5. $(D_1 + D_2)^3$
6. $(D_1 + D_2)^4$
7. $(2D_1 - 3D_2)(D_1 + D_2)$
8. $(D_1 - D_3)(D_2 + 5D_3)$
9. $\left(\frac{\partial}{\partial x} + 4\,\frac{\partial}{\partial y}\right)^3$
10. $\left(2\,\frac{\partial}{\partial x} + \frac{\partial}{\partial y}\right)^2$
11. $\left(h\,\frac{\partial}{\partial x} + k\,\frac{\partial}{\partial y}\right)^2$
12. $\left(h\,\frac{\partial}{\partial x} + k\,\frac{\partial}{\partial y}\right)^3$

Find the values of the differential operator of Exercise 10 applied to the following functions at the given point.

13. $x^2 y$ at $(0, 1)$
14. xy at $(1, 1)$
15. $\sin(xy)$ at $(0, \pi)$
16. e^{xy} at $(0, 0)$.

17. Let f, g be two functions (of two variables) with continuous partial derivatives of order ≤ 2 in an open set U. Assume that

$$\frac{\partial f}{\partial x} = -\frac{\partial g}{\partial y} \quad \text{and} \quad \frac{\partial f}{\partial y} = \frac{\partial g}{\partial x}.$$

Show that

$$\frac{\partial^2 f}{\partial x^2} + \frac{\partial^2 f}{\partial y^2} = 0.$$

18. Let f be a function of three variables, defined for $X \neq O$ by $f(X) = 1/\|X\|$. Show that

$$\frac{\partial^2 f}{\partial x^2} + \frac{\partial^2 f}{\partial y^2} + \frac{\partial^2 f}{\partial z^2} = 0.$$

19. In Exercise 20 of the preceding section, compute

$$\left(\frac{\partial}{\partial x}\right)^2 + \left(\frac{\partial}{\partial y}\right)^2$$

in terms of $\partial/\partial r$ and $\partial/\partial\theta$. Watch out! The coefficients are not constant.

§3. *Taylor's formula*

Let f be a function defined on an open set U. Let P be a point in this set, and let H be a non-zero vector. If t is a small number, then tH is small, and hence $P + tH$ will lie in U. Thus $f(P + tH)$ will be defined, and there always exists an open interval (possibly small) such that $f(P + tH)$ is defined. For t in such an interval, we can take the derivative, by the chain rule, as in Chapter IV:

$$\frac{d}{dt}\left(f(P + tH)\right) = \operatorname{grad} f\,(P + tH) \cdot H.$$

We are now interested in taking the derivative once more. To do this and see clearly what is happening, we need to use another notation.

Let $H = (h_1, \ldots, h_n)$. Instead of writing $\operatorname{grad} f$ we shall write

$$\nabla f$$

where ∇ stands for the symbol

$$\left(\frac{\partial}{\partial x_1}, \ldots, \frac{\partial}{\partial x_n}\right) = (D_1, \ldots, D_n).$$

(This is *not* a differential operator in the sense of §2 because ∇f is not a function!)

We shall write $H \cdot \nabla$ for the differential operator

$$h_1 \frac{\partial}{\partial x_1} + \cdots + h_n \frac{\partial}{\partial x_n}.$$

Example 1. If $H = (3, -1)$ and $\nabla = \left(\dfrac{\partial}{\partial x}, \dfrac{\partial}{\partial y}\right)$ then

$$H \cdot \nabla = 3\frac{\partial}{\partial x} - \frac{\partial}{\partial y}.$$

The expression giving us the derivative

$$\frac{d}{dt} f(P + tH)$$

can be written as $H \cdot (\text{grad } f \, (P + tH))$, or in terms of coordinates:

$$h_1 D_1 f(P + tH) + \cdots + h_n D_n f(P + tH).$$

The advantage of our abbreviated notation now becomes clear. We recognize this expression to be none other than $Df(P + tH)$, where D is the differential operator $H \cdot \nabla$. In other words, our expression is equal to

$$((H \cdot \nabla)f)(P + tH),$$

which we write also as

$$(H \cdot \nabla)f(P + tH),$$

eliminating a set of parentheses for simplicity.

We are now in a position to give the general formula for the iterated derivatives of $f(P + tH)$.

THEOREM 2. *Let r be a positive integer. Let f be a function defined on an open set U, and having continuous partial derivatives of orders $\leq r$. Let P be a point of U, and H a vector. Then*

$$\left(\frac{d}{dt}\right)^r (f(P + tH)) = (H \cdot \nabla)^r f(P + tH),$$

for all values of t such that $P + tH$ lies in U.

Proof. For $r = 1$, we have just verified our assertion. Consider next $r = 2$. Let

$$g = (H \cdot \nabla)f.$$

We must find the derivative

$$\frac{d}{dt} (g(P + tH)).$$

As we have seen, it is equal to

$$((H \cdot \nabla)g)(P + tH).$$

Substituting the value for g, we get

$$((H \cdot \nabla)^2 f)(P + tH).$$

This proves our assertion for $r = 2$.

We can proceed stepwise, and use a similar argument for $r = 3$. In general, we shall now show how to go from one step to the next. Suppose we have proved our result for step number s. Thus we have proved that

$$\left(\frac{d}{dt}\right)^s (f(P + tH)) = (H \cdot \nabla)^s f(P + tH).$$

To find the next derivative, we let

$$g = (H \cdot \nabla)^s f.$$

We must then find

$$\frac{d}{dt} (g(P + tH)).$$

We know that this is equal to

$$(H \cdot \nabla) g(P + tH).$$

Substituting the expression defining g, we obtain

$$((H \cdot \nabla)^{s+1} f)(P + tH),$$

as desired.

Taylor's formula for functions of several variables is an easy application of Theorem 2.

TAYLOR'S FORMULA. *Let f be a function defined on an open set U, and having continuous partial derivatives up to order s. Let P be a point of U, and let H be a vector. Assume that the line segment*

$$P + tH, \quad 0 \leqq t \leqq 1,$$

is contained in U. Let D be the differential operator $H \cdot \nabla$. Then there exists a number τ between 0 and 1 such that

$$f(P + H) = f(P) + \frac{Df(P)}{1!} + \frac{D^2f(P)}{2!} + \cdots + \frac{D^{s-1}f(P)}{(s-1)!} + \frac{D^sf(P + \tau H)}{s!}.$$

Proof. Let $g(t) = f(P + tH)$. Then g is a differentiable function of t in the old sense of functions of one variable, and we can apply the ordinary Taylor formula, between $t = 0$ and $t = 1$. In that case, all powers of $(1 - 0) = 1$ are equal to 1. Hence Taylor's formula in one variable applied to g yields:

$$g(1) = g(0) + \frac{g'(0)}{1!} + \frac{g''(0)}{2!} + \cdots + \frac{g^{(s-1)}(0)}{(s-1)!} + \frac{g^{(s)}(\tau)}{s!},$$

for some number τ between 0 and 1.

The successive derivatives of g are given by Theorem 2. If we evaluate them for $t = 0$ in the terms up to order $s - 1$, and for $t = \tau$ in the s-th term, then we see that the formula of the theorem simply drops out! That's the proof.

Usually one takes P to be the origin and $H = X$. In the case of two variables, for instance,

$$X \cdot \nabla = x \frac{\partial}{\partial x} + y \frac{\partial}{\partial y}.$$

The terms of the formula up to order 2 would be:

$$f(x, y) = f(0, 0) + x \frac{\partial f}{\partial x} (0, 0) + y \frac{\partial f}{\partial y} (0, 0)$$

$$+ \frac{1}{2!} \left[x^2 \frac{\partial^2 f}{\partial x^2} (0, 0) + 2xy \frac{\partial^2 f}{\partial x \, \partial y} (0, 0) + y^2 \frac{\partial^2 f}{\partial y^2} (0, 0) \right] + \cdots.$$

Writing down explicitly the terms as above is useful for computations, but obviously unwieldy to carry out a general discussion of the situation.

In general, we would have

$$f(x, y) = \sum_{i=0}^{n-1} \binom{n}{i} b_{i,n-i} x^i y^{n-i} + R_n,$$

where R_n is the remainder term, $\binom{n}{i}$ is the binomial coefficient, and $b_{i,n-i}$ is the *number* given by

$$b_{i,n-i} = \frac{\partial^n f}{\partial x^i \, \partial y^{n-i}} (0, 0) = (D_1^i D_2^{n-i} f)(0, 0).$$

Let us denote the above sum, from $i = 0$ to $n - 1$, by $G_{n-1}(x, y)$. Then G_{n-1} is a polynomial, which differs from f by the remainder term R_n. If $n - 1 = 3$, for instance, we have

$$G_3(x, y) = G_2(x, y)$$

$$+ \frac{1}{3!} \left[D_1^3 f(0, 0) x^3 + 3 D_1^2 D_2 f(0, 0) x^2 y + 3 D_1 D_2^2 f(0, 0) xy^2 + D_2^3 f(0, 0) y^3 \right].$$

Usually, as n becomes large, the polynomials G_{n-1} give increasingly good approximations to the function f. How good an approximation must of course be determined in each case, by estimating the remainder, just as we did for functions of one variable.

The above polynomial G_{n-1} will be called the *polynomial approximation* of f up to degree $n - 1$.

Example 2. Find the polynomial approximation of the function

$$f(x, y) = \log (1 + x + 2y)$$

up to degree 2.

To do this, we first compute the partial derivatives. They are:

$$f(0, 0) = 0$$

$$D_1 f(x, y) = \frac{1}{1 + x + 2y}, \qquad D_1 f(0, 0) = 1,$$

$$D_2 f(x, y) = \frac{2}{1 + x + 2y}, \qquad D_3 f(0, 0) = 2,$$

$$D_1^2 f(x, y) = -\frac{1}{(1 + x + 2y)^2}, \qquad D_1^2 f(0, 0) = -1,$$

$$D_2^2 f(x, y) = -\frac{4}{(1 + x + 2y)^2}, \qquad D_2^2 f(0, 0) = -4,$$

$$D_1 D_2 f(0, 0) = -\frac{2}{(1 + x + 2y)^2}, \qquad D_1 D_2 f(0, 0) = -2.$$

Hence the polynomial approximation of f up to degree 2 is

$$G_2(x, y) = x + 2y - \tfrac{1}{2}(x^2 + 4xy + 4y^2).$$

In some cases, one can avoid computing partial derivatives. For instance, let g be a function of one variable, having 3 continuous derivatives in some interval containing 0. Then the Taylor formula for g yields:

$$g(t) = g(0) + \frac{g'(0)}{1!} t + \frac{g''(0)}{2!} t^2 + \frac{g'''(\tau)}{3!} t^3$$

for some number τ between 0 and t.

If $\varphi(x, y)$ is some function of two variables whose values are such that $g(\varphi(x, y))$ is defined, then we can substitute $\varphi(x, y)$ for t in the expression above.

For instance, let $g(t) = e^t$. To find e^{xy}, we do not work out the partial derivatives. We apply our knowledge of the Taylor series for e^t, which is

$$e^t = 1 + t + \frac{t^2}{2!} + \cdots.$$

We obtain therefore

$$e^{xy} = 1 + xy + \frac{x^2 y^2}{2!} + \cdots.$$

It can be shown that the terms which we obtain by this method will be the same as those using the Taylor formula in several variables.

In any case, we see that our function e^{xy} can be approximated by polynomials in x and y. For instance,

$$1 + xy + \frac{x^2 y^2}{2!}$$

is such a polynomial, and to determine the degree of accuracy of the approximation, we have of course to estimate the remainder term.

EXERCISES

Find the terms up to order 2 in the Taylor formula of the following functions (taking $P = 0$).

1. $\sin (xy)$ 2. $\cos (xy)$ 3. $\log (1 + xy)$

4. $\sin (x^2 + y^2)$ 5. e^{x+y} 6. $\cos (x^2 + y)$

7. $(\sin x)(\cos y)$ 8. $e^x \sin y$ 9. $x + xy + 2y^2$

10. Does $\dfrac{\sin (xy)}{y}$ approach a limit as (x, y) approaches $(0, 0)$? If so, what limit?

11. Same questions for

$$\frac{e^{xy} - 1}{x} \quad \text{and} \quad \frac{\log (1 + x^2 + y^2)}{x^2 + y^2} .$$

12. Same questions for

$$\frac{\cos (xy) - 1}{x} .$$

13. Same questions for

$$\frac{\sin (xy) - xy}{x^2 y} .$$

14. Find the terms up to order 3 in Taylor's formula for the function $e^x \cos y$.

15. What is the term of degree 7 in Taylor's formula for the function

$$x^3 - 2xy^4 + (x - 1)^2 y^{10}?$$

16. Show that if $f(x, y, z)$ is a polynomial in x, y, z, then it is equal to its own Taylor series, i.e. there exists an integer n such that $R_n = 0$.

17. Find the polynomial approximation of the function

$$f(x, y) = \log (1 + x + 2y)$$

up to degree 3.

§4. Estimate for the remainder

Let us take $P = 0$ in Taylor's formula, and $H = X$. Then the formula reads:

$$f(X) = f(0) + \frac{(X \cdot \nabla)f(0)}{1!} + \cdots + \frac{(X \cdot \nabla)^{s-1}f(0)}{(s - 1)!} + \frac{(X \cdot \nabla)^s f(\tau X)}{s!} .$$

We wish to estimate the remainder.

THEOREM 3. *Let a be a number > 0 and such that the closed ball of radius a around O is contained in the open set of definition of f. There exists a number C such that for all X with $\|X\| \leq a$, we have*

$$|(X \cdot \nabla)^s f(\tau X)| \leq C\|X\|^s.$$

Proof. For simplicity we limit ourselves to the case of two variables. We take $X = (x, y)$. Then

$$X \cdot \nabla = x D_1 + y D_2.$$

If we take its s-th power, then

$$(x D_1 + y D_2)^s = x^s D_1^s + \cdots + y^s D_2^s.$$

The terms in between come from the binomial expansion, and are of type

$$c_{ij} x^i y^j D_1^i D_2^j$$

with $i + j = s$, and suitable binomial coefficients $c_{ij} = \binom{s}{i}$.

All the repeated partial derivatives

$$D_1^i D_2^j f$$

are continuous. We shall take for granted without proof that there is a number C' such that these partials are bounded by C' in the disc of radius a. In other words,

$$|D_1^i D_2^j f(Q)| \leq C'$$

whenever $\|Q\| \leq a$ and $i + j = s$.

We know that

$$|x| \leq \|X\| \qquad \text{and} \qquad |y| \leq \|X\|$$

because $\|X\| = (x^2 + y^2)^{1/2}$. Hence

$$|x^i y^j| \leq \|X\|^i \|X\|^j = \|X\|^s.$$

The numbers c_{ij} are fixed (binomial coefficients) and bounded by a constant C''. We want to estimate the absolute value of the sum of the terms

$$c_{ij} x^i y^j D_1^i D_2^j f(Q)$$

for $Q = \tau X$ (and hence $\|Q\| \leq a$). According to the estimates we have made above each such term is bounded in absolute value by

$$C'' \|X\|^i \|X\|^j C' = C'' \|X\|^s C'.$$

The sum consists of a finite number of terms. Hence we get

$$|(X \cdot \nabla)^s f(Q)| \leq C \|X\|^s$$

(with the constant C equal to $C'C''$ times the number of terms in the sum). This proves what we wanted.

When $\|X\|$ approaches 0, then $\|X\|^s$ approaches 0 much more rapidly if $s \geq 2$. Thus the more terms we can take in the Taylor formula, the better approximation to the function do we get.

Exercises

1. Let f be a function as in the theorem concerning Taylor's formula, with $P = O$. Let a be a number > 0. Let $G(X)$ be a polynomial in $x_1, \ldots, x_n$, of degree $\leq s - 1$, such that

$$|f(X) - G(X)| \leq C\|X\|^s$$

for all X satisfying $\|X\| \leq a$. Show that there is only one polynomial $G(X)$ satisfying this condition, and that $G(X)$ consists of the terms of order $\leq s - 1$ in Taylor's formula.

2. Let $f(x_1, x_2)$ be a function with continuous partial derivatives of order ≤ 2. Assume that $f(0, 0) = 0$. Show that there exist functions g_1, g_2 with continuous partials of order ≤ 1 such that

$$f(x_1, x_2) = x_1 g_1(x_1, x_2) + x_2 g_2(x_1, x_2).$$

[*Hint:* Use the fact that

$$f(X) = \int_0^1 \frac{d}{dt} f(tX)\, dt.]$$

3. In the preceding exercise, assume that $D_i f(O) = 0$ for $i = 1, 2$. Show that there exist continuous functions $h_{ij}(X)$ such that

$$f(X) = \sum x_i x_j h_{ij}(X),$$

the sum being taken for $i, j = 1$ and 2, and $h_{ij} = h_{ji}$.

4. Let f be a differentiable function defined on all of n-space. Assume that $f(O) = 0$, and that $f(tX) = tf(X)$ for all numbers t and vectors X. Show that for all vectors X, we have

$$f(X) = \operatorname{grad} f(O) \cdot X.$$

5. Let f be a function with continuous partial derivatives of order ≤ 3. Assume that $f(O) = 0$ and also that $f(tX) = t^2 f(X)$ for all numbers t and vectors X. Show that for all vectors X we have

$$f(X) = \frac{(X \cdot \nabla)^2 f(O)}{2!}.$$

6. Let U be an open set having the following property: Given two points X, Y in U, the line segment joining X and Y is contained in the open set.

    (a) What is the parametric equation for this line segment?

    (b) Let f have continuous partial derivatives in U. Assume that $\|\operatorname{grad} f(P)\| \leq M$ for some number M, and all points P in U. Show that for any two points X, Y in U, we have

$$|f(X) - f(Y)| \leq M\|X - Y\|.$$

7. Let f be differentiable on the open set U. Let X be a point of U, let H be a vector such that the line segment between X and $X + H$ is contained in U. Using the fact that

$$f(X + H) - f(X) = \int_0^1 \frac{d}{dt} f(X + tH)\, dt,$$

show that

$$|f(X + H) - f(X)| \leq M\|H\|,$$

if M is a number such that $\|\text{grad } f(P)\| \leq M$ for all P on the above-mentioned line segment.

CHAPTER VII

Maximum and Minimum

When we studied functions of one variable, we found maxima and minima by first finding critical points, i.e. points where the derivative is equal to 0, and then determining by inspection which of these are maxima or minima. We can carry out a similar investigation for functions of several variables. The condition that the derivative is equal to 0 must be replaced by the vanishing of all partial derivatives.

§1. *Critical points*

Let f be a differentiable function defined on an open set U. Let P be a point of U. If all partial derivatives of f are equal to 0 at P, then we say that P is a *critical point* of the function. In other words, for P to be a critical point, we must have

$$D_1f(P) = 0, \ldots, D_nf(P) = 0.$$

Example. Find the critical points of the function $f(x, y) = e^{-(x^2+y^2)}$. Taking the partials, we see that

$$\frac{\partial f}{\partial x} = -2xe^{-(x^2+y^2)} \quad \text{and} \quad \frac{\partial f}{\partial y} = -2ye^{-(x^2+y^2)}.$$

The only value of (x, y) for which both these quantities are equal to 0 is $x = 0$ and $y = 0$. Hence the only critical point is $(0, 0)$.

A critical point of a function of one variable is a point where the derivative is equal to 0. We have seen examples where such a point need not be a local maximum or a local minimum, for instance as in the following picture:

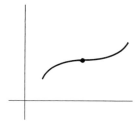

A fortiori, a similar thing may occur for functions of several variables. However, once we have found critical points, it is usually not too difficult to tell by inspection whether they are of this type or not.

Let f be any function (differentiable or not), defined on an open set U. We shall say that a point P of U is a *local maximum* for the function if there exists an open ball (of positive radius) B, centered at P, such that for all points X of B, we have

$$f(X) \leqq f(P).$$

As an exercise, define *local minimum* in an analogous manner.

In the case of functions of one variable, we took an open interval instead of an open ball around the point P. Thus our notion of local maximum in n-space is the natural generalization of the notion in 1-space.

THEOREM 1. *Let f be a function which is defined and differentiable on an open set U. Let P be a local maximum for f in U. Then P is a critical point of f.*

Proof. The proof is exactly the same as for functions of one variable. In fact, we shall prove that the directional derivative of f at P in any direction is 0. Let H be a non-zero vector. For small values of t, $P + tH$ lies in the open set U, and $f(P + tH)$ is defined. Furthermore, for small values of t, tH is small, and hence $P + tH$ lies in our open ball such that

$$f(P + tH) \leqq f(P).$$

Hence the function of one variable $g(t) = f(P + tH)$ has a local maximum at $t = 0$. Hence its derivative $g'(0)$ is equal to 0. By the chain rule, we obtain as usual:

$$\operatorname{grad} f(P) \cdot H = 0.$$

This equation is true for every non-zero vector H, and hence

$$\operatorname{grad} f(P) = O.$$

This proves what we wanted.

EXERCISES

Find the critical points of the following functions.

1. $x^2 + 4xy - y^2 - 8x - 6y$ 2. $x + y \sin x$
3. $x^2 + y^2 + z^2$ 4. $(x + y)e^{-xy}$
5. $xy + xz$ 6. $\cos(x^2 + y^2 + z^2)$
7. x^2y^2 8. $x^4 + y^2$
9. $(x - y)^4$ 10. $x \sin y$
11. $x^2 + 2y^2 - x$ 12. $e^{-(x^2 + y^2 + z^2)}$
13. $e^{(x^2 + y^2 + z^2)}$

14. In the preceding exercises, find the minimum value of the given function, and give all points where the value of the function is equal to this minimum.

§2. *The quadratic form*

Let f be a differentiable function on an open set U, and assume that all partial derivatives up to order 3 exist and are continuous. Let P be a point of U.

According to Taylor's formula, we have

$$f(P + H) = f(P) + (H \cdot \nabla)f(P) + \tfrac{1}{2}(H \cdot \nabla)^2 f(P) + R_3,$$

where R_3, the remainder term, satisfies the estimate

$$|R_3| \leqq C\|H\|^3,$$

provided $\|H\| \leqq a$ for some number $a > 0$.

If $\operatorname{grad} f(P) = O$, then

$$(H \cdot \nabla)f(P) = 0.$$

In that case, the next best approximation to the function f near P is given by the term

$$\tfrac{1}{2}(H \cdot \nabla)^2 f(P),$$

which we shall call the *quadratic term* (or term of order 2) in Taylor's formula.

Let K be a fixed vector $\neq O$ and let $H = tK$ with small values of t. Then

$$(tK \cdot \nabla)^2 f(P) = t^2 (K \cdot \nabla)^2 f(P)$$

and

$$\|H\|^3 = |t^3|\,\|K\|^3.$$

If $(K \cdot \nabla)^2 f(P) \neq 0$, then the quadratic term is much larger than the error term R_3. Hence the quadratic term describes the value of the function to within the approximation given by a cubic term.

In practice, the quadratic term is the most important. We write it out in full in the case of two variables:

$$\frac{1}{2}\left(h \frac{\partial}{\partial x} + k \frac{\partial}{\partial y}\right)^2 f(P) = \frac{1}{2}\left[h^2 \frac{\partial^2 f}{\partial x^2}(P) + 2hk \frac{\partial^2 f}{\partial x\,\partial y}(P) + k^2 \frac{\partial^2 f}{\partial y^2}(P)\right].$$

The *function* of x, y given by

$$\tfrac{1}{2}[x^2 D_1^2 f(P) + 2xy D_1 D_2 f(P) + y^2 D_2^2 f(P)]$$

is called the *quadratic form* associated to f at P (whenever $\operatorname{grad} f(P) = O$).

Example. Let $f(x, y) = e^{-(x^2+y^2)}$. Then you will verify immediately that

$$\operatorname{grad} f(0, 0) = 0.$$

Taking $P = (0,0)$ to be the origin, we see that the quadratic form associated to f at P is

$$-(x^2 + y^2).$$

Indeed, an easy computation shows that $D_1^2 f(O) = -2$, $D_1 D_2 f(O) = 0$ and $D_2^2 f(O) = -2$. Substituting these values in the general formula gives the desired expression $-(x^2 + y^2)$.

EXERCISE

1. Find the quadratic form associated to the function f at the critical points P in the Exercises of §1.

§3. *Boundary points*

In considering intervals, we had to distinguish between closed and open intervals. We must do an analogous distinction when considering sets of points in space.

Let S be a set of points, in some n-space. Let P be a point of S. We shall say that P is an *interior point* of S if there exists an open ball B of positive radius, centered at P, and such that B is contained in S. The next picture illustrates an interior point (for the set consisting of the region enclosed by the curve).

We have also drawn an open ball around P.

From the very definition, we conclude that the set consisting of all interior points of S is an open set.

A point P (not necessarily in S) is called a *boundary point* of S if every open ball B centered at P includes a point of S, and also a point which is not in S. We illustrate a boundary point in the following picture:

For example, the set of boundary points of the closed ball of radius $a > 0$ is the sphere of radius a. In 2-space, the plane, the region consisting of all points with $y > 0$ is open. Its boundary points are the points lying on the x-axis.

If a set contains all of its boundary points, then we shall say that the set is *closed*.

Finally, a set is said to be *bounded* if there exists a number $b > 0$ such that, for every point X of the set, we have

$$\|X\| \leqq b.$$

We are now in a position to state the existence of maxima and minima for continuous functions.

THEOREM 2. *Let S be a closed and bounded set. Let f be a continuous function defined on S. Then f has a maximum and a minimum in S. In other words, there exists a point P in S such that*

$$f(P) \geqq f(X)$$

for all X in S, and there exists a point Q in S such that

$$f(Q) \leqq f(X)$$

for all X in S.

We shall not prove this theorem. It depends on an analysis which is beyond the level of this course.

When trying to find a maximum (say) for a function f, one should first determine the critical points of f in the interior of the region under consideration. If a maximum lies in the interior, it must be among these critical points.

Next, one should investigate the function on the boundary of the region. By parametrizing the boundary, one frequently reduces the problem of finding a maximum on the boundary to a lower-dimensional problem, to which the technique of critical points can also be applied.

Finally, one has to compare the possible maximum of f on the boundary and in the interior to determine which points are maximum points.

Example. In the Example in §1, we observe that the function $f(x, y) = e^{-(x^2+y^2)}$ becomes very small as x or y becomes large. Consider some big closed disc centered at the origin. We know by Theorem 2 that the function has a maximum in this disc. Since the value of the function is small on the boundary, it follows that this maximum must be an interior point, and hence that the maximum is a critical point. But we found in the Example in §1 that the only critical point is at the origin. Hence we conclude that the origin is *the* only maximum of the function $f(x, y)$. The value of f at the origin is $f(0, 0) = 1$. Furthermore, the function has no minimum, because $f(x, y)$ is always positive and approaches 0 as x and y become large.

Find the maximum and minimum points of the following functions in the indicated region.

1. $x + y$ in the square with corners at $(\pm 1, \pm 1)$.

2. $x + y + z$ in the region $x^2 + y^2 + z^2 \leqq 1$.

3. $xy - (1 - x^2 - y^2)^{1/2}$ in the region $x^2 + y^2 \leqq 1$.

4. $144x^3y^2(1 - x - y)$ in the region $x \geqq 0$ and $y \geqq 0$ (the first quadrant together with its boundary).

5. $(x^2 + 2y^2)e^{-(x^2+y^2)}$ in the plane.

6. $(x^2 + y^2)^{-1}$ in the region $(x - 2)^2 + y^2 \leqq 1$.

7. Which of the following functions have a maximum and which have a minimum in the whole plane?

(a) $(x + 2y)e^{-x^2-y^4}$ (b) e^{x-y}

(c) $e^{x^2-y^2}$ (d) $e^{x^2+y^{10}}$

(e) $(3x^2 + 2y^2)e^{-(4x^2+y^2)}$ (f) $-x^2e^{x^4+y^{10}}$

(g) $\begin{cases} \dfrac{x^2 + y^2}{|x| + |y|} & \text{if } (x, y) \neq (0, 0) \\ 0 & \text{if } (x, y) = (0, 0) \end{cases}$

8. What is the point on the curve $(\cos t, \sin t, \sin (t/2))$ farthest from the origin?

§4. Lagrange multipliers

In this section, we shall investigate another method for finding the maximum or minimum of a function on some set of points. This method is particularly well adapted to the case when the set of points is described by means of an equation.

We shall work in 3-space. Let g be a differentiable function of three variables x, y, z. We consider the surface

$$g(X) = 0.$$

Let U be an open set containing this surface, and let f be a differentiable function defined for all points of U. We wish to find those points P on the surface $g(X) = 0$ such that $f(P)$ is a maximum or a minimum on the surface. In other words, we wish to find all points P such that $g(P) = 0$, and either

$$f(P) \geqq f(X) \quad \text{for all } X \text{ such that } g(X) = 0,$$

or

$$f(P) \leqq f(X) \quad \text{for all } X \text{ such that } g(X) = 0.$$

Any such point will be called an *extremum for f subject to the constraint g*.

In what follows, we consider only points P such that $g(P) = 0$ but grad g $(P) \neq 0$.

We shall now show that for any extremum point P for f subject to the constraint g, there exists a number λ such that

$$\text{grad } f \ (P) = \lambda \text{ grad } g \ (P).$$

Indeed, let $X(t)$ be a (differentiable) curve on the surface passing through P, say $X(t_0) = P$. Then the function $f(X(t))$ has a maximum or a minimum at t_0. Its derivative

$$\frac{d}{dt} f(X(t))$$

is therefore equal to 0 at t_0. But this derivative is equal to

$$\text{grad } f \ (P) \cdot \dot{X}(t_0) = 0.$$

Hence grad f (P) is perpendicular to every curve on the surface passing through P. It can be shown that under these circumstances, and the hypothesis that grad g $(P) \neq O$, there exists a number λ such that

(1) $$\text{grad } f \ (P) = \lambda \text{ grad } g \ (P),$$

or in other words, grad f (P) has the same, or opposite direction, as grad g (P), provided it is not O. Intuitively, this is rather clear, since the direction of grad g (P) is the direction perpendicular to the surface, and we have seen that grad f (P) is also perpendicular to the surface. To give a complete proof would require technical arguments in linear algebra, which we shall omit.

Conversely, when we want to find an extremum point for f subject to the constraint g, we find all points P such that $g(P) = 0$, and such that relation (1) is satisfied. We can then find our extremum points among these by inspection.

(Note that this procedure is analogous to the procedure used to find maxima or minima for functions of one variable. We first determined all points at which the derivative is equal to 0, and then determined maxima or minima by inspection.)

Example. Find the extrema for the function $x^2 + y^2 + z^2$ subject to the constraint $x^2 + 2y^2 - z^2 - 1 = 0$.

Computing the partial derivatives of the functions f and g, we find that we must solve the system of equations

(a) $2x = \lambda \cdot 2x$,   (b) $2y = \lambda \cdot 4y$,

(c) $2z = \lambda \cdot (-2z)$,   (d) $g(X) = x^2 + 2y^2 - z^2 - 1 = 0$.

Let (x_0, y_0, z_0) be a solution. If $z_0 \neq 0$, then from (c) we conclude that $\lambda = -1$. The only way to solve (a) and (b) with $\lambda = -1$ is that $x = y = 0$. In that case, from (d), we would get

$$z_0^2 = -1,$$

which is impossible. Hence any solution must have $z_0 = 0$.

If $x_0 \neq 0$, then from (a) we conclude that $\lambda = 1$. From (b) and (c) we then conclude that $y_0 = z_0 = 0$. From (d), we must have $x_0 = \pm 1$. In this manner, we have obtained two solutions satisfying our conditions, namely

$$(1, 0, 0) \quad \text{and} \quad (-1, 0, 0).$$

Similarly, if $y_0 \neq 0$, we find two more solutions, namely

$$(0, \sqrt{\tfrac{1}{2}}, 0) \quad \text{and} \quad (0, -\sqrt{\tfrac{1}{2}}, 0).$$

These four points are therefore the extrema of the function f subject to the constraint g.

If we ask for the minimum of f, then a direct computation shows that the last two points

$$(0, \pm\sqrt{\tfrac{1}{2}}, 0)$$

are the only possible solutions (because $1 > \tfrac{1}{2}$).

EXERCISES

1. Find the minimum of the function $x + y^2$ subject to the constraint $2x^2 + y^2 = 1$.

2. Find the maximum value of $x^2 + xy + y^2 + yz + z^2$ on the sphere of radius 1.

3. Let $A = (1, 1, -1)$, $B = (2, 1, 3)$, $C = (2, 0, -1)$. Find the point at which the function

$$f(X) = (X - A)^2 + (X - B)^2 + (X - C)^2$$

reaches its minimum, and find the minimum value.

4. Do Exercise 3 in general, for any three distinct vectors

$$A = (a_1, a_2, a_3), \quad B = (b_1, b_2, b_3), \quad C = (c_1, c_2, c_3).$$

5. Find the maximum of the function $3x^2 + 2\sqrt{2}\,xy + 4y^2$ on the circle of radius 3 in the plane.

6. Find the maximum of the functions xyz subject to the constraints $x \geq 0$, $y \geq 0$, $z \geq 0$ and $xy + yz + xz = 2$.

7. Find the maximum and minimum distance from points on the curve

$$5x^2 + 6xy + 5y^2 = 0$$

and the origin in the plane.

8. Find the extreme values of the function $\cos^2 x + \cos^2 y$ subject to the constraint $x - y = \pi/4$ and $0 \leq x \leq \pi$.

9. Find the points on the surface $z^2 - xy = 1$ nearest to the origin.

10. Find the extreme values of the function xy subject to the condition $x + y = 1$.

11. Find the shortest distance from the point $(1, 0)$ and the curve $y^2 = 4x$.

12. Let x, y be two positive numbers. Show that

$$(xy)^{1/2} \leq \frac{x + y}{2}.$$

13. Let x, y, z be three positive numbers. Show that

$$(xyz)^{1/3} \leq \frac{x + y + z}{3}.$$

14. Generalize Exercise 13 to n numbers.

CHAPTER VIII

Multiple Integrals

When studying functions of one variable, it was possible to give essentially complete proofs for the existence of an integral of a continuous function over an interval. The investigation of the integral involved lower sums and upper sums.

In order to develop a theory of integration for functions of several variables, it becomes necessary to have techniques whose degree of sophistication is somewhat greater than that which is available to us. Hence we shall only state results, and omit proofs. These results will allow us to compute multiple integrals.

We shall also list various formulas giving double and triple integrals in terms of polar coordinates, and we give a geometric argument to make them plausible. Here again, the general formula for changing variables in a multiple integral can be handled theoretically (and elegantly) only when much more machinery is available than we have at present. These topics properly belong to an advanced calculus course, and no good purpose would be achieved by giving here a half-baked treatment.

§1. Double integrals

We begin by discussing the analogue of upper and lower sums associated with partitions.

Let R be a region of the plane, and let f be a function defined on R. We shall say that f is *bounded* if there exists a number M such that $|f(X)| \leq M$ for all X in R.

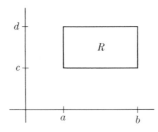

Let a, b be two numbers with $a \leq b$, and let c, d be two numbers with $c \leq d$. We consider the closed interval $[a, b]$ on the x-axis and the closed interval $[c, d]$ on the y-axis. These determine a rectangle R in the plane, consisting of all pairs of points (x, y) with $a \leq x \leq b$ and $c \leq y \leq d$.

The rectangle R above will be denoted by $[a, b] \times [c, d]$.

Consider a partition of the interval $[a, b]$, in other words a sequence of numbers:

$$x_1 = a \leqq x_2 \leqq \cdots \leqq x_{n+1} = b$$

and a partition of $[c, d]$, namely

$$y_1 = c \leqq y_2 \leqq \cdots \leqq y_{m+1} = d.$$

Each pair of small intervals $[x_i, x_{i+1}]$ and $[y_j, y_{j+1}]$ determines a small rectangle as indicated on the next figure. We shall call this small rectangle R_{ij}. Thus we may view our partitions together as determining a partition of the big rectangle into small rectangles.

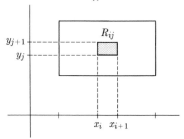

Let f be a function defined on R, and assume that f is bounded. For each pair i, j let M_{ij} be the least upper bound of the values of f on R_{ij}, in other words, M_{ij} is the least upper bound of all numbers $f(X)$, where X ranges over points in R_{ij}. This least upper bound exists because we assumed f bounded, and we can apply a standard property of the real numbers.

We take the sum of all terms

$$M_{ij}(y_{j+1} - y_j)(x_{i+1} - x_i)$$

with $1 \leqq i \leqq n$ and $1 \leqq j \leqq m$, and write this sum with the usual $\sum$ notation, namely:

$$\sum M_{ij}(y_{j+1} - y_j)(x_{i+1} - x_i).$$

This sum will be called an *upper sum* associated with the partitions and the function f.

Similarly, if m_{ij} denotes the greatest lower bound of the values of f on the small rectangle R_{ij}, then we can form a lower sum

$$\sum m_{ij}(y_{j+1} - y_j)(x_{i+1} - x_i).$$

If P_{ij} is any point in the rectangle R_{ij}, then

$$m_{ij} \leqq f(P_{ij}) \leqq M_{ij},$$

and hence the sum

$$\sum f(P_{ij})(y_{j+1} - y_j)(x_{i+1} - x_i)$$

lies between the lower and upper sum.

We shall state a theorem which gives us conditions under which there exists a unique number which is greater than or equal to every lower sum, and less than or equal to every upper sum. If such a number exists, we say that f is *integrable* on R, and we call this number its *integral* over R. We denote it by

$$\iint\limits_R f \qquad \text{or} \qquad \iint\limits_R f(x, y) \, dy \, dx.$$

Under suitable conditions, we can interpret the integral as a volume. Indeed, suppose that f is continuous, and that $f(x, y) \geqq 0$ for all (x, y) in the rectangle. The value $f(x, y)$ at a point (x, y) may be viewed as a height above the point (x, y), and we may consider the integral of f as the volume of the 3-dimensional region lying above the rectangle and bounded from above by the values of f.

We can also interpret S as a metal sheet, and a function f as giving a density distribution on S. Then the integral is interpreted as the mass of the sheet.

To state the next theorem, we need some terminology.

Let s, t be numbers with $s \leqq t$. Let f be a function defined on the closed interval $[s, t]$. If f is differentiable, and if its derivative is continuous, we shall say that f is *smooth*. Let f, g be two functions defined on $[s, t]$. If both f and g are smooth, then the set of points $(f(x), g(x))$ as x ranges over the interval will be called a *smooth curve*. (In preceding chapters we had considered curves arising from open intervals, but for this chapter, we change our meaning and deal only with closed intervals. If the interval consists of a single point, we *define* any function of that point to be differentiable, and we agree to say that its derivative is 0. If $s < t$, then at the end points, the derivative is meant to be the right or left derivative respectively.)

Let S be a region in the plane. We say as usual that S is *bounded* if there exists a number M such that $\|X\| \leqq M$ for all points X in S. The set of boundary points of S will also be called the boundary of S. We shall say that the boundary of S is *smooth* if it consists of a finite number of smooth curves.

Let S be a region in the plane, and let f be a function defined on S. As usual, we say that f is *continuous* at a point P of S if

$$\lim_{X \to P} f(X) = f(P).$$

We say that f is continuous on S if it is continuous at every point of S.

THEOREM 1. *Let R be a rectangle as above, and let f be a function defined on R, bounded, and continuous except possibly at the points lying on a finite number of smooth curves. Then f is integrable on R.*

To compute the integral we shall investigate double integrals.

Let f be a function defined on our rectangle. For each x in the interval $[a, b]$ we have a function φ of y given by $\varphi(y) = f(x, y)$, and this function φ is defined on the interval $[c, d]$. Assume that for each x this function φ is integrable over this interval (in the old sense of the word, for functions of one variable). We may then form the integral

$$\int_c^d \varphi(y) \, dy = \int_c^d f(x, y) \, dy.$$

The expression we obtain depends on the particular value of x chosen in the interval $[a, b]$, and is thus a function of x. Assume that this function is integrable over the interval $[a, b]$. We can then take the integral

$$\int_a^b \left[\int_c^d f(x, y) \, dy \right] dx, \qquad \text{also written} \qquad \int_a^b \int_c^d f(x, y) \, dy \, dx,$$

which is called the *repeated integral* of f.

Example 1. Let $f(x, y) = x^2 y$. Find the repeated integral of f over the rectangle determined by the intervals $[1, 2]$ on the x-axis and $[-3, 4]$ on the y-axis.

We find the double integral

$$\int_1^2 \int_{-3}^4 f(x, y) \, dy \, dx.$$

To do this, we first compute the integral with respect to y, namely

$$\int_{-3}^4 x^2 y \, dy.$$

For a fixed value of x, we can take x^2 out of the integral, and hence this inner integral is equal to

$$x^2 \int_{-3}^4 y \, dy = x^2 \left. \frac{y^2}{2} \right|_{-3}^4 = \frac{7x^2}{2}.$$

We then integrate with respect to x, namely

$$\int_1^2 \frac{7x^2}{2} \, dx = \frac{49}{6}.$$

Thus the integral of f over the rectangle is equal to $\frac{49}{6}$.

We shall now extend the definition of the integral to more general regions than rectangles. Let S be a bounded region, and assume that the boundary of S consists of a finite number of smooth curves. Let f be a function defined on S, which is bounded and continuous except at a finite number of smooth curves. We can always find intervals $[a, b]$ and $[c, d]$ such that S is contained in the rectangle

$$R = [a, b] \times [c, d],$$

because S is bounded. We define f on R to be equal to 0 at points lying outside S. It can be shown that the integral

$$\iint_R f$$

does not depend on the choice of rectangle R containing S, and we define the integral

$$\iint_S f$$

to be the integral of f over R.

We shall now make a list of the properties of the integral. In order to avoid repetitions, we shall assume throughout that any region we speak of is bounded, has a boundary consisting of a finite number of smooth curves, and that any function defined on a region is bounded, and continuous except on a finite number of smooth curves.

Property 1. If f, g are two functions defined on a region S, then

$$\iint_S (f + g) = \iint_S f + \iint_S g.$$

If c is a number, then

$$\iint_S cf = c\iint_S f.$$

Property 2. If f, g are two functions defined on a region S, and $f(X) \leqq g(X)$ for all points X in S, then

$$\iint_S f \leqq \iint_S g.$$

Property 3. If S can be expressed as a union of two regions S_1, S_2 having no point in common except possibly boundary points, and f is a function defined on S, then

$$\iint_S f = \iint_{S_1} f + \iint_{S_2} f.$$

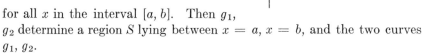

The following situation will arise frequently in practice.

Let g_1, g_2 be two smooth functions on
a closed interval $[a, b]$ $(a \leq b)$ such that
$g_1(x) \leq g_2(x)$ for all x in that interval.
Let c, d be numbers such that

$$c < g_1(x) \leq g_2(x) < d$$

for all x in the interval $[a, b]$. Then g_1,
g_2 determine a region S lying between $x = a$, $x = b$, and the two curves
g_1, g_2.

Let f be a function which is continuous on the region S, and define f
on the rectangle $[a, b] \times [c, d]$ to be equal to 0 at any point of the rectangle not lying in the region S. For any value x in the interval $[a, b]$
the integral

$$\int_c^d f(x, y) \, dy$$

can be written as a sum:

$$\int_c^{g_1(x)} f(x, y) \, dy + \int_{g_1(x)}^{g_2(x)} f(x, y) \, dy + \int_{g_2(x)}^d f(x, y) \, dy.$$

Since $f(x, y) = 0$ whenever $c \leq y < g_1(x)$ and $g_2(x) < y \leq d$, it follows
that the two extreme integrals are equal to 0. Thus the repeated integral
of f over the rectangle is in fact equal to the repeated integral

$$\int_a^b \left[\int_{g_1(x)}^{g_2(x)} f(x, y) \, dy \right] dx.$$

Regions of the type described by two functions g_1, g_2 as above are the
most common type of regions with which we deal.

The repeated integral is useful to compute a double integral because of
the following theorem.

THEOREM 2. *Let* g_1, g_2 *be two smooth functions defined on a closed
interval* $[a, b]$ $(a \leq b)$ *such that* $g_1(x) \leq g_2(x)$ *for all* x *in that interval.
Let* f *be a continuous function on the region* S *lying between* $x = a$, $x = b$,
and the two curves $g_1(x)$ *and* $g_2(x)$. *Then*

$$\iint_S f = \int_a^b \left[\int_{g_1(x)}^{g_2(x)} f(x, y) \, dy \right] dx;$$

in other words, the double integral is equal to the repeated integral.

Since we know how to evaluate the integral of a function of one variable in many cases, the preceding theorem makes it possible to compute double integrals in terms of integrals of functions of one variable.

Given a region S it is frequently possible to break it up into smaller regions having only boundary points in common, and such that each smaller region is of the type we have just described. In that case, to compute the integral of a function over S, we can apply Property 3.

Example 2. Let $f(x, y) = 2xy$. Find the integral of f over the triangle bounded by the lines $y = 0$, $y = x$, and the line $x + y = 2$.

The region is as shown at the right.

We break up our region into the portion from 0 to 1 and the portion from 1 to 2. These correspond to the small triangles S_1, S_2 indicated in the picture. Then

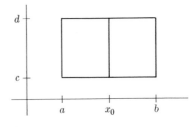

$$\iint_{S_1} f = \int_0^1 \left[\int_0^x 2xy\, dy \right] dx$$

and

$$\iint_{S_2} f = \int_1^2 \left[\int_0^{2-x} 2xy\, dy \right] dx.$$

There is no difficulty in evaluating these integrals, and we leave them to you.

Remark. In the statement of Theorem 2, one might ask why we required f to be continuous in the whole region S. The reason is that if we allow discontinuities on smooth curves, then there will be values of x such that the integral

$$\int_c^d f(x_0, y)\, dy$$

is not defined. As an example, consider a rectangle, and a function f which is equal to 1 at every point except on one vertical line.

If one defines f in a sufficiently horrible way on this line, then

$$\int_c^d f(x_0, y)\, dy$$

is not defined, i.e. the function $\varphi(y) = f(x_0, y)$ is not integrable.

EXERCISES

1. Find the value of the following repeated integrals.

(a) $\displaystyle\int_0^2 \int_1^3 (x+y)\,dx\,dy$

(b) $\displaystyle\int_0^2 \int_1^{x^2} y\,dy\,dx$

(c) $\displaystyle\int_0^1 \int_{y^2}^{y} \sqrt{x}\,dx\,dy$

(d) $\displaystyle\int_0^{\pi} \int_0^{x} x \sin y\,dy\,dx$

(e) $\displaystyle\int_1^2 \int_{y}^{y^2} dx\,dy$

(f) $\displaystyle\int_0^{\pi} \int_0^{\sin x} y\,dy\,dx$

2. Find the integral of the following functions.
   (a) $x \cos(x+y)$ over the triangle whose vertices are $(0,0)$, $(\pi,0)$, and (π,π).
   (b) e^{x+y} over the region defined by $|x| + |y| \leq 1$.
   (c) $x^2 - y^2$ over the region bounded by the curve $y = \sin x$ between 0 and π.
   (d) $x^2 + y$ over the triangle whose vertices are $(-\tfrac{1}{2}, \tfrac{1}{2})$, $(1, 2)$, $(1, -1)$.

3. Find the numerical answer in Example 2.

4. (a) Let a be a number > 0. Show that the area of the region consisting of all points (x, y) such that $|x| + |y| \leq a$, is $(2a)^2/2!$.
   (b) After you have read the beginning of the next section, show that the volume of the 3-dimensional region consisting of all points (x_1, x_2, x_3) such that $|x_1| + |x_2| + |x_3| \leq a$, is equal to $(2a)^3/3!$.
   (c) Generalize to n-space, showing that the volume of the analogous n-dimensional region is $(2a)^n/n!$.

§2. *Polar coordinates*

It is frequently more convenient to describe a region by means of polar coordinates than with the "rectangular" coordinates used in the preceding section.

Let us consider two numbers a, b with $a \leq b$ and an interval

$$a \leq \theta \leq b.$$

We shall also assume that $b \leq a + 2\pi$. Let c, d be two numbers with $0 \leq c \leq d$. Then the set of points S whose polar coordinates (θ, r) satisfy $a \leq \theta \leq b$ and $c \leq r \leq d$ form a region as shown in the figure at the right.

Consider partitions

$$a = \theta_1 \leq \theta_2 \leq \cdots \leq \theta_n = b,$$
$$c = r_1 \leq r_2 \leq \cdots \leq r_m = d$$

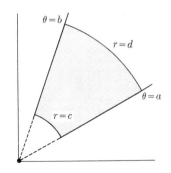

of the two intervals $[a, b]$ and $[c, d]$. Each pair of intervals $[\theta_i, \theta_{i+1}]$ and $[r_j, r_{j+1}]$ determines a small region as shown on the following figure.

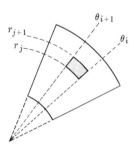

The area of such a region is equal to the difference between the area of the sector having angle $\theta_{i+1} - \theta_i$ and radius r_{j+1}, and the area of the sector having the same angle but radius r_j. The area of a sector having angle θ and radius r is equal to

$$\frac{\theta}{2\pi} \pi r^2 = \frac{\theta r^2}{2}.$$

Consequently the difference mentioned above is equal to

$$\frac{(\theta_{i+1} - \theta_i)r_{j+1}^2}{2} - \frac{(\theta_{i+1} - \theta_i)r_j^2}{2} = (\theta_{i+1} - \theta_i)\frac{(r_{j+1} + r_j)}{2}(r_{j+1} - r_j).$$

We note that

$$r_j \leqq \frac{r_{j+1} + r_j}{2} \leqq r_{j+1}.$$

Let f be a continuous function of (θ, r) on the region S, and let $\varphi(\theta, r) = f(\theta, r)r$. Then

$$\sum_{j=1}^{m} \sum_{i=1}^{n} f(\theta_i, r_j)r_j(r_{j+1} - r_j)(\theta_{i+1} - \theta_i)$$

is a Riemann sum for the function φ on the product $[a, b] \times [c, d]$. The function $f(\theta, r)$ can be viewed as a function of (x, y), since θ, r are functions of x and y. Thus there is a function $f^*(x, y)$ such that, when we put $x = r \cos \theta$ and $y = r \sin \theta$, we have $f^*(x, y) = f(\theta, r)$. Then our Riemann sum above makes the following assertion very plausible.

THEOREM 3. *Let f be a function of (θ, r) which is defined on the region S discussed above, and is bounded, continuous except at a finite number of smooth curves. Let f^* be the corresponding function of (x, y). Then*

$$\iint_S f(\theta, r)r \, dr \, d\theta = \iint_S f^*(x, y) \, dy \, dx.$$

As with rectangular coordinates, we can deal with more general regions S. Let g_1, g_2 be two smooth functions defined on the interval $[a, b]$ and assume

$$0 \leq g_1(\theta) \leq g_2(\theta)$$

for all θ in that interval. Let S be the region consisting of all points (θ, r) such that $a \leq \theta \leq b$ and $g_1(\theta) \leq r \leq g_2(\theta)$. We can select two numbers $c, d \geq 0$ such that

$$c \leq g_1(\theta) \leq g_2(\theta) \leq d$$

for all θ in the interval $[c, d]$. Let f be continuous on S, and extend f to the circular sector of radius d between $\theta = a$ and $\theta = b$ by giving it the value 0 outside S. *Then the integral of Theorem 3 taken over this sector is equal to the repeated integral*

$$\int_a^b \int_{g_1(\theta)}^{g_2(\theta)} f(\theta, r) r \, dr \, d\theta.$$

The following picture shows a typical region S under consideration. The important thing to remember about the formula of Theorem 3 is the appearance of an extra r inside the integral.

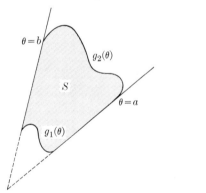

We also remark that a region could be described by taking θ as a function of r, and letting r vary between two constant values. In view of Theorem 2, we can evaluate the double integral of Theorem 3 by repeated integration first with respect to θ and then with respect to r.

In dealing with polar coordinates, it is useful to remember the equation of a circle. Let $a > 0$. Then

$$r = a \cos \theta, \qquad -\frac{\pi}{2} \leq \theta \leq \frac{\pi}{2},$$

is the equation of a circle of radius $a/2$ and center $(a/2, 0)$. Similarly,

$$r = a \sin \theta, \qquad 0 \leq \theta \leq \pi,$$

is the equation of a circle of radius $a/2$ and center $(0, a/2)$. You can easily show this, as an exercise, using the relations

$$r = \sqrt{x^2 + y^2}, \qquad x = r \cos \theta, \qquad y = r \sin \theta.$$

(*Note.* The coordinates of the center above are given in rectangular coordinates.)

EXERCISES

1. By changing to polar coordinates, find the integral of $e^{x^2+y^2}$ over the region consisting of the points (x, y) such that $x^2 + y^2 \leq 1$.

2. Find the volume of the region lying over the disc $x^2 + (y - 1)^2 \leq 1$ and bounded from above by the function $z = x^2 + y^2$.

3. Find the integral of $e^{-(x^2+y^2)}$ over the circular disc bounded by

$$x^2 + y^2 = a^2, \qquad a > 0.$$

4. What is

$$\int_{-\infty}^{\infty} \int_{-\infty}^{\infty} e^{-(x^2+y^2)} \, dx \, dy?$$

5. Find the mass of a square plate of side a if the density is proportional to the square of the distance from a vertex.

6. Find the mass of a circular disk of radius a if the density is proportional to the square of the distance from a point on the circumference. [*Hint:* Center the disk at the origin, and let the point be $(a, 0)$ in rectangular coordinates.]

7. Find the mass of a plate bounded by one arch of the curve $y = \sin x$, and the x-axis, if the density is proportional to the distance from the x-axis.

§3. *Triple integrals*

The discussion given in §1 and §2 concerning double integrals can be applied to triple integrals, or multiple integrals of any number of variables.

We shall consider only triple integrals, since our main purpose is not to give a general theoretical treatment of the subject, but some concrete, rather computational comments.

Instead of considering rectangles, we consider rectangular boxes determined by the product of three intervals. Everything we said concerning Riemann sums would apply. It must be pointed out, however, that the boundaries of our 3-dimensional regions cannot consist only of curves. They have to be parametrized surfaces. These can be defined as follows. Let a, b, c, d be numbers, $a \leq b$ and $c \leq d$. We consider the rectangle defined by $a \leq t \leq b$ and $c \leq u \leq d$. Let $f_1(t, u)$, $f_2(t, u)$, $f_3(t, u)$ be three functions defined on the rectangle, and having continuous partial derivatives. We call these *smooth*. The set of points (x, y, z) in 3-space consisting of all points

$$(f_1(t, u), f_2(t, u), f_3(t, u))$$

as (t, u) ranges over the square is called a smooth piece of surface. In 3-dimensions, we consider regions S whose boundary consists of a finite number of smooth pieces of surface. These are the analogues of the smooth curves considered in §1.

With this modification, the three properties of §1 and Theorems 1 and 2 are true, taking a triple integral instead of a double integral.

We shall enumerate the formulas for triple integrals as repeated integrals when a region is determined by inequalities as in §1 and §2. If S now denotes a 3-dimensional region, and f a suitable function on S, we denote the integral of f over S by

$$\iiint_S f \qquad \text{or} \qquad \iiint_S f(x, y, z) \, dz \, dy \, dx.$$

If f is positive, the integral can be viewed as a 4-dimensional volume of a region lying above S in 4-space. Furthermore, if S is viewed as a solid piece of material, and f is regarded as representing a density distribution over S, then the integral may be interpreted as the mass of S.

Case 1. Rectangular coordinates. Let a, b be numbers, $a \leqq b$. Let g_1, g_2 be two smooth functions defined on the interval $[a, b]$ such that

$$g_1(x) \leqq g_2(x),$$

and let $h_1(x, y) \leqq h_2(x, y)$ be two smooth functions defined on the region consisting of all points (x, y) such that

$$a \leqq x \leqq b \qquad \text{and} \qquad g_1(x) \leqq y \leqq g_2(x).$$

(By smooth functions of several variables, we shall mean functions having continuous partial derivatives.) Let S be the set of points (x, y, z) such that

$$a \leqq x \leqq b, \quad g_1(x) \leqq y \leqq g_2(x), \quad \text{and} \quad h_1(x, y) \leqq z \leqq h_2(x, y).$$

Let f be continuous on S. Then

$$\iiint_S f = \int_a^b \left[\int_{g_1(x)}^{g_2(x)} \left(\int_{h_1(x,y)}^{h_2(x,y)} f(x, y, z) \, dz \right) dy \right] dx.$$

For simplicity, the integral on the right will also be written without the brackets.

Case 2. Cylindrical coordinates. We now take polar coordinates in the (x, y)-plane, and keep our z-coordinate as before. Consider a region S

consisting of all points (θ, r, z) satisfying conditions:

$$a \leq \theta \leq b \qquad (b \leq a + 2\pi)$$
$$0 \leq g_1(\theta) \leq r \leq g_2(\theta)$$

with smooth functions g_1, g_2 defined on the interval $[a, b]$, and

$$h_1(\theta, r) \leq z \leq h_2(\theta, r)$$

with smooth functions h_1, h_2 defined on the 2-dimensional region bounded by $\theta = a$, $\theta = b$, and g_1, g_2, i.e. the region consisting of all points (θ, r) satisfying the above inequalities.

Let f be continuous on this region S. Then

$$\iiint\limits_{S} f = \int_a^b \int_{g_1(\theta)}^{g_2(\theta)} \int_{h_1(\theta,r)}^{h_2(\theta,r)} f(\theta, r, z) r \, dz \, dr \, d\theta.$$

(Observe the factor r on the right!)

Case 3. *Spherical coordinates.* Let (x, y, z) be the ordinary coordinates of a point in 3-space. We let

$$\rho = \sqrt{x^2 + y^2 + z^2}$$

and call this the *spherical* ρ in 3-space, to distinguish it from its analogue in the plane, namely the polar r.

Let E_1, E_2, E_3 be the three ordinary unit vectors in 3-space, giving rise to the coordinates (x, y, z) of a point. If X is a vector, we let φ be the angle between X and E_3, $0 \leq \varphi \leq \pi$. Then

$$X \cdot E_3 = z = \rho \cos \varphi.$$

Using the value $\rho^2 = x^2 + y^2 + z^2$, we find

$$x^2 + y^2 = \rho^2 - z^2 = \rho^2 \sin^2 \varphi.$$

Hence

$$r = \sqrt{x^2 + y^2} = \rho \sin \varphi$$

(because both r and $\sin \varphi$ are ≥ 0).

Let θ be the usual polar θ in the plane. Then

$$x = \rho \sin \varphi \cos \theta,$$
$$y = \rho \sin \varphi \sin \theta,$$

and we had

$$z = \rho \cos \varphi.$$

We call (φ, θ, ρ) the *spherical coordinates* of a point (x, y, z). Any point other than the origin has unique spherical coordinates provided we take $\rho > 0$, $0 \leqq \varphi \leqq \pi$, and $0 \leqq \theta < 2\pi$.

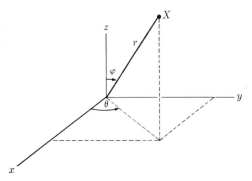

Consider now the elementary spherical region defined by the inequalities

$$\theta_1 \leqq \theta \leqq \theta_2, \qquad (\theta_2 \leqq \theta_1 + 2\pi)$$
$$0 \leqq \rho_1 \leqq \rho \leqq \rho_2,$$
$$0 \leqq \varphi_1 \leqq \varphi \leqq \varphi_2 \leqq \pi.$$

Then the volume of this box is equal to

$$\bar{\rho}^2 \sin \bar{\varphi} (\rho_2 - \rho_1)(\varphi_2 - \varphi_1)(\theta_2 - \theta_1)$$

for some number $\bar{\rho}$ between ρ_1 and ρ_2, and some number $\bar{\varphi}$ between φ_1 and φ_2.

We leave the proof of this statement as an exercise (cf. Exercise 1). It is then plausible that the following assertion is true.

Let a, b be numbers such that $0 < b - a \leqq 2\pi$.

Let $g_1(\theta)$, $g_2(\theta)$ be smooth functions of θ, defined on the interval $a \leqq \theta \leqq b$, and such that

$$0 \leqq g_1(\theta) \leqq g_2(\theta) \leqq \pi.$$

Let h_1, h_2 be functions of two variables, defined and smooth on the region consisting of all points (θ, φ) such that

$$a \leqq \theta \leqq b$$
$$g_1(\theta) \leqq \varphi \leqq g_2(\theta),$$

and such that $0 \leqq h_1(\theta, \varphi) \leqq h_2(\theta, \varphi)$ for all (θ, φ) in this region.

Let S be the 3-dimensional region consisting of all points (θ, φ, ρ) such that

$$a \leqq \theta \leqq b, \qquad g_1(\theta) \leqq \varphi \leqq g_2(\theta), \qquad h_1(\theta, \varphi) \leqq \rho \leqq h_2(\theta, \varphi).$$

Let f be a function which is continuous on S. Then

$$\iiint_S f = \int_a^b \int_{g_1(\theta)}^{g_2(\theta)} \int_{h_1(\theta,\varphi)}^{h_2(\theta,\varphi)} f(\theta, \varphi, \rho)\rho^2 \sin \varphi \, d\rho \, d\varphi \, d\theta.$$

(Observe the factor $\rho^2 \sin \varphi$ on the right!)

Example. Find the mass of a solid body S determined by the inequalities of spherical coordinates:

$$0 \leq \theta \leq \frac{\pi}{2}, \qquad \frac{\pi}{4} \leq \varphi \leq \arctan 2, \qquad 0 \leq \rho \leq \sqrt{6},$$

if the density, given as a function of the spherical coordinates (θ, φ, ρ), is equal to $1/\rho$.

To find the mass, we have to integrate the given function over the region. The integral is given by

$$\iiint_S f = \int_0^{\pi/2} \int_{\pi/4}^{\arctan 2} \int_0^{\sqrt{6}} \frac{1}{\rho}\rho^2 \sin \varphi \, d\rho \, d\varphi \, d\theta.$$

Performing the repeated integral, we obtain $\dfrac{3\pi}{2}\left(\dfrac{1}{\sqrt{2}} - \dfrac{1}{\sqrt{5}}\right)$. We note that in the present example, the limits of integration are constants, and hence the repeated integral is equal to a product of the integrals

$$\int_0^{\pi/2} d\theta \cdot \int_{\pi/4}^{\arctan 2} \sin \varphi \, d\varphi \cdot \int_0^{\sqrt{6}} \rho \, d\rho.$$

Each integration can be performed separately. Of course, this does not hold when the limits of integration are non-constant functions.

EXERCISES

1. Prove the assertion concerning the volume of the elementary spherical region made in the text by proceeding as follows.
   (a) Let $\theta_1, \theta_2, \rho_1, \varphi_1$ be numbers such that

$$0 < \theta_2 - \theta_1 \leq 2\pi, \qquad \rho_1 > 0, \qquad 0 < \varphi_1 \leq \pi.$$

Let S be the region defined by the inequalities

$$\theta_1 \leq \theta \leq \theta_2, \qquad 0 \leq \rho \leq \rho_1, \qquad 0 \leq \varphi \leq \varphi_1.$$

This region is illustrated in the figure at the left on the next page.
   The region S can be denoted by $S(\varphi_1, \rho_1)$. Show that the volume of S is

$$\tfrac{1}{3}\rho_1^3(1 - \cos \varphi_1)(\theta_2 - \theta_1).$$

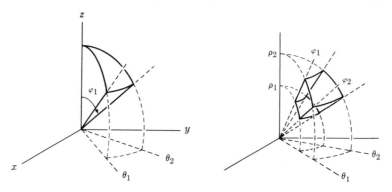

Do this by transforming to cylindrical coordinates, using the relations

$$r = \rho \sin \varphi \qquad \text{and} \qquad z = \rho \cos \varphi.$$

Assume first that $\varphi_1 \leqq \pi/2$. In cylindrical coordinates, the region can be described by the inequalities

$$\theta_1 \leqq \theta \leqq \theta_2, \qquad 0 \leqq r \leqq \rho_1 \sin \varphi_1, \qquad r \cot \varphi_1 \leqq z \leqq \sqrt{\rho_1^2 - r^2}.$$

Thus θ, r vary between fixed limits, and z varies on limits depending on r. The integral is then easy to evaluate. If $\pi/2 \leqq \varphi_1 \leqq \pi$, use a symmetry argument to show that the volume of $S(\varphi_1, \rho_1)$ is still given by the same formula.

(b) Let $\theta_1, \theta_2, \varphi_1, \varphi_2, \rho_1, \rho_2$ describe the elementary spherical region as in the text. Then the volume of this elementary spherical region can be expressed as a difference of volumes of type occurring in (a), namely:

[Volume of $S(\varphi_2, \rho_2)$ — Volume of $S(\varphi_1, \rho_2)$]
$$- \text{[Volume of } S(\varphi_2, \rho_1) - \text{Volume of } S(\varphi_1, \rho_1)].$$

These volumes are those taken first with the larger value ρ_2, with φ lying between φ_1 and φ_2, and secondly with the smaller value ρ_1, again with φ lying between φ_1 and φ_2. The situation is illustrated in the figure at the right above. You will find that the volume of the elementary spherical region is then *exactly*

$$\tfrac{1}{3}(\rho_2^3 - \rho_1^3)(\cos \varphi_1 - \cos \varphi_2)(\theta_2 - \theta_1).$$

To obtain the assertion in the text, use the mean value theorem on the first factors in this product.

2. Find the integral

$$\int_0^\pi \int_0^{\sin \theta} \int_0^{\rho \cos \theta} \rho^2 \, dz \, d\rho \, d\theta.$$

3. Find the mass of a spherical ball of radius $a > 0$ if the density at any point is equal to a constant k times the distance of that point to the center.

4. Find the mass of a spherical shell of inside radius a and outside radius b if the density at any point is inversely proportional to the distance from the center.

5. Find the integral of the function $f(x, y, z) = x^2$ over that portion of the cylinder $x^2 + y^2 = a^2$ lying between the planes $z = 0$ and $z = b > 0$.

6. Find the mass of a sphere of radius a if the density at any point is proportional to the distance from a fixed plane passing through a diameter.

7. Find the volume of the region bounded by the cylinder $y = \cos x$, and the planes

$$z = y, \qquad x = 0, \qquad x = \frac{\pi}{2}, \qquad \text{and} \qquad z = 0.$$

8. Find the volume of the region bounded above by the sphere

$$x^2 + y^2 + z^2 = 1$$

and below by the surface $z = x^2 + y^2$.

9. Find the volume of that portion of the sphere $x^2 + y^2 + z^2 = a^2$, which is inside the cylinder $r = a \sin \theta$, using cylindrical coordinates.

10. Find the volume above the cone $z^2 = x^2 + y^2$ and inside the sphere $\rho = 2a \cos \varphi$ (spherical coordinates). [Draw a picture. What is the center of the sphere? What is the equation of the cone in spherical coordinates?]

11. Find the volumes of the following regions, in 3-space.

    (a) Bounded above by the plane $z = 1$, and below by the top half of $z^2 = x^2 + y^2$.

    (b) Bounded above and below by $z^2 = x^2 + y^2$, and on the sides by $x^2 + y^2 + z^2 = 1$.

    (c) Bounded above by $z = x^2 + y^2$, below by $z = 0$, and on the sides by $x^2 + y^2 = 1$.

    (d) Bounded above by $z = x$, and below by $z = x^2 + y^2$.

12. Find the integral of the following functions over the indicated region, in 3-space.

    (a) $f(x, y, z) = x^2$ over the tetrahedron bounded by the plane $12x + 20y + 15z = 60$, and the coordinate planes.

    (b) $f(x, y, z) = y$ over the tetrahedron as in (a).

    (c) $f(x, y, z) = 7yz$ over the region on the positive side of the xz-plane, bounded by the planes $y = 0$, $z = 0$, and $z = a$ (for some positive number a), and the cylinder $x^2 + y^2 = b^2$ ($b > 0$).

CHAPTER IX

Vector Spaces

This chapter and all subsequent ones (except Chapter XIII) can be read immediately after Chapter I. In fact, we start where we left off, introducing the notions of linear independence and bases, which allow us to speak of dimension.

As usual, a collection of objects will be called a *set*. A member of the collection is also called an *element* of the set. It is useful in practice to use short symbols to denote certain sets. For instance we denote by **R** the set of all numbers. To say that "x is a number" or that "x is an element of **R**" amounts to the same thing. The set of n-tuples of numbers will be denoted by $\mathbf{R}^n$. Thus "X is an element of $\mathbf{R}^n$" and "X is an n-tuple" mean the same thing. Instead of saying that u is an element of a set S, we shall also frequently say that u *lies in* S. If S and S' are two sets, and if every element of S' is an element of S, then we say that S' is a *subset* of S. Thus the set of rational numbers is a subset of the set of (real) numbers. To say that S is a subset of S' is to say that S is part of S'.

§1. Definition

We have met already several types of objects which can be added and multiplied by numbers. Among these are vectors (of the same dimension) and functions. It is now convenient to define in general a notion which includes these as a special case.

A *vector space* V is a set of objects which can be added and multiplied by numbers, in such a way that the sum of two elements of V is again an element of V, the product of an element of V by a number is an element of V, and the following properties are satisfied:

VS 1. *Given elements u, v, w of V we have*

$$(u + v) + w = u + (v + w).$$

VS 2. *There is an element of V, denoted by O, such that*

$$O + u = u + O = u$$

for all elements u of V.

VS 3. *Given an element u of V, the element $(-1)u$ is such that*

$$u + (-1)u = O.$$

VS 4. *For all elements u, v of V, we have*

$$u + v = v + u.$$

VS 5. *If c is a number, then* $c(u + v) = cu + cv$.

VS 6. *If a, b are two numbers, then* $(a + b)v = av + bv$.

VS 7. *If a, b are two numbers, then* $(ab)v = a(bv)$.

VS 8. *For all elements u of V, we have* $1 \cdot u = u$ *(1 here is the number one).*

We have used all these rules when dealing with vectors, or with functions but we wish to be more systematic from now on, and hence have made a list of them. Further properties which can be easily deduced from these are listed as exercises and will be assumed from now on.

The sum $u + (-1)v$ is usually written $u - v$. We also write $-v$ instead of $(-1)v$.

We shall use 0 to denote the number zero, and O to denote the element of any vector space V satisfying property VS 2. We also call it zero, but there is never any possibility of confusion. We observe that this zero element O is uniquely determined by condition VS 2 (cf. Exercise 5).

It is possible to add several elements of a vector space. Suppose we wish to add four elements, say u, v, w, z. We first add any two of them, then a third, and finally a fourth. Using the rules VS 1 and VS 4, we see that it does not matter in which order we perform the additions. This is exactly the same situation as we had with vectors. For example, we have

$$\begin{aligned}
((u + v) + w) + z &= (u + (v + w)) + z \\
&= ((v + w) + u) + z \\
&= (v + w) + (u + z)
\end{aligned}$$

etc.

Thus it is customary to leave out the parentheses, and write simply

$$u + v + w + z.$$

The same remark applies to the sum of any number n of elements of V, and a formal proof could easily be given by induction.

Let V be a vector space, and let W be a subset of V. Assume that W satisfies the following conditions.

(i) If v, w are elements of W, their sum $v + w$ is also an element of W.

(ii) If v is an element of W and c a number, then cv is an element of W.

(iii) The element O of V is also an element of W.

Then W itself is a vector space. Indeed, properties VS 1 through VS 8 being satisfied for all elements of V are satisfied a fortiori for the elements of W. We shall call W a *subspace* of V.

Example 1. Let $V = \mathbf{R}^n$ and let W be the set of vectors in V whose last coordinate is equal to 0. Then W is a subspace of V, which we could identify with $\mathbf{R}^{n-1}$.

Example 2. Let V be an arbitrary vector space, and let $v_1, \ldots, v_n$ be elements of V. Let $x_1, \ldots, x_n$ be numbers. An expression of type

$$x_1 v_1 + \cdots + x_n v_n$$

is called a *linear combination* of $v_1, \ldots, v_n$. The set of all linear combinations of $v_1, \ldots, v_n$ is a subspace of V.

Proof. Let $y_1, \ldots, y_n$ be numbers. Then

$$(x_1 v_1 + \cdots + x_n v_n) + (y_1 v_1 + \cdots + y_n v_n) = (x_1 + y_1)v_1 + \cdots + (x_n + y_n)v_n.$$

Thus the sum of two elements of W is again an element of W, i.e. a linear combination of $v_1, \ldots, v_n$. Futhermore, if c is a number, then

$$c(x_1 v_1 + \cdots + x_n v_n) = c x_1 v_1 + \cdots + c x_n v_n$$

is a linear combination of $v_1, \ldots, v_n$, and hence is an element of W. Finally,

$$O = 0 v_1 + \cdots + 0 v_n$$

is an element of W. This proves that W is a subspace of V.

In Example 2, the subspace W is called the subspace *generated* by $v_1, \ldots, v_n$. If $W = V$, i.e. if every element of V is a linear combination of $v_1, \ldots, v_n$, then we say that $v_1, \ldots, v_n$ *generate* V.

Example 3. Let V be the set of all functions defined for all numbers. If f, g are two functions, then we know how to form their sum $f + g$. It is the function whose value at a number t is $f(t) + g(t)$. We also know how to multiply f by a number c. It is the function cf whose value at a number t is $cf(t)$. In dealing with functions, we have used properties VS 1 through VS 8 many times. We now realize that the set of functions is a vector space.

If f, g are two continuous functions, then $f + g$ is continuous. If c is a number, then cf is continuous. The zero function is continuous. Hence the continuous functions form a subspace of the vector space of all functions.

If f, g are two differentiable functions, then their sum $f + g$ is differentiable. If c is a number, then cf is differentiable. The zero function is differentiable. Hence the differentiable functions form a subspace of the vector space of all functions. Furthermore, every differentiable function is continuous. Hence the differentiable functions form a subspace of the vector space of continuous functions.

Consider the two functions e^t, e^{2t}. These generate a subspace of the space of all differentiable functions. The function $3e^t + 2e^{2t}$ is an element of this subspace. So is the function $\sqrt{2}\, e^t + \pi e^{2t}$.

Exercises

1. Let V be a vector space. Using the properties VS 1 through VS 8, show that if v is an element of V and 0 is the number zero, then $0v = O$.

2. Let c be a number $\neq 0$, and v an element of V. Prove that if $cv = O$, then $v = O$.

3. In the vector space of functions, what is the function satisfying the condition VS 2?

4. Let V be a vector space and v, w two elements of V. If $v + w = O$, show that $w = -v$.

5. Let V be a vector space, and v, w two elements of V such that $v + w = v$. Show that $w = O$.

§2. *Bases*

Let V be a vector space, and let $v_1, \ldots, v_n$ be elements of V. We shall say that $v_1, \ldots, v_n$ are *linearly dependent* if there exist numbers $a_1, \ldots, a_n$ not all equal to 0 such that

$$a_1 v_1 + \cdots + a_n v_n = O.$$

If there do not exist such numbers, then we say that $v_1, \ldots, v_n$ are *linearly independent*.

Example 1. Let $V = \mathbf{R}^n$ and consider the vectors

$$E_1 = (1, 0, \ldots, 0)$$
$$\vdots$$
$$E_n = (0, 0, \ldots, 1).$$

Then $E_1, \ldots, E_n$ are linearly independent. Indeed, let $a_1, \ldots, a_n$ be numbers such that $a_1 E_1 + \cdots + a_n E_n = O$. Since

$$a_1 E_1 + \cdots + a_n E_n = (a_1, \ldots, a_n),$$

it follows that all $a_i = 0$.

Example 2. Let V be the vector space of all functions of a variable t. Let $f_1(t), \ldots, f_n(t)$ be n functions. To say that they are linearly dependent is to say that there exist n numbers $a_1, \ldots, a_n$ not all equal to 0 such that

$$a_1 f_1(t) + \cdots + a_n f_n(t) = 0$$

for *all* values of t.

The two functions e^t, e^{2t} are linearly independent. To prove this, suppose that there are numbers a, b such that

$$ae^t + be^{2t} = 0$$

(for all values of t). Differentiate this relation. We obtain

$$ae^t + 2be^{2t} = 0.$$

Subtract the first from the second relation. We obtain $be^t = 0$, and hence $b = 0$. From the first relation, it follows that $ae^t = 0$, and hence $a = 0$. Hence e^t, e^{2t} are linearly independent.

Consider again an arbitrary vector space V. Let $v_1, \ldots, v_n$ be linearly independent elements of V. Let $x_1, \ldots, x_n$ and $y_1, \ldots, y_n$ be numbers. Suppose that we have

$$x_1 v_1 + \cdots + x_n v_n = y_1 v_1 + \cdots + y_n v_n.$$

In other words, two linear combinations of $v_1, \ldots, v_n$ are equal. Then we must have $x_i = y_i$ for each $i = 1, \ldots, n$. Indeed, subtracting the right-hand side from the left-hand side, we get

$$x_1 v_1 - y_1 v_1 + \cdots + x_n v_n - y_n v_n = O.$$

We can write this relation also in the form

$$(x_1 - y_1)v_1 + \cdots + (x_n - y_n)v_n = O.$$

By definition, we must have $x_i - y_i = 0$ for all $i = 1, \ldots, n$, thereby proving our assertion.

If elements $v_1, \ldots, v_n$ of V generate V and in addition are linearly independent, then the set consisting of these elements is called a *basis* of V. We shall also say that the elements $v_1, \ldots, v_n$ *constitute* or *form* a basis of V.

As a matter of notation, if $s_1, \ldots, s_n$ are objects, then the set consisting of these objects is denoted by $\{s_1, \ldots, s_n\}$. If elements $v_1, \ldots, v_n$ of V generate V and are linearly independent, then we shall say that $\{v_1, \ldots, v_n\}$ is a basis.

The vectors $E_1, \ldots, E_n$ of Example 1 form a basis of $\mathbf{R}^n$.

Let W be the vector space of functions generated by the two functions e^t, e^{2t}. Then $\{e^t, e^{2t}\}$ is a basis of W.

Let V be a vector space, and let $\{v_1, \ldots, v_n\}$ be a basis of V. The elements of V can be represented by n-tuples relative to this basis, as follows

If an element v of V is written as a linear combination

$$v = x_1 v_1 + \cdots + x_n v_n$$

of the basis elements, then we call $(x_1, \ldots, x_n)$ the *coordinates* of v with respect to our basis, and we call x_i the i-th coordinate.

For example, let V be the vector space of functions generated by the two functions e^t, e^{2t}. Then the coordinates of the function

$$3e^t + 5e^{2t}$$

with respect to the basis e^t, e^{2t} are $(3, 5)$.

Example 3. Show that the vectors $(1, 1)$ and $(-3, 2)$ are linearly independent.

Let a, b be two numbers such that

$$a(1, 1) + b(-3, 2) = O.$$

Writing this equation in terms of components, we find

$$a - 3b = 0,$$
$$a + 2b = 0.$$

This is a system of two equations which we solve for a and b. Subtracting the second from the first, we get $-5b = 0$, whence $b = 0$. Substituting in either equation, we find $a = 0$. Hence a, b are both 0, and our vectors are linearly independent.

Example 4. Find the coordinates of $(1, 0)$ with respect to the two vectors $(1, 1)$ and $(-1, 2)$.

We must find numbers a, b such that

$$a(1, 1) + b(-1, 2) = (1, 0).$$

Writing this equation in terms of coordinates, we find

$$a - b = 1,$$
$$a + 2b = 0.$$

Solving for a and b in the usual manner yields $b = -\frac{1}{3}$ and $a = \frac{2}{3}$. Hence the coordinates of $(1, 0)$ with respect to $(1, 1)$ and $(-1, 2)$ are $(\frac{2}{3}, -\frac{1}{3})$.

Let $\{v_1, \ldots, v_n\}$ be a set of elements of a vector space V. Let r be a positive integer $\leq n$. We shall say that $\{v_1, \ldots, v_r\}$ is a *maximal* subset of linearly independent elements if $v_1, \ldots, v_r$ are linearly independent, and if in addition, given any v_i with $i > r$, the elements $v_1, \ldots, v_r, v_i$ are linearly dependent.

The next theorem gives us a useful criterion to determine when a set of elements of a vector space is a basis.

THEOREM 1. *Let* $\{ v_1, \ldots, v_n \}$ *be a set of generators of a vector space* V. *Let* $\{ v_1, \ldots, v_r \}$ *be a maximal subset of linearly independent elements. Then* $\{ v_1, \ldots, v_r \}$ *is a basis of* V.

Proof. We must prove that $v_1, \ldots, v_r$ generate V. We shall first prove that each v_i (for $i > r$) is a linear combination of $v_1, \ldots, v_r$. By hypothesis, given v_i, there exist numbers $x_1, \ldots, x_r, y$ not all 0, such that

$$x_1 v_1 + \cdots + x_r v_r + y v_i = O.$$

Furthermore, $y \neq 0$, because otherwise, we would have a relation of linear dependence for $v_1, \ldots, v_r$. Hence we can solve for v_i, namely

$$v_i = \frac{x_1}{-y} v_1 + \cdots + \frac{x_r}{-y} v_r,$$

thereby showing that v_i is a linear combination of $v_1, \ldots, v_r$.

Next, let v be any element of V. There exist numbers $c_1, \ldots, c_n$ such that

$$v = c_1 v_1 + \cdots + c_n v_n.$$

In this relation, we can replace each v_i ($i > r$) by a linear combination of $v_1, \ldots, v_r$. If we do this, and then collect terms, we find that we have expressed v as a linear combination of $v_1, \ldots, v_r$. This proves that $v_1, \ldots, v_r$ generate V, and hence form a basis of V.

EXERCISES

1. Show that the following vectors are linearly independent.

    (a) $(1, 1, 1)$ and $(0, 1, -1)$ (b) $(1, 0)$ and $(1, 1)$
    (c) $(-1, 1, 0)$ and $(0, 1, 2)$ (d) $(2, -1)$ and $(1, 0)$
    (e) $(\pi, 0)$ and $(0, 1)$ (f) $(1, 2)$ and $(1, 3)$
    (g) $(1, 1, 0)$, $(1, 1, 1)$ and $(0, 1, -1)$
    (h) $(0, 1, 1)$, $(0, 2, 1)$ and $(1, 5, 3)$

2. Express the given vector X as a linear combination of the given vectors A, B, and find the coordinates of X with respect to A, B.

    (a) $X = (1, 0)$, $A = (1, 1)$, $B = (0, 1)$
    (b) $X = (2, 1)$, $A = (1, -1)$, $B = (1, 1)$
    (c) $X = (1, 1)$, $A = (2, 1)$, $B = (-1, 0)$
    (d) $X = (4, 3)$, $A = (2, 1)$, $B = (-1, 0)$

3. Find the coordinates of the vector X with respect to the vectors A, B, C.

(a) $X = (1, 0, 0)$, $A = (1, 1, 1)$, $B = (-1, 1, 0)$, $C = (1, 0, -1)$
(b) $X = (1, 1, 1)$, $A = (0, 1, -1)$, $B = (1, 1, 0)$, $C = (1, 0, 2)$
(c) $X = (0, 0, 1)$, $A = (1, 1, 1)$, $B = (-1, 1, 0)$, $C = (1, 0, -1)$

4. Let (a, b) and (c, d) be two vectors in the plane. If $ad - bc = 0$, show that they are linearly dependent. If $ad - bc \neq 0$, show that they are linearly independent.

5. Consider the vector space of all functions of a variable t. Show that the following pairs of functions are linearly independent.

(a) $1, t$ (b) t, t^2 (c) t, t^4 (d) e^t, t (e) te^t, e^{2t} (f) $\sin t, \cos t$ (g) $t, \sin t$
(h) $\sin t, \sin 2t$ (i) $\cos t, \cos 3t$

6. Consider the vector space of functions defined for $t > 0$. Show that the following pairs of functions are linearly independent.

(a) $t, 1/t$ (b) $e^t, \log t$

7. What are the coordinates of the function $3 \sin t + 5 \cos t = f(t)$ with respect to the basis $\{\sin t, \cos t\}$?

8. Let D be the derivative d/dt. Let $f(t)$ be as in Exericse 7. What are the coordinates of the function $Df(t)$ with respect to the basis of Exercise 7?

9. Let $A_1, \ldots, A_r$ be vectors in $\mathbf{R}^n$ and assume that they are mutually perpendicular (i.e. any two of them are perpendicular), and that none of them is equal to O. Prove that they are linearly independent.

10. Let V be the vector space of continuous functions on the interval $[-\pi, \pi]$. If f, g are two continuous functions on this interval, define their scalar product $\langle f, g \rangle$ to be

$$\langle f, g \rangle = \int_{-\pi}^{\pi} f(t)g(t) \, dt.$$

Show that the functions $\sin nt$ $(n = 1, 2, 3, \ldots)$ are mutually perpendicular, i.e. that the scalar product of any two of them is equal to 0.

11. Show that the functions $\sin t$, $\sin 2t$, $\sin 3t$, $\ldots$, $\sin nt$ are linearly independent, for any integer $n \geq 1$.

CHAPTER X

Linear Equations and Bases

You have met linear equations in elementary school. Linear equations are simply equations like

$$2x + y + z = 1,$$
$$5x - y + 7z = 0.$$

You have learned to solve such equations by the successive elimination of the variables. In this chapter, we shall review the theory of such equations, dealing with equations in n variables, and interpreting our results from the point of view of vectors. Several geometric interpretations for the solutions of the equations will be given.

§1. Matrices

We consider a new kind of object, matrices.

Let n, m be two integers ≥ 1. An array of numbers

$$\begin{pmatrix} a_{11} & a_{12} & a_{13} & \cdots & a_{1n} \\ a_{21} & a_{22} & a_{23} & \cdots & a_{2n} \\ \vdots & \vdots & \vdots & & \vdots \\ a_{m1} & a_{m2} & a_{m3} & \cdots & a_{mn} \end{pmatrix}$$

is called a *matrix*. We can abbreviate the notation for this matrix by writing it (a_{ij}), $i = 1, \ldots, m$ and $j = 1, \ldots, n$. We say that it is an m by n matrix, or an $m \times n$ matrix. The matrix has m *rows* and n *columns*. For instance, the first column is

$$\begin{pmatrix} a_{11} \\ a_{21} \\ \vdots \\ a_{m1} \end{pmatrix}$$

and the second row is $(a_{21}, a_{22}, \ldots, a_{2n})$. We call a_{ij} the *ij-entry* or *ij-component* of the matrix.

Example 1. The following is a 2×3 matrix:

$$\begin{pmatrix} 1 & 1 & -2 \\ -1 & 4 & -5 \end{pmatrix}.$$

It has two rows and three columns.

113

The rows are $(1, 1, -2)$ and $(-1, 4, -5)$. The columns are

$$\begin{pmatrix} 1 \\ -1 \end{pmatrix}, \quad \begin{pmatrix} 1 \\ 4 \end{pmatrix}, \quad \begin{pmatrix} -2 \\ -5 \end{pmatrix}.$$

Thus the rows of a matrix may be viewed as n-tuples, and the columns may be viewed as vertical m-tuples. A vertical m-tuple is also called a *column vector*.

A vector $(x_1, \ldots, x_n)$ is a $1 \times n$ matrix. A column vector

$$\begin{pmatrix} x_1 \\ \vdots \\ x_n \end{pmatrix}$$

is an $n \times 1$ matrix.

When we write a matrix in the form (a_{ij}), then i denotes the row and j denotes the column. In Example 1, we have for instance $a_{11} = 1$, $a_{23} = -5$.

A single number (a) may be viewed as a 1×1 matrix.

Let (a_{ij}), $i = 1, \ldots, m$ and $j = 1, \ldots, n$ be a matrix. If $m = n$, then we say that it is a *square* matrix. Thus

$$\begin{pmatrix} 1 & 2 \\ -1 & 0 \end{pmatrix} \quad \text{and} \quad \begin{pmatrix} 1 & -1 & 5 \\ 2 & 1 & -1 \\ 3 & 1 & -1 \end{pmatrix}$$

are both square matrices.

We have a *zero matrix*, in which $a_{ij} = 0$ for all i, j. It looks like this:

$$\begin{pmatrix} 0 & 0 & 0 & \cdots & 0 \\ 0 & 0 & 0 & \cdots & 0 \\ \vdots & \vdots & \vdots & & \vdots \\ 0 & 0 & 0 & \cdots & 0 \end{pmatrix}.$$

We shall write it O. We note that we have met so far with the zero number, zero vector, and zero matrix.

We shall now define addition of matrices and multiplication of matrices by numbers.

We define addition of matrices only when they have the same size. Thus let m, n be fixed integers ≥ 1. Let $A = (a_{ij})$ and $B = (b_{ij})$ be two $m \times n$ matrices. We define $A + B$ to be the matrix whose entry in the i-th row and j-th column is $a_{ij} + b_{ij}$. In other words, we add matrices of the same size componentwise.

Example 2. Let

$$A = \begin{pmatrix} 1 & -1 & 0 \\ 2 & 3 & 4 \end{pmatrix} \quad \text{and} \quad B = \begin{pmatrix} 5 & 1 & -1 \\ 2 & 1 & -1 \end{pmatrix}.$$

Then

$$A + B = \begin{pmatrix} 6 & 0 & -1 \\ 4 & 4 & 3 \end{pmatrix}.$$

If A, B are both $1 \times n$ matrices, i.e. n-tuples, then we note that our addition of matrices coincides with the addition which we defined in Chapter I for n-tuples.

If O is the zero matrix, then for any matrix A (of the same size, of course), we have $O + A = A + O = A$. This is trivially verified.

We shall now define the multiplication of a matrix by a number. Let c be a number, and $A = (a_{ij})$ be a matrix. We define cA to be the matrix whose ij-component is ca_{ij}. We write $cA = (ca_{ij})$. Thus we multiply each component of A by c.

Example 3. Let A, B be as in Example 2. Let $c = 2$. Then

$$2A = \begin{pmatrix} 2 & -2 & 0 \\ 4 & 6 & 8 \end{pmatrix} \quad \text{and} \quad 2B = \begin{pmatrix} 10 & 2 & -2 \\ 4 & 2 & -2 \end{pmatrix}.$$

We also have:

$$(-1)A = -A = \begin{pmatrix} -1 & 1 & 0 \\ -2 & -3 & -4 \end{pmatrix}.$$

For all matrices A, we find that $A + (-1)A = O$.

We leave it as an exercise to verify that all properties VS1 through VS8 are satisfied by our rules for addition of matrices and multiplication of matrices by numbers. The main thing to observe here is that addition of matrices is defined in terms of the components, and for the addition of components, the conditions analogous to VS1 through VS4 are satisfied. They are standard properties of numbers. Similarly, VS5 through VS8 are true for multiplication of matrices by numbers, because the corresponding properties for the multiplication of numbers are true.

We see that the matrices (of a given size $m \times n$) form a vector space, which we may denote by $\mathfrak{M}_{m,n}$.

We define one more notion related to a matrix. Let $A = (a_{ij})$ be an $m \times n$ matrix. The $n \times m$ matrix $B = (b_{ji})$ such that $b_{ji} = a_{ij}$ is called the *transpose* of A, and is also denoted by ${}^t A$. Taking the transpose of a matrix amounts to changing rows into columns and vice versa. If A is the matrix which we wrote down at the beginning of this section, then ${}^t A$ is the matrix

$$\begin{pmatrix} a_{11} & a_{21} & a_{31} & \cdots & a_{m1} \\ a_{12} & a_{22} & a_{32} & \cdots & a_{m2} \\ \vdots & \vdots & \vdots & & \vdots \\ a_{1n} & a_{2n} & a_{3n} & \cdots & a_{mn} \end{pmatrix}.$$

To take a special case:

$$\text{If } A = \begin{pmatrix} 2 & 1 & 0 \\ 1 & 3 & 5 \end{pmatrix} \quad \text{then} \quad {}^t A = \begin{pmatrix} 2 & 1 \\ 1 & 3 \\ 0 & 5 \end{pmatrix}.$$

If $A = (2, 1, -4)$ is a *row vector*, then

$$ {}^t A = \begin{pmatrix} 2 \\ 1 \\ -4 \end{pmatrix} $$

is a *column vector*.

EXERCISES

1. Let
$$ A = \begin{pmatrix} 1 & 2 & 3 \\ -1 & 0 & 2 \end{pmatrix} \quad \text{and} \quad B = \begin{pmatrix} -1 & 5 & -2 \\ 1 & 1 & -1 \end{pmatrix}. $$

Find $A + B$, $3B$, $-2B$, $A + 2B$, $2A + B$, $A - B$, $A - 2B$, $B - A$.

2. Let
$$ A = \begin{pmatrix} 1 & -1 \\ 2 & 1 \end{pmatrix} \quad \text{and} \quad B = \begin{pmatrix} -1 & 1 \\ 0 & -3 \end{pmatrix}. $$

Find $A + B$, $3B$, $-2B$, $A + 2B$, $A - B$, $B - A$.

3. In Exercise 1, find ${}^t A$ and ${}^t B$.

4. In Exercise 2, find ${}^t A$ and ${}^t B$.

5. If A, B are arbitrary $m \times n$ matrices, show that ${}^t(A + B) = {}^t A + {}^t B$.

6. If c is a number, show that ${}^t(cA) = c\, {}^t A$.

7. If $A = (a_{ij})$ is a square matrix, then the elements a_{ii} are called the *diagonal* elements. How do the diagonal elements of A and ${}^t A$ differ?

8. Find ${}^t(A + B)$ and ${}^t A + {}^t B$ in Exercise 2.

9. Find $A + {}^t A$ and $B + {}^t B$ in Exercise 2.

10. A matrix A is said to be *symmetric* if $A = {}^t A$. Show that for any square matrix A, the matrix $A + {}^t A$ is symmetric.

11. Write down the row vectors and column vectors of the matrices A, B in Exercise 1.

12. Write down the row vectors and column vectors of the matrices A, B in Exercise 2.

§2. *Homogeneous linear equations*

Let $A = (a_{ij})$, $i = 1, \ldots, m$ and $j = 1, \ldots, n$ be a matrix. Let $b_1, \ldots, b_m$ be numbers. Equations like

(*)
$$ \begin{aligned} a_{11}x_1 + \cdots + a_{1n}x_n &= b_1 \\ &\vdots \\ a_{m1}x_1 + \cdots + a_{mn}x_n &= b_m \end{aligned} $$

are called linear equations. We also say that (*) is a system of linear equations. The system is said to be *homogeneous* if all the numbers $b_1, \ldots, b_m$ are equal to 0. The number n is called the number of *unknowns*, and m is the number of equations.

The system of equations

$$
\begin{aligned}
a_{11}x_1 + \cdots + a_{1n}x_n &= 0 \\
&\vdots \\
a_{m1}x_1 + \cdots + a_{mn}x_n &= 0
\end{aligned}
$$

(**)

will be called the *homogeneous system associated with* (*). In this section, we study the homogeneous system (**).

The system (**) always has a solution, namely the solution obtained by letting all $x_i = 0$. This solution will be called the *trivial* solution. A solution $(x_1, \ldots, x_n)$ such that some x_i is $\neq 0$ is called *non-trivial*.

We shall be interested in the case when the number of unknowns is greater than the number of equations, and we shall see that in that case, there always exists a non-trivial solution.

Before dealing with the general case, we shall study examples.

First, suppose that we have a single equation, like

$$2x + y - 4z = 0.$$

To find a non-trivial solution, we give all the variables except the first a special value $\neq 0$, say $y = 1$, $z = 1$. We then solve for x. We find $2x - (-y) + 4z = 3$, whence $x = \frac{2}{3}$.

Next, consider a pair of equations, say

$$(1) \qquad\qquad 2x + 3y - z = 0,$$

$$(2) \qquad\qquad x + y + z = 0.$$

We reduce the problem of solving these simultaneous equations to the preceding case of one equation, by eliminating one variable. Thus we multiply the second equation by 2 and subtract it from the first equation, getting

$$(3) \qquad\qquad y - 3z = 0.$$

Now we meet one equation in more than one variable. We give z any value $\neq 0$, say $z = 1$, and solve for y, namely $y = 3$. We then solve for x from the second equation, and obtain $x = -4$. The values which we have obtained for x, y, z are also solutions of the first equation, because the first equation is (in an obvious sense) the sum of equation (2) multiplied by 2, and equation (3).

The procedure which we shall use in general is merely the general formulation of the elimination carried out above on numerical examples.

Consider our system of homogeneous equations (**). Let $A_1, \ldots, A_m$ be the row vectors of the matrix (a_{ij}). Then we can rewrite our equations (**) in the form

$$A_1 \cdot X = 0$$

(**)
$$\vdots$$

$$A_m \cdot X = 0.$$

Geometrically, to find a solution of (**) amounts to finding a vector X which is perpendicular to $A_1, \ldots, A_m$. Using the notation of the dot product will make it easier to formulate the proof of our main theorem, namely:

THEOREM 1. *Let*

$$a_{11}x_1 + \cdots + a_{1n}x_n = 0$$
$$\vdots$$
$$a_{m1}x_1 + \cdots + a_{mn}x_n = 0$$

be a system of m linear equations in n unknowns, and assume that $n > m$. Then the system has a non-trivial solution.

Proof. The proof will be carried out by induction (cf. the Appendix), i.e. a stepwise procedure.

Consider first the case of one equation in n unknowns, $n > 1$:

$$a_1x_1 + \cdots + a_nx_n = 0.$$

If all coefficients $a_1, \ldots, a_n$ are equal to 0, then any value of the variables will be a solution, and a non-trivial solution certainly exists. Suppose that some coefficient a_i is $\neq 0$. After renumbering the variables and the coefficients, we may assume that it is a_1. Then we give $x_2, \ldots, x_n$ arbitrary values, for instance we let $x_2 = \cdots = x_n = 1$, and solve for x_1, letting

$$x_1 = \frac{-1}{a_1}(a_2 + \cdots + a_n).$$

In that manner, we obtain a nontrivial-solution for our system of equations.

Let us now assume that our theorem is true for a system of $m - 1$ equations in more than $m - 1$ unknowns. We shall prove that it is true for m equations in n unknowns when $n > m$. We consider the system (**).

If all coefficients (a_{ij}) are equal to 0, we can give any non-zero value to our variables to get a solution. If some coefficient is not equal to 0, then after renumbering the equations and the variables, we may assume that it is a_{11}. We shall subtract a multiple of the first equation from the others to eliminate x_1. Namely, we consider the system of equations

$$\left(A_2 - \frac{a_{21}}{a_{11}} A_1\right) \cdot X = 0$$

$$\vdots$$

$$\left(A_m - \frac{a_{m1}}{a_{11}} A_1\right) \cdot X = 0,$$

which can also be written in the form

$$A_2 \cdot X - \frac{a_{21}}{a_{11}} A_1 \cdot X = 0$$

(***)
$$\vdots$$

$$A_m \cdot X - \frac{a_{m1}}{a_{11}} A_1 \cdot X = 0.$$

In this system, the coefficient of x_1 is equal to 0. Hence we may view (***) as a system of $m - 1$ equations in $n - 1$ unknowns, and $n - 1 > m - 1$.

According to our assumption, we can find a non-trivial solution $(x_2, \ldots, x_n)$ for this system. We can then solve for x_1 in the first equation, namely

$$x_1 = \frac{-1}{a_{11}} (a_{12}x_2 + \cdots + a_{1n}x_n).$$

In that way, we find a solution of $A_1 \cdot X = 0$. But according to (***), we have

$$A_i \cdot X = \frac{a_{i1}}{a_{11}} A_1 \cdot X$$

for $i = 2, \ldots, m$. Hence $A_i \cdot X = 0$ for $i = 2, \ldots, m$ and therefore we have found a non-trivial solution to our original system (**).

The argument we have just given allows us to proceed stepwise from one equation to two equations, then from two to three, and so forth. This concludes the proof.

EXERCISES

1. Let V be a subspace of $\mathbf{R}^n$. Let W be the set of elements of $\mathbf{R}^n$ which are perpendicular to every element of V. Show that W is a subspace of $\mathbf{R}^n$.

2. Let $A_1, \ldots, A_r$ be generators of a subspace V of $\mathbf{R}^n$. Let W be the set of all elements of $\mathbf{R}^n$ which are perpendicular to $A_1, \ldots, A_r$. Show that the vectors of W are perpendicular to every element of V.

3. Interpret the solutions of a homogeneous system of linear equations in the light of Exercises 1 and 2.

4. Consider the inhomogeneous system (*) consisting of all X such that $X \cdot A_i = b_i$ for $i = 1, \ldots, m$. If X and X' are two solutions of this system,

show that there exists a solution Y of the homogeneous system (**) such that $X' = X + Y$. Conversely, if X is any solution of (*), and Y a solution of (**), show that $X + Y$ is a solution of (*).

§3. *Invariance of dimension*

This section consists of applications of Theorem 1.

THEOREM 2. *Let V be a vector space, and let $\{v_1, \ldots, v_m\}$ be a basis of V. Let $w_1, \ldots, w_n$ be elements of V and assume that $n > m$. Then $w_1, \ldots, w_n$ are linearly dependent.*

Proof. Since $\{v_1, \ldots, v_m\}$ is a basis, there exist numbers (a_{ij}) such that we can write

$$w_1 = a_{11}v_1 + \cdots + a_{m1}v_m$$
$$\vdots$$
$$w_n = a_{1n}v_1 + \cdots + a_{mn}v_m.$$

If $x_1, \ldots, x_n$ are numbers, then

$$x_1w_1 + \cdots + x_nw_n$$
$$= (x_1a_{11} + \cdots + x_na_{1n})v_1 + \cdots + (x_1a_{m1} + \cdots + x_na_{mn})v_n$$

(just add up the coefficients of $v_1, \ldots, v_n$ vertically downwards). According to Theorem 1, the system of equations

$$x_1a_{11} + \cdots + x_na_{1n} = 0$$
$$\vdots$$
$$x_1a_{m1} + \cdots + x_na_{mn} = 0$$

has a non-trivial solution, because $n > m$. In view of the preceding remark, such a solution $(x_1, \ldots, x_n)$ is such that

$$x_1w_1 + \cdots + x_nw_n = 0,$$

as desired.

THEOREM 3. *Let V be a vector space and suppose that one basis has n elements, and another basis has m elements. Then $m = n$.*

Proof. We apply Theorem 2 to the two bases. Theorem 2 implies that both alternatives $n > m$ and $m > n$ are impossible, and hence $m = n$.

Let V be a vector space having a basis consisting of n elements. We shall say that n is the *dimension* of V. If V consists of O alone, then V does not have a basis, and we shall say that V has dimension 0.

We shall now give criteria which allow us to tell when elements of a vector space constitute a basis.

Let $v_1, \ldots, v_n$ be linearly independent elements of a vector space V. We shall say that they form a *maximal set of linearly independent elements* of V if given any element w of V, the elements $w, v_1, \ldots, v_n$ are linearly dependent.

THEOREM 4. *Let V be a vector space, and $\{v_1, \ldots, v_n\}$ a maximal set of linearly independent elements of V. Then $\{v_1, \ldots, v_n\}$ is a basis of V.*

Proof. We must show that $v_1, \ldots, v_n$ generate V, i.e. that every element of V can be expressed as a linear combination of $v_1, \ldots, v_n$. Let w be an element of V. The elements $w, v_1, \ldots, v_n$ of V must be linearly dependent by hypothesis, and hence there exist numbers $x_0, x_1, \ldots, x_n$ not all 0 such that

$$x_0 w + x_1 v_1 + \cdots + x_n v_n = O.$$

We cannot have $x_0 = 0$, because if that were the case, we would obtain a relation of linear dependence among $v_1, \ldots, v_n$. Therefore we can solve for w in terms of $v_1, \ldots, v_n$, namely

$$w = -\frac{x_1}{x_0} v_1 - \cdots - \frac{x_n}{x_0} v_n.$$

This proves that w is a linear combination of $v_1, \ldots, v_n$, and hence that $\{v_1, \ldots, v_n\}$ is a basis.

THEOREM 5. *Let V be a vector space of dimension n, and let $v_1, \ldots, v_n$ be linearly independent elements of V. Then $v_1, \ldots, v_n$ constitute a basis of V.*

Proof. According to Theorem 2, $\{v_1, \ldots, v_n\}$ is a maximal set of linearly independent elements of V. Hence it is a basis by Theorem 4.

THEOREM 6. *Let V be a vector space having a basis consisting of n elements. Let W be a subspace which does not consist of O alone. Then W has a basis, and the dimension of W is $\leq n$.*

Proof. Let w_1 be a non-zero element of W. If $\{w_1\}$ is not a maximal set of linearly independent elements of W, we can find an element w_2 of W such that w_1, w_2 are linearly independent. Proceeding in this manner one element at a time, there must be an integer $m \leq n$ such that we can find linearly independent elements $w_1, w_2, \ldots, w_m$, and such that $\{w_1, \ldots, w_m\}$ is a maximal set of linearly independent elements of W (by Theorem 2, we cannot go on indefinitely finding linearly independent elements, and the number of such elements is at most n). If we now use Theorem 4, we conclude that $\{w_1, \ldots, w_m\}$ is a basis for W.

§4. *Orthonormal bases*

We return to the notion of scalar product. Now that we know what a vector space is in general, we shall generalize our notion of scalar product to apply to arbitrary vector spaces.

Let V be a vector space. A *scalar product* on V is a rule which to any pair of elements v, w of V associates a number, denoted by $\langle v, w \rangle$, satisfying the following properties:

SP 1. *We have* $\langle v, w \rangle = \langle w, v \rangle$.

SP 2. *If u, v, w are elements of V, then*

$$\langle u, v + w \rangle = \langle u, v \rangle + \langle u, w \rangle.$$

SP 3. *If x is a number, then*

$$\langle xu, v \rangle = x\langle u, v \rangle \qquad \text{and} \qquad \langle u, xv \rangle = x\langle u, v \rangle.$$

SP 4. *If $v = O$ then $\langle v, v \rangle = 0$, and otherwise, $\langle v, v \rangle > 0$.*

(It is actually customary to say that the scalar product is *positive definite* because of property SP 4, but we shall not deal with any other type, and hence simply speak of a scalar product.)

The definitions of Chapter I, §4 and the properties proved there apply to arbitrary scalar products. You should now verify this in detail. For instance, we can define the *norm* $\|v\|$ of an element of V, by letting $\|v\| = \sqrt{\langle v, v \rangle}$ and the following three properties hold:

For all v in V, we have $\|v\| \geq 0$, and $= 0$ if and only if $v = O$.
For any number x, we have $\|xv\| = |x|\|v\|$.
For any elements v, w of V, we have $\|v + w\| \leq \|v\| + \|w\|$.

We also define two elements v, w of V to be *perpendicular*, or *orthogonal*, if $\langle v, w \rangle = 0$.

The notation $\langle v, w \rangle$ is used because in dealing with vector spaces of functions, it might be confusing to write $f \cdot g$ for the scalar product (i.e. this might be confused with the ordinary product of functions). However, in dealing with abstract vector spaces, there is a certain simplicity about the dot notation, and hence we shall sometimes write $v \cdot w$ instead of writing $\langle v, w \rangle$.

We shall also refer to elements of a vector space as vectors. If V is a vector space with a scalar product, and v is an element of V, then we say that v is a *unit vector* if $\|v\| = 1$ (or equivalently, if $\langle v, v \rangle = 1$).

For the rest of this section, we let V be a vector space with a scalar product. A basis $\{v_1, \ldots, v_n\}$ of V is said to be *orthogonal* if its elements are mutually perpendicular, i.e. if $v_i \cdot v_j = 0$ whenever $i \neq j$. If in addition each element of the basis has norm 1, then the basis is called *orthonormal*.

The unit vectors $E_1, \ldots, E_n$ of $\mathbf{R}^n$ form an orthonormal basis of $\mathbf{R}^n$. We shall see below that any subspace V of $\mathbf{R}^n$ which does not consist of O alone has an orthonormal basis.

THEOREM 7. *Let V be a vector space with a scalar product. Let n be the dimension of V, and assume $n > 0$. Let W be a subspace of V, and let $\{w_1, \ldots, w_m\}$ be an orthonormal basis of W. If $W \neq V$, then there exist elements $w_{m+1}, \ldots, w_n$ of V such that $\{w_1, \ldots, w_n\}$ is an orthonormal basis of V.*

Proof. We shall proceed inductively according to the following pattern. Suppose that we have found elements $w_1, \ldots, w_r$ of V which are mutually perpendicular and of norm 1. Let V_r be the subspace of V generated by $w_1, \ldots, w_r$. If V_r is not all of V, let v be an element of V which does not lie in V_r, i.e. v is not a linear combination of $w_1, \ldots, w_r$. We subtract from v its projections on $w_1, \ldots, w_r$. In other words, let

$$c_1 = v \cdot w_1, \ldots, c_r = v \cdot w_r.$$

Let $v' = v - c_1 w_1 - \cdots - c_r w_r$. Then v' is perpendicular to $w_1, \ldots, w_r$ because for any integer i such that $1 \leq i \leq r$ we have

$$v' \cdot w_i = v \cdot w_i - c_i w_i \cdot w_i = c_i - c_i = 0.$$

Furthermore, $v' \neq O$ (otherwise v would lie in V_r). Let

$$w_{r+1} = \frac{v'}{||v'||}.$$

Then w_{r+1} has norm 1, and is perpendicular to every element $w_1, \ldots, w_r$, hence perpendicular to every element in V_r.

According to Theorem 2, we cannot continue the above procedure indefinitely, and there is an integer r such that $r \leq n$ and $V_r = V$. Then $\{w_1, \ldots, w_r\}$ is an orthonormal basis of V.

COROLLARY. *Let V be a vector space with a scalar product. Let n be the dimension of V and assume that $n > 0$. Then V has an orthonormal basis.*

Proof. By hypothesis, there exists an element v of V such that $v \neq O$. We let

$$w_1 = \frac{v}{||v||}.$$

Then $||w_1|| = 1$. We let W be the space generated by w_1, and we apply the theorem to get the desired basis.

Example 1. Find an orthonormal basis for the vector space generated by the vectors $(1, 1, 0, 1)$, $(1, -2, 0, 0)$, and $(1, 0, -1, 2)$.

Let us denote these vectors by A, B, C. Let

$$B' = B - \frac{B \cdot A}{A \cdot A}\, A.$$

In other words, we subtract from B its projection along A. Then B' is perpendicular to A. We find

$$B' = \tfrac{1}{3}(4, -5, 0, 1).$$

Now we subtract from C its projection along A and B', and thus we let

$$C' = C - \frac{C \cdot A}{A \cdot A}\, A - \frac{C \cdot B'}{B' \cdot B'}\, B'.$$

Since A and B' are perpendicular, taking the scalar product of C' with A and B' shows that C' is perpendicular to both A and B'. We find:

$$C' = \tfrac{1}{7}(-4, -2, -1, 6).$$

The vectors A, B', C' are non-zero and mutually perpendicular. They lie in the space generated by A, B, C. Hence they constitute an orthogonal basis for that space. If we wish an orthonormal basis, then we divide these vectors by their length, and thus obtain

$$\frac{A}{\|A\|} = \frac{1}{\sqrt{3}}\,(1, 1, 0, 1), \qquad \frac{B'}{\|B'\|} = \frac{1}{\sqrt{42}}\,(4, -5, 0, 1),$$

$$\frac{C'}{\|C'\|} = \frac{1}{\sqrt{57}}\,(-4, -2, -1, 6),$$

as an orthonormal basis.

In the proof of Theorem 7, we divided the vectors at each step by their norm. If we wish, we may postpone this step till the end. For instance, suppose V is a vector space with a scalar product, and we have found non-zero elements $v_1, \ldots, v_r$ which are mutually perpendicular. Let v be another element of V. To "orthogonalize" this new element, we subtract from it its projections on $v_1, \ldots, v_r$. Thus we let

$$v' = v - \frac{v \cdot v_1}{v_1 \cdot v_1}\, v_1 - \cdots - \frac{v \cdot v_r}{v_r \cdot v_r}\, v_r.$$

Then v' is perpendicular to $v_1, \ldots, v_r$, as one sees at once by taking the scalar product with these. Then either $v' = 0$, in which case v' is in the space generated by $v_1, \ldots, v_r$, or $v' \neq 0$, in which case we have $r + 1$ linearly independent mutually perpendicular elements $v_1, \ldots, v_r, v'$. If we divide each one of these by its norm, then we obtain vectors of norm 1, which are again mutually perpendicular.

Let V be a vector space with a scalar product. Let S be a subset of V. Let U be the set of elements of V which are perpendicular to every element of S. Then you will verify easily (as an exercise) that U is a subspace of V. In practice, we shall take S to be a subspace. An element of V which is perpendicular to every element of S is also said to be *perpendicular to S*.

THEOREM 8. *Let V be a vector space with a scalar product, of dimension n. Let W be a subspace of V of dimension r. Let U be the subspace of V consisting of all elements which are perpendicular to W. Then U has dimension $n - r$.*

Proof. If W consists of O alone, or if $W = V$, then our assertion is obvious. We therefore assume that $W \neq V$ and that $W \neq \{O\}$. Let $\{w_1, \ldots, w_r\}$ be an orthonormal basis of W. By Theorem 7, there exist elements $u_{r+1}, \ldots, u_n$ of V such that

$$\{w_1, \ldots, w_r, u_{r+1}, \ldots, u_n\}$$

is an orthonormal basis of V. We shall prove that $\{u_{r+1}, \ldots, u_n\}$ is an orthonormal basis of U.

Let u be an element of U. Then there exist numbers $x_1, \ldots, x_n$ such that

$$u = x_1 w_1 + \cdots + x_r w_r + x_{r+1} u_{r+1} + \cdots + x_n u_n.$$

Since u is perpendicular to W, taking the dot product with any w_i $(i = 1, \ldots, r)$, we find

$$0 = u \cdot w_i = x_i(w_i \cdot w_i) = x_i.$$

Hence all $x_i = 0$ $(i = 1, \ldots, r)$. Therefore u is a linear combination of $u_{r+1}, \ldots, u_n$.

Conversely, let $u = x_{r+1} u_{r+1} + \cdots + x_n u_n$ be a linear combination of $u_{r+1}, \ldots, u_n$. Taking the dot product with any w_i yields 0. Hence u is perpendicular to all w_i $(i = 1, \ldots, r)$, and hence is perpendicular to W. This proves that $u_{r+1}, \ldots, u_n$ generate U. Since they are mutually perpendicular, and of norm 1, they form an orthonormal basis of U, whose dimension is therefore $n - r$.

Example 2. Theorem 8 has an interesting interpretation in terms of linear equations. Let $A_1, \ldots, A_m$ be row vectors in $\mathbf{R}^n$. Let $X = (x_1, \ldots, x_n)$ as usual. The set of solutions X of the homogeneous system of linear equations

(**) $$A_1 \cdot X = 0, \ldots, A_m \cdot X = 0$$

is a vector space. In fact, let W be the space generated by $A_1, \ldots, A_m$. Then the space U consisting of all vectors perpendicular to $A_1, \ldots, A_m$ is precisely the vector space of solutions of (**). The vectors $A_1, \ldots, A_m$ may not be linearly independent. However, if r is the dimension of W, then we may now say that the space of solutions has dimension $n - r$. Note that $r \leq m$. The dimension of U is called the *dimension of the space of solutions* of the system of linear equations.

Let $b_1, \ldots, b_m$ be numbers, and consider once more the inhomogeneous system of linear equations

$$
\begin{aligned}
A_1 \cdot X &= b_1 \\
&\vdots \\
A_m \cdot X &= b_m.
\end{aligned}
$$

(*)

It may happen that this system has no solution at all, i.e. that the equations are inconsistent. For instance, the system

$$
\begin{aligned}
2x + 3y - z &= 1, \\
2x + 3y - z &= 2
\end{aligned}
$$

has no solution. However, if there is at least one solution, then all solutions are obtainable from this one by adding an arbitrary solution of the associated homogeneous system (**) (cf. Exercise 4 of §2). Hence in this case again, we can speak of the dimension of the set of solutions. In the next section, we shall give a criterion which guarantees us the existence of at least one solution.

Example 3. Consider $\mathbf{R}^3$. Let A, B be two linearly independent vectors in $\mathbf{R}^3$. Then the space of vectors which are perpendicular to both A and B is a 1-dimensional space. If $\{N\}$ is a basis for this space, any other basis for this space is of type $\{tN\}$, where t is a number $\neq 0$.

Again in $\mathbf{R}^3$, let N be a non-zero vector. The space of vectors perpendicular to N is a 2-dimensional space, i.e. a plane, passing through the origin O.

EXERCISES

1. Let V be a vector space with a scalar product. Show that $\langle 0, v \rangle = 0$ for every element v of V.

2. Let V be a vector space with a scalar product, and let $v_1, \ldots, v_n$ be non-zero elements of V which are mutually perpendicular. Show that they are linearly independent.

3. Let V be as in Exercise 2, and let $w_1, \ldots, w_m$ be elements of V. Let W be the subspace generated by $w_1, \ldots, w_m$. Show that a vector v perpendicular to each w_i is also perpendicular to W.

4. What is the dimension of the subspace of $\mathbf{R}^6$ perpendicular to the two vectors $(1, 1, -2, 3, 4, 5)$ and $(0, 0, 1, 1, 0, 7)$?

5. Let V be a vector space with a scalar product and let W be a subspace, $W \neq V$. Show that there exists a non-zero element of V which is perpendicular to W (assuming that the dimension of W is finite).

6. Find an orthonormal basis for the subspaces of $\mathbf{R}^3$ generated by the following vectors: (a) $(1, 1, -1)$ and $(1, 0, 1)$,　(b) $(2, 1, 1)$ and $(1, 3, -1)$.

7. Find an orthonormal basis for the subspace of $\mathbf{R}^4$ generated by the vectors $(1, 2, 1, 0)$ and $(1, 2, 3, 1)$.

8. Find an orthonormal basis for the subspace of $\mathbf{R}^4$ generated by $(1, 1, 0, 0)$, $(1, -1, 1, 1)$, and $(-1, 0, 2, 1)$.

In the next exercises, we consider the vector space of continuous functions on the interval $[0, 1]$. We define the scalar product of two such functions f, g by the rule

$$\langle f, g \rangle = \int_0^1 f(t)g(t)\, dt.$$

9. Let V be the subspace of functions generated by the two functions $f(t) = t$ and $g(t) = t^2$. Find an orthonormal basis for V.

10. Let V be the subspace generated by the three functions 1, t, t^2 (where 1 is the constant function). Find an orthonormal basis for V.

11. What is the dimension of the space of solutions of the following systems of linear equations:

(a) $2x - 3y + z = 0$
　　$x + y - z = 0$

(b) $2x + 7y = 0$
　　$x - 2y + z = 0$

(c) $2x - 3y + z = 0$
　　$x + y - z = 0$
　　$3x + 4y = 0$
　　$5x + y + z = 0$

(d) $x + y + z = 0$
　　$2x + 2y + 2z = 0$

12. Let A be a non-zero vector in n-space. Let P be a point in n-space. What is the dimension of the set of solutions of the equation

$$X \cdot A = P \cdot A?$$

13. Let A, B be two linearly independent vectors in n-space. What is the dimension of the space perpendicular to both A and B?

§5. A geometric interpretation

Let $A = (a_{ij})$, $i = 1, \ldots, n$ and $j = 1, \ldots, m$ be a matrix, and let $b_1, \ldots, b_m$ be numbers. Consider the system of linear equations

(*)
$$a_{11}x_1 + \cdots + a_{1n}x_n = b_1$$
$$\vdots$$
$$a_{m1}x_1 + \cdots + a_{mn}x_n = b_m.$$

Let X be the vector $(x_1, \ldots, x_n)$ and let $A^1, \ldots, A^n$ be the *column* vectors of the matrix A. Let B be the column vector

$$B = \begin{pmatrix} b_1 \\ b_2 \\ \vdots \\ b_m \end{pmatrix}.$$

To say that X is a solution of the system of linear equations is to say that B is a linear combination of the vectors $A^1, \ldots, A^m$, namely

$$x_1 A^1 + x_2 A^2 + \cdots + x_n A^n = B,$$

or written in full:

$$x_1 \begin{pmatrix} a_{11} \\ \vdots \\ a_{m1} \end{pmatrix} + \cdots + x_n \begin{pmatrix} a_{1n} \\ \vdots \\ a_{mn} \end{pmatrix} = \begin{pmatrix} b_1 \\ \vdots \\ b_m \end{pmatrix}.$$

THEOREM 9. *Assume that $m = n$ in the system (*) above, and that the vectors $A^1, \ldots, A^n$ are linearly independent. Then the system (*) has a solution, and this solution is unique.*

Proof. From Theorem 5, we know that $\{A^1, \ldots, A^n\}$ is a basis of $\mathbf{R}^n$. Hence any vector can be expressed as a unique linear combination of these basis vectors, as contended.

For simplicity we shall also denote the system (*) by $AX = B$.

EXERCISES

1. Let A be a square $n \times n$ matrix and let $AX = O$ be the associated system of n linear equations in n unknowns. Prove that if the column vectors of A are linearly independent then the only solution is the trivial solution.

2. Let A be a square matrix again. Prove that if the row vectors of A are linearly independent, then the only solution of the system of equations $AX = O$ is the trivial solution.

CHAPTER XI

Linear Mappings

We shall first define the general notion of a mapping, which generalizes the notion of a function. Among mappings, the linear mappings are the most important. A good deal of mathematics is devoted to reducing questions concerning arbitrary mappings to linear mappings. For one thing, they are interesting in themselves, and many mappings are linear. On the other hand, it is often possible to approximate an arbitrary mapping by a linear one, whose study is much easier than the study of the original mapping. (Cf. Chapter XIII.)

§1. Mappings

Let S, S' be two sets. A *mapping* from S to S' is a rule which to every element of S associates an element of S'. Instead of saying that F is a mapping from S into S', we shall often write the symbols $F:S \to S'$. A mapping will also be called a *map*, for the sake of brevity.

A function is a special type of mapping, namely it is a mapping from a set into the set of numbers, i.e. into **R**.

We extend to mappings some of the terminology we have used for functions. For instance, if $T:S \to S'$ is a mapping, and if u is an element of S, then we denote by $T(u)$, or Tu, the element of S' associated to u by T. We call $T(u)$ the *value* of T at u, or also the *image* of u under T. The symbols $T(u)$ are read "*T* of *u*". The set of all elements $T(u)$, when u ranges over all elements of S, is called the *image* of T. If W is a subset of S, then the set of elements $T(w)$, when w ranges over all elements of W, is called the *image* of W under T, and is denoted by $T(W)$.

Example 1. Let S and S' be both equal to **R**. Let $f:\mathbf{R} \to \mathbf{R}$ be the function $f(x) = x^2$ (i.e. the function whose value at a number x is x^2). Then f is a mapping from **R** into **R**.

Example 2. Let S be the set of numbers ≥ 0, and let $S' = \mathbf{R}$. Let $g:S \to S'$ be the function such that $g(x) = x^{1/2}$. Then g is a mapping from S into **R**.

Example 3. Let S be the set of functions having derivatives of all orders on the interval $0 < t < 1$, and let $S' = S$. Then the derivative $D = d/dt$ is a mapping from S into S. Indeed, our rule D associates the function $df/dt = Df$ to the function f. According to our terminology, Df is the value of the mapping D at f.

Example 4. Let S be the set of continuous functions on the interval $[0, 1]$ and let S' be the set of differentiable functions on that interval. We shall define a mapping $\mathcal{S}: S \to S'$ by giving its value at any function f in S. Namely, we let $\mathcal{S}f$ (or $\mathcal{S}(f)$) be the function whose value at x is

$$\int_0^x f(t)\, dt.$$

Then $\mathcal{S}(f)$ is a differentiable function.

Example 5. Let S be the set $\mathbf{R}^3$, i.e. the set of 3-tuples. Let $A = (2, 3, -1)$. Let $L: \mathbf{R}^3 \to \mathbf{R}$ be the mapping whose value at a vector $X = (x, y, z)$ is $A \cdot X$. Then $L(X) = A \cdot X$. If $X = (1, 1, -1)$, then the value of L at X is 6.

Just as we did with functions, we describe a mapping by giving its values. Thus, instead of making the statement in Example 5 describing the mapping L, we would also say: Let $L: \mathbf{R}^3 \to \mathbf{R}$ be the mapping $L(X) = A \cdot X$. This is somewhat incorrect, but is briefer, and does not usually give rise to confusion.

Example 6. Let $F: \mathbf{R}^2 \to \mathbf{R}^2$ be the mapping given by

$$F(x, y) = (2x, 2y).$$

Describe the image under F of the points lying on the circle $x^2 + y^2 = 1$.

Let (x, y) be a point on the circle of radius 1.

Let $u = 2x$ and $v = 2y$. Then u, v satisfy the relation

$$(u/2)^2 + (v/2)^2 = 1$$

or in other words,

$$\frac{u^2}{4} + \frac{v^2}{4} = 1.$$

Hence (u, v) is a point on the circle of radius 2. Hence the image under F of the circle of radius 1 is a subset of the circle of radius 2. Conversely, given a point (u, v) such that

$$u^2 + v^2 = 4,$$

let $x = u/2$ and $y = v/2$. Then the point (x, y) satisfies the equation $x^2 + y^2 = 1$, and hence is a point on the circle of radius 1. Furthermore, $F(x, y) = (u, v)$. Hence every point on the circle of radius 2 is the image of some point on the circle of radius 1. We conclude finally that the image of the circle of radius 1 under F is precisely the circle of radius 2.

Note. In general, let S, S' be two sets. To prove that $S = S'$, one frequently proves that S is a subset of S' and that S' is a subset of S. This is what we did in the preceding argument.

Example 7. Let S be a set. A mapping from S into $\mathbf{R}$ will be called a *function*, and the set of such functions will be called the set of functions defined on S. Let f, g be two functions defined on S. We can define their sum just as we did for functions of numbers, namely $f + g$ is the function whose value at an element t of S is $f(t) + g(t)$. We can also define the product of f by a number c. It is the function whose value at t is $cf(t)$. Then the set of mappings from S into $\mathbf{R}$ is a vector space.

Example 8. Let S be a set and let V be a vector space. Let F, G be two mappings from S into V. We can define their sum in the same way as we defined the sum of functions, namely the sum $F + G$ is the mapping whose value at an element t of S is $F(t) + G(t)$. We also define the product of F by a number c to be the mapping whose value at an element t of S is $cF(t)$. It is easy to verify that conditions VS1 through VS8 are satisfied.

Example 9. Let $F : \mathbf{R} \to \mathbf{R}^n$ be a mapping. For each number t, the value of F at t is a vector $F(t)$. The coordinates of $F(t)$ depend on t. Hence there are functions $f_1, \ldots, f_n$ such that

$$F(t) = \big(f_1(t), \ldots, f_n(t)\big).$$

Each f_i is a function from $\mathbf{R}$ into $\mathbf{R}$. These functions are called the *coordinate functions* of F.

Let $G : \mathbf{R} \to \mathbf{R}^n$ be another mapping from $\mathbf{R}$ into $\mathbf{R}^n$, and let $g_1, \ldots, g_n$ be its coordinate functions. Then

$$G(t) = \big(g_1(t), \ldots, g_n(t)\big).$$

Then

$$(F + G)(t) = F(t) + G(t) = \big(f_1(t) + g_1(t), \ldots, f_n(t) + g_n(t)\big)$$

and for any number c,

$$(cF)(t) = cF(t) = \big(cf_1(t), \ldots, cf_n(t)\big).$$

If all the functions $f_1, \ldots, f_n$ are differentiable, then we say that the mapping F above is *differentiable*. The set of all differentiable mappings from $\mathbf{R}$ into $\mathbf{R}^n$ is a subspace of the vector space of all mappings.

EXERCISES

1. In Example 3, give Df when f is the function:
   (a) $f(x) = \sin x$ (b) $f(x) = e^x$ (c) $f(x) = \log x$

2. In Example 4, give $g(f)$ when f is the function:

   (a) $f(x) = e^x$ · (b) $f(x) = \dfrac{1}{1 + x^2}$ (c) $f(x) = \cos x$

3. In Example 5, give $L(X)$ when X is the vector:

(a) $(1, 2, -3)$ (b) $(-1, 5, 0)$ (c) $(2, 1, 1)$

4. Let $F : \mathbf{R} \to \mathbf{R}^2$ be the mapping such that $F(t) = (e^t, t)$. What is $F(1)$, $F(0)$, $F(-1)$?

5. Let $G : \mathbf{R} \to \mathbf{R}^2$ be the mapping such that $G(t) = (t, 2t)$. Let F be as in Exercise 4. What is $(F + G)(1)$, $(F + G)(2)$, $(F + G)(0)$?

6. Let F be as in Exercise 4. What is $(2F)(0)$, $(\pi F)(1)$?

7. Let $A = (1, 1, -1, 3)$. Let $F : \mathbf{R}^4 \to \mathbf{R}$ be the mapping such that for any vector $X = (x_1, x_2, x_3, x_4)$ we have $F(X) = X \cdot A + 2$. What is the value of $F(X)$ when (a) $X = (1, 1, 0, -1)$ and (b) $X = (2, 3, -1, 1)$?

(In Exercises 8 through 12, refer to Example 6. In each case, to prove that the image is equal to a certain set S, you must prove that the image is contained in S, and also that every element of S is in the image.)

8. Let $F : \mathbf{R}^2 \to \mathbf{R}^2$ be the mapping defined by $F(x, y) = (2x, 3y)$. Describe the image of the points lying on the circle $x^2 + y^2 = 1$.

9. Let $F : \mathbf{R}^2 \to \mathbf{R}^2$ be the mapping defined by $F(x, y) = (xy, y)$. Describe the image under F of the straight line $x = 2$.

10. Let F be the mapping defined by $F(x, y) = (e^x \cos y, e^x \sin y)$. Describe the image under F of the line $x = 1$. Describe more generally the image under F of a line $x = c$, where c is a constant.

11. Let F be the mapping defined by $F(t, u) = (\cos t, \sin t, u)$. Describe geometrically the image of the (t, u)-plane under F.

12. Let F be the mapping defined by $F(x, y) = (x/3, y/4)$. What is the image under F of the ellipse

$$\frac{x^2}{9} + \frac{y^2}{16} = 1?$$

§2. Linear mappings

Let V, V' be two vector spaces. A *linear mapping*

$$T : V \to V'$$

is a mapping which satisfies the following two properties. First, for any elements u, v in V, we have

LM1. $T(u + v) = T(u) + T(v).$

Secondly, for any number c, we have

LM2. $T(cu) = cT(u).$

Example 1. Let V be the set of functions which have derivatives of all orders. Then the derivative $D : V \to V$ is a linear mapping. This is simply a brief way of summarizing properties of the derivative which we have known a long time, namely

$$D(f + g) = Df + Dg,$$
$$D(cf) = cD(f).$$

Example 2.   Let $V = \mathbf{R}^3$ be the vector space of vectors in 3-space. Let $V' = \mathbf{R}^2$ be the vector space of vectors in 2-space. We can define a mapping

$$F:\mathbf{R}^3 \to \mathbf{R}^2$$

by the projection, namely $F(x, y, z) = (x, y)$. We leave it to you to check that the conditions LM1 and LM2 are satisfied.

Example 3.   Let $A = (1, 2, -1)$. Let $V = \mathbf{R}^3$ and $V' = \mathbf{R}$. We can define a mapping $L = L_A:\mathbf{R}^3 \to \mathbf{R}$ by the rule

$$L(X) = X \cdot A$$

for any vector X in 3-space. The fact that L is linear summarizes two known properties of the scalar product, namely, for any two vectors X, Y we have

$$(X + Y) \cdot A = X \cdot A + Y \cdot A$$
$$(cX) \cdot A = c(X \cdot A).$$

Example 4.   Let V be any vector space. The mapping which associates to any element u of V this element itself is obviously a linear mapping, which is called the *identity* mapping. We denote it by Id or simply I. Thus $Id(u) = u$.

Example 5.   Let V, V' be any vector spaces. The mapping which associates the element O in V' to any element u of V is called the *zero* mapping and is obviously linear.

Example 6.   Let V, V' be two vector spaces. We consider the set of all linear mappings from V into V', and denote this set by $\mathfrak{L}$. We shall define the addition of linear mappings and their multiplication by numbers in such a way as to make $\mathfrak{L}$ into a vector space.

Let $T:V \to V'$ and let $F:V \to V'$ be two linear mappings. We define their *sum* $T + F$ to be the map whose value at an element u of V is $T(u) + F(u)$. Thus we may write

$$(T + F)(u) = T(u) + F(u).$$

The map $T + F$ is then a linear map. Indeed, it is easy to verify that the two conditions which define a linear map are satisfied. For any elements u, v of V, we have

$$
\begin{aligned}
(T + F)(u + v) &= T(u + v) + F(u + v) \\
&= T(u) + T(v) + F(u) + F(v) \\
&= T(u) + F(u) + T(v) + F(v) \\
&= (T + F)(u) + (T + F)(v).
\end{aligned}
$$

Furthermore, if c is a number, then

$$
\begin{aligned}
(T + F)(cu) &= T(cu) + F(cu) \\
&= cT(u) + cF(u) \\
&= c[T(u) + F(u)] \\
&= c[(T + F)(u)].
\end{aligned}
$$

Hence $T + F$ is a linear map.

If a is a number, and $T : V \to V'$ is a linear map, we define a map aT from V into V' by giving its value at an element u of V, namely $(aT)(u) = aT(u)$. Then it is easily verified that aT is a linear map. We leave this as an exercise.

We have just defined operations of addition and multiplication by numbers in our set $\mathcal{L}$. Furthermore, if $T : V \to V'$ is a linear map, i.e. an element of $\mathcal{L}$, then we can define $-T$ to be $(-1)T$, i.e. the product of the number -1 by T. Finally, we have the *zero-map*, which to every element of V associates the element O of V'. Then $\mathcal{L}$ is a vector space. In other words, the set of linear maps from V into V' is itself a vector space. The verification that the rules VS1 through VP8 for a vector space are satisfied are easy and left to the reader.

Example 7. Let $V = V'$ be the vector space of functions which have derivatives of all orders. Let D be the derivative, and let Id be the identity. If f is in V, then

$$(D + Id)f = Df + f.$$

Thus, when $f(x) = e^x$, then $(D + Id)f$ is the function whose value at x is $e^x + e^x = 2e^x$.

If $f(x) = \sin x$, then $((D + Id)f)(x) = \cos x + \sin x$.

We note that $3 \cdot Id$ is a linear map, whose value at f is $3f$. Thus $(D + 3 \cdot Id)f = Df + 3f$. At any number x, the value of $(D + 3 \cdot Id)f$ is $Df(x) + 3f(x)$.

Instead of writing $D + 3 \cdot Id$, it is customary to abbreviate the notation, and write $D + 3$. Thus we would write

$$(D + 3)f(x) = Df(x) + 3f(x).$$

Let $T: V \to V'$ be a linear mapping. Let u, v, w be elements of V. Then

$$T(u + v + w) = T(u) + T(v) + T(w).$$

This can be seen stepwise, using the definition of linear mappings. Thus

$$T(u + v + w) = T(u + v) + T(w) = T(u) + T(v) + T(w).$$

Similarly, given a sum of more than three elements, an analogous property is satisfied. For instance, let $u_1, \ldots, u_n$ be elements of V. Then

$$T(u_1 + \cdots + u_n) = T(u_1) + \cdots + T(u_n).$$

The sum on the right can be taken in any order. A formal proof can easily be given by induction, and we omit it.

If $a_1, \ldots, a_n$ are numbers, then

$$T(a_1 u_1 + \cdots + a_n u_n) = a_1 T(u_1) + \cdots + a_n T(u_n).$$

We show this for three elements.

$$
\begin{aligned}
T(a_1 u + a_2 v + a_3 w) &= T(a_1 u) + T(a_2 v) + T(a_3 w) \\
&= a_1 T(u) + a_2 T(v) + a_3 T(w).
\end{aligned}
$$

The next theorem will show us how a linear map is determined when we know its value on basis elements.

THEOREM 1. *Let V and W be vector spaces. Let $\{v_1, \ldots, v_n\}$ be a basis of V, and let $w_1, \ldots, w_n$ be arbitrary elements of W. Then there exists a unique linear mapping $T: V \to W$ such that $T(v_1) = w_1, \ldots, T(v_n) = w_n$. If $x_1, \ldots, x_n$ are numbers, then*

$$T(x_1 v_1 + \cdots + x_n v_n) = x_1 w_1 + \cdots + x_n w_n.$$

Proof. We shall prove that a linear map T satisfying the required conditions exists. Let v be an element of V, and let $x_1, \ldots, x_n$ be the unique numbers such that $v = x_1 v_1 + \cdots + x_n v_n$. We let $T(v) = x_1 w_1 + \cdots + x_n w_n$. We then have defined a mapping T from V into W, and we contend that T is linear. If v' is an element of V, and if $v' = y_1 v_1 + \cdots + y_n v_n$, then

$$v + v' = (x_1 + y_1) v_1 + \cdots + (x_n + y_n) v_n.$$

By definition, we obtain

$$
\begin{aligned}
T(v + v') &= (x_1 + y_1) w_1 + \cdots + (x_n + y_n) w_n \\
&= x_1 w_1 + y_1 w_1 + \cdots + x_n w_n + y_n w_n \\
&= T(v) + T(v').
\end{aligned}
$$

Let c be a number. Then $cv = cx_1v_1 + \cdots + cx_nv_n$, and hence

$$T(cv) = cx_1w_1 + \cdots + cx_nw_n = cT(v).$$

We have therefore proved that T is linear, and hence that there exists a linear map as asserted in the theorem.

Such a map is unique, because for any element $x_1v_1 + \cdots + x_nv_n$ of V, any linear map $F : V \to W$ such that $F(v_i) = w_i$ $(i = 1, \ldots, n)$ must also satisfy

$$F(x_1v_1 + \cdots + x_nv_n) = x_1F(v_1) + \cdots + x_nF(v_n)$$
$$= x_1w_1 + \cdots + x_nw_n.$$

This concludes the proof.

EXERCISES

1. Determine which ones of the following mappings F are linear.

   (a) $F : \mathbf{R}^3 \to \mathbf{R}^2$ defined by $F(x, y, z) = (x, z)$.
   (b) $F : \mathbf{R}^4 \to \mathbf{R}^4$ defined by $F(X) = -X$.
   (c) $F : \mathbf{R}^3 \to \mathbf{R}^3$ defined by $F(X) = X + (0, -1, 0)$.
   (d) $F : \mathbf{R}^2 \to \mathbf{R}^2$ defined by $F(x, y) = (2x + y, y)$.
   (e) $F : \mathbf{R}^2 \to \mathbf{R}^2$ defined by $F(x, y) = (2x, y - x)$.
   (f) $F : \mathbf{R}^2 \to \mathbf{R}^2$ defined by $F(x, y) = (y, x)$.
   (g) $F : \mathbf{R}^2 \to \mathbf{R}$ defined by $F(x, y) = xy$.
   (h) Let U be an open subset of $\mathbf{R}^3$, and let V be the vector space of differentiable functions on U. Let V' be the vector space of vector fields on U. Then
   $$\mathrm{grad} : V \to V'$$
   is a mapping. Is it linear?

2. Let $T : V \to W$ be a linear map from one vector space into another. Show that $T(O) = O$.

3. Let T be as in Exercise 2. Let u, v be elements of V, and let $Tu = w$. If $Tv = O$, show that $T(u + v)$ is also equal to w.

4. Determine all elements z of V such that $Tz = w$.

5. Let $T : V \to W$ be a linear map. Let v be an element of V. Show that $T(-v) = -T(v)$.

6. Let V be a vector space, and $f : V \to \mathbf{R}$, $g : V \to \mathbf{R}$ two linear mappings. Let $F : V \to \mathbf{R}^2$ be the mapping defined by $F(v) = (f(v), g(v))$. Show that F is linear. Generalize.

7. Let V, W be two vector spaces and let $F : V \to W$ be a linear map. Let U be the subset of V consisting of all elements v such that $F(v) = O$. Prove that U is a subspace of V.

8. Which of the mappings in Exercises 4, 7, 8, 9 of §1 are linear?

9. Let $F:\mathbf{R}^3 \to \mathbf{R}^4$ be a linear map. Let P be a point of $\mathbf{R}^3$, and A a non-zero element of $\mathbf{R}^3$. Describe the image of the straight line $P + tA$ under F. [Distinguish the cases when $F(A) = O$ and $F(A) \neq O$.]

Let V be a vector space, and let v_1, v_2 be two elements of V which are linearly independent. The set of elements of V which can be written in the form $t_1v_1 + t_2v_2$ with numbers t_1, t_2 satisfying $0 \leq t_1 \leq 1$ and $0 \leq t_2 \leq 1$, is called a *parallelogram*, spanned by v_1, v_2.

10. Let V and W be vector spaces, and let $F:V \to W$ be a linear map. Let v_1, v_2 be linearly independent elements of V, and assume that $F(v_1)$, $F(v_2)$ are linearly independent. Show that the image under F of the parallelogram spanned by v_1 and v_2 is the parallelogram spanned by $F(v_1)$, $F(v_2)$.

11. Let F be a linear map from $\mathbf{R}^2$ into itself such that

$$F(E_1) = (1, 1) \quad \text{and} \quad F(E_2) = (-1, 2).$$

Let S be the square whose corners are at $(0, 0)$, $(1, 0)$, $(1, 1)$, and $(0, 1)$. Show that the image of this square under F is a parallelogram.

12. Let A, B be two non-zero vectors in the plane such that there is no constant $c \neq 0$ such that $B = cA$. Let T be a linear mapping of the plane into itself such that $T(E_1) = A$ and $T(E_2) = B$. Describe the image under T of the rectangle whose corners are $(0, 1)$, $(3, 0)$, $(0, 0)$, and $(3, 1)$.

13. Let A, B be two non-zero vectors in the plane such that there is no constant $c \neq 0$ such that $B = cA$. Describe geometrically the set of points $tA + uB$ for values of t and u such that $0 \leq t \leq 5$ and $0 \leq u \leq 2$.

14. Let S be a set in $\mathbf{R}^n$. We say that S is *convex* if given two points P, Q in S, the line segment joining P to Q is contained in S. [The points on this line segment are those which can be written in the form $tP + (1 - t)Q$, $0 \leq t \leq 1$.] Let $L:\mathbf{R}^n \to \mathbf{R}^m$ be a linear map. Show that the image under L of a convex set is convex.

15. Let $L:\mathbf{R}^n \to \mathbf{R}$ be a linear map. Let S be the set of all points A in $\mathbf{R}^n$ such that $L(A) \geq 0$. Show that S is convex.

16. Let $L:\mathbf{R}^n \to \mathbf{R}$ be a linear map, and let c be a number. Show that the set S consisting of all points A in $\mathbf{R}^n$ such that $L(A) > c$ is convex.

17. Let S_1, S_2 be two convex sets in $\mathbf{R}^n$. Show that the set of points S common to both S_1 and S_2 is convex.

18. State the results of Exercises 14 through 17 for arbitrary vector spaces.

19. Let A be a non-zero vector in $\mathbf{R}^n$, and c a number. Show that the set of points X such that $X \cdot A \geq c$ is convex.

20. Let A, B, C be three distinct points in $\mathbf{R}^n$, satisfying the condition that $B - A$ and $C - A$ are linearly independent. Show that this condition is equivalent with the fact that they do not lie on a straight line.

21. Let A, B, C be three points in $\mathbf{R}^n$ such that $B - A$ and $C - A$ are linearly independent. The set of points of type

$$t_1 A + t_2 B + t_3 C$$

where t_i are numbers, $0 \leq t_i$ for $i = 1, 2, 3$ and $t_1 + t_2 + t_3 = 1$ is called a *triangle,* determined by A, B, C.

(a) Show that a triangle is convex.
(b) Show that any convex set containing A, B, C also contains the triangle determined by A, B, C.
(c) Let $F : \mathbf{R}^n \to \mathbf{R}^m$ be a linear map such that $F(A)$, $F(B)$, and $F(C)$ are distinct and do not lie on a straight line. Show that the image under F of the triangle determined by A, B, C is the triangle determined by $F(A)$, $F(B)$, $F(C)$.
(d) Do Exercises 3 and 4 of Appendix 1.

22. Let V, W be two vector spaces, and $F : V \to W$ a linear map. Let $w_1, \dots, w_n$ be elements of W which are linearly independent, and let $v_1, \dots, v_n$ be elements of V such that $F(v_i) = w_i$ for $i = 1, \dots, n$. Show that $v_1, \dots, v_n$ are linearly independent.

23. Let V be a vector space and $F : V \to \mathbf{R}$ a linear map. Let W be the subset of V consisting of all elements v such that $F(v) = O$. Assume that $W \neq V$, and let v_0 be an element of V which does not lie in W. Show that every element of V can be written as a sum $w + cv_0$, with some w in W and some number c.

24. In Exercise 23, show that W is a subspace of V. Let $\{v_1, \dots, v_n\}$ be a basis of W. Show that $\{v_0, v_1, \dots, v_n\}$ is a basis of V.

§3. *The kernel of a linear map*

Let V, W be vector spaces, and let $F : V \to W$ be a linear map. We contend that the following two conditions are equivalent:

(1) If v is an element of V such that $F(v) = O$, then $v = O$.
(2) If v, w are elements of V such that $F(v) = F(w)$, then $v = w$.

To prove our contention, assume first that F satisfies the first condition, and suppose that v, w are such that $F(v) = F(w)$. Then $F(v - w) = F(v) - F(w) = O$. By assumption, $v - w = O$, and hence $v = w$.

Conversely, assume that F satisfies the second condition. If v is such that $F(v) = F(O) = O$, we conclude that $v = O$.

Let $F : V \to W$ be as above. The set of elements v of V such that $F(v) = O$ is called the *kernel* of F. We leave it as an exercise to prove that the kernel of F is a subspace of V.

THEOREM 2. *Let $F : V \to W$ be a linear map whose kernel is $\{O\}$. If $v_1, \dots, v_n$ are linearly independent elements of V, then $F(v_1), \dots, F(v_n)$ are linearly independent elements of W.*

Proof. Let $x_1, \dots, x_n$ be numbers such that

$$x_1 F(v_1) + \cdots + x_n F(v_n) = O.$$

By linearity, we get
$$F(x_1v_1 + \cdots + x_nv_n) = O.$$

Hence $x_1v_1 + \ldots + x_nv_n = O$. Since $v_1, \ldots, v_n$ are linearly independent it follows that $x_i = 0$ for $i = 1, \ldots, n$. This proves our theorem.

Example. Let A, B be two linearly independent vectors in n-space. Let P be a point in n-space. The set of all points

$$X = P + tA + uB$$

where t, u range over all numbers is called a *plane,* passing through P, *parallel* to A and B.

Let $T : \mathbf{R}^n \to \mathbf{R}^m$ be a linear mapping, and assume that the kernel of T is $\{O\}$. Then the image of a plane under T is again a plane. Indeed, consider a plane consisting of all points $P + tA + uB$ as above. Then the image of such a point is

$$T(P) + tT(A) + uT(B),$$

and since the kernel of T is $\{O\}$, $T(A)$ and $T(B)$ are linearly independent. Consequently the image of our plane is a plane passing through $T(P)$, parallel to $T(A)$ and $T(B)$.

The equation $X = P + tA + uB$ is sometimes called the *parametric equation* of a plane.

Let $F : V \to W$ be a linear map. The *image* of F is the set of elements w in W such that there exists an element v of V such that $F(v) = w$. The image of F is a subspace of W. To prove this, observe first that $F(O) = O$, and hence O is in the image. Next, suppose that w_1, w_2 are in the image. Then there exist elements v_1, v_2 of V such that $F(v_1) = w_1$ and $F(v_2) = w_2$. Hence $F(v_1 + v_2) = F(v_1) + F(v_2) = w_1 + w_2$, thereby proving that $w_1 + w_2$ is in the image. If c is a number, then $F(cv_1) = cF(v_1) = cw_1$. Hence cw_1 is in the image. This proves that the image is a subspace of W.

EXERCISES

1. Let A, B be two vectors in $\mathbf{R}^2$ forming a basis of $\mathbf{R}^2$. Let $F : \mathbf{R}^2 \to \mathbf{R}^n$ be a linear map. Show that either $F(A), F(B)$ are linearly independent, or the image of F has dimension 1, or the image of F is $\{O\}$.

2. Find a parametric equation for the plane in $\mathbf{R}^4$ passing through the three points $(1, 1, 0, -1)$, $(2, -1, 1, 3)$, and $(4, -2, 1, -1)$.

3. Let $F : V \to W$ be a linear map, whose kernel is $\{O\}$. Assume that V and W have both the same dimension n. Show that the image of F is all of W.

4. Let $F:V \to W$ be a linear map and assume that the image of F is all of W. Assume that V and W have the same dimension n. Show that the kernel of F is $\{O\}$.

5. Let $L:V \to W$ be a linear map. Let w be an element of W. Let v_0 be an element of V such that $L(v_0) = w$. Show that any solution of the equation $L(X) = w$ is of type $v_0 + u$, where u is an element of the kernel of L.

6. Let V be the vector space of functions which have derivatives of all orders, and let $D:V \to V$ be the derivative. What is the kernel of D?

7. Let D^2 be the second derivative (i.e. the iteration of D taken twice). What is the kernel of D^2? In general, what is the kernel of D^n (n-th derivative)?

8. Let V be as in Exercise 6. We write the functions as functions of a variable t, and let $D = d/dt$. Let $a_1, \ldots, a_m$ be numbers. Let g be an element of V. Describe how the problem of finding a solution of the differential equation

$$a_m \frac{d^m f}{dt^m} + a_{m-1} \frac{d^{m-1} f}{dt^{m-1}} + \cdots + a_0 f = g$$

can be interpreted as fitting the abstract situation described in Exercise 5.

9. Let V, D be as in Exercise 6. Let $L = D - I$, where I is the identity mapping of V. What is the kernel of L?

10. Same question of $L = D - aI$, where a is a number.

§4. Kernel and image

The main theorem relating the kernel and image of a linear map is the following.

THEOREM 3. *Let V be a vector space. Let $L:V \to W$ be a linear map of V into another space W. Let n be the dimension of V, q the dimension of the kernel of L, and s the dimension of the image of L. Then $n = q + s$.*

Proof. If the image of L consists of O only, then our assertion is trivial. We may therefore assume that $s > 0$. Let $\{w_1, \ldots, w_s\}$ be a basis of the image of L. Let $v_1, \ldots, v_s$ be elements of V such that $L(v_i) = w_i$ for $i = 1, \ldots, s$. If the kernel of L is not $\{O\}$, let $\{u_1, \ldots, u_q\}$ be a basis of the kernel. If the kernel is $\{O\}$, it is understood that all reference to $\{u_1, \ldots, u_q\}$ is to be omitted in what follows. We contend that $\{v_1, \ldots, v_s, u_1, \ldots, u_q\}$ is a basis of V. This will suffice to prove our assertion. Let v be any element of V. Then there exist numbers $x_1, \ldots, x_s$ such that

$$L(v) = x_1 w_1 + \cdots + x_s w_s,$$

because $\{w_1, \ldots, w_s\}$ is a basis of the image of L. By linearity,

$$L(v) = L(x_1 v_1 + \cdots + x_s v_s),$$

and again by linearity, subtracting the right-hand side from the left-hand side, it follows that

$$L(v - x_1v_1 - \cdots - x_sv_s) = O.$$

Hence $v - x_1v_1 - \ldots - x_sv_s$ lies in the kernel of L, and there exist numbers $y_1, \ldots, y_q$ such that

$$v - x_1v_1 - \cdots - x_sv_s = y_1u_1 + \cdots + y_qu_q.$$

Hence

$$v = x_1v_1 + \cdots + x_sv_s + y_1u_1 + \cdots + y_qu_q$$

is a linear combination of $v_1, \ldots, v_s, u_1, \ldots, u_q$. This proves that these $s + q$ elements of V generate V.

We now show that they are linearly independent, and hence that they constitute a basis. Suppose that there exists a linear relation

$$x_1v_1 + \cdots + x_sv_s + y_1u_1 + \cdots + y_qu_q = O.$$

Applying L to this relation, and using the fact that $L(u_j) = O$ for $j = 1, \ldots, q$, we obtain

$$x_1L(v_1) + \cdots + x_sL(v_s) = O.$$

But $L(v_1), \ldots, L(v_s)$ are none other than $w_1, \ldots, w_s$, which have been assumed linearly independent. Hence $x_i = 0$ for $i = 1, \ldots, s$. Hence

$$y_1u_1 + \cdots + y_qu_q = 0.$$

But $u_1, \ldots, u_q$ constitute a basis of the kernel of L, and in particular, are linearly independent. Hence all $y_j = 0$ for $j = 1, \ldots, q$. This concludes the proof of our assertion.

§5. The rank of a matrix

Let A be an $m \times n$ matrix:

$$A = \begin{pmatrix} a_{11} & \cdots & a_{1n} \\ & \vdots & \\ a_{m1} & \cdots & a_{mn} \end{pmatrix}.$$

Let $A^1, \ldots, A^n$ be its column vectors as usual, and let $A_1, \ldots, A_m$ be its row vectors. Then the column vectors generate a subspace of m-space, and the row vectors generate a subspace of n-space. The *column rank* of the matrix is defined to be the maximum number of linearly independent columns among the column vectors of A. It is also equal to the dimension of the subspace generated by these column vectors. Similarly, the *row rank* of A is defined to be the maximum number of linearly independent rows among the row vectors of A. It is also equal to the dimension of the subspace generated by these row vectors. (Cf. Exercise 12 of Chapter IX, §2.) The main theorem concerning the rank is the following.

THEOREM 4. *The column rank of a matrix is equal to its row rank.*

Proof. Let r be the row rank, and let s be the column rank. According to Theorem 8 of Chapter X, §4, the dimension of the space of solutions of the system of homogeneous linear equations determined by A is equal to $n - r$. Indeed, it is the dimension of the space of vectors which are perpendicular to the space generated by the row vectors.

We shall now use another interpretation for this space of solutions. Let W be the vector space generated by the column vectors of A. According to Theorem 1 of Chapter XI, §2, there exists a unique linear map $L: \mathbf{R}^n \to W$ such that for any vector $X = (x_1, \ldots, x_n)$ we have

$$L(X) = x_1 A^1 + \cdots + x_n A^n.$$

The image of L is therefore the space generated by the column vectors of A, and the dimension of this image is s. The kernel of L is by definition the space of solutions of the linear equations determined by A, namely it is the space consisting of those vectors X such that

$$x_1 A^1 + \cdots + x_n A^n = O.$$

According to Theorem 3 of §4, the dimension of this kernel is $n - s$ (we apply the statement to the case $V = \mathbf{R}^n$). Hence we now see that $n - r = n - s$, or in other words, $r = s$, as was to be shown.

The row rank, or column rank, will simply be called the *rank* of the matrix.

Example. What is the rank of the matrix

$$\begin{pmatrix} 2 & 0 & 1 \\ -1 & 1 & 5 \end{pmatrix}?$$

It is easy to check that the first two columns are linearly independent. Hence the rank is 2.

In order to compute easily the rank of a matrix, we observe that the following operations on the columns of a matrix do not change its rank.

(1) Multiplying one column by a non-zero number.
(2) Interchanging two columns
(3) Adding one column to another.

[Prove that (1), (2), (3) do not change the rank as an exercise.] Furthermore, since the row rank is equal to the column rank, the same three operations applied to rows instead of to columns also do not change the rank. By applying these operations to a given matrix, it is usually possible to change the matrix into another one whose rank is more easily computable.

In the proof of Theorem 4, the kernel of our linear map $L:\mathbf{R}^n \to \mathbf{R}^m$ consists precisely of the solutions X of the system of linear equations

$$a_{11}x_1 + \cdots + a_{1n}x_n = 0$$
$$\vdots$$
$$a_{m1}x_1 + \cdots + a_{mn}x_n = 0.$$

THEOREM 5. *Let U be the space of solutions of the preceding system of linear equations. Let r be the rank of the matrix (a_{ij}). Then the dimension of U is equal to $n - r$.*

Proof. We know that U consists of all vectors perpendicular to the row vectors of the matrix (a_{ij}). By Theorem 8 of Chapter X, §4 we know that $\dim U = n - r$.

EXERCISES

1. Find the rank of the following matrices.

(a) $\begin{pmatrix} 2 & 1 & 3 \\ 7 & 2 & 0 \end{pmatrix}$ (b) $\begin{pmatrix} -1 & 2 & -2 \\ 3 & 4 & -5 \end{pmatrix}$ (c) $\begin{pmatrix} 1 & 2 & 7 \\ 2 & 4 & -1 \end{pmatrix}$

(d) $\begin{pmatrix} 1 & 2 & -3 \\ -1 & -2 & 3 \\ 4 & 8 & -12 \\ 0 & 0 & 0 \end{pmatrix}$

2. Let A, B be two matrices which can be multiplied. Show that rank of $AB \leqq$ rank of A, and also rank of $AB \leqq$ rank of B.

3. Let A be a triangular matrix:

$$A = \begin{pmatrix} a_{11} & \cdots & a_{1n} \\ 0 & a_{22} & \vdots \\ \vdots & \ddots & \vdots \\ 0 & \cdots & 0 \; a_{nn} \end{pmatrix}$$

and assume that none of the diagonal elements is equal to 0. What is the rank at A?

4. Find the dimension of the space of solutions of the following systems of linear equations.

(a) $2x + y - z = 0$
$\qquad y + z = 0$

(b) $x - y + z = 0$

(c) $4x + 7y - \pi z = 0$
$\quad\ 2x - y + z = 0$

(d) $x + y + z = 0$
$\quad\ x - y = 0$
$\quad\ y + z = 0$

§6. *Orthogonal maps*

All the assertions of this section are very easy to prove, and furnish pleasant exercises. We shall not spoil your pleasure in working these out, and we shall only state the results, occasionally giving some hints for the proofs.

Let V be a vector space with a scalar product, as in Chapter X, §4. If you wish, you may assume that $V = \mathbf{R}^n$, but this will not make any statement or proof easier to understand. Let $F : V \to V$ be a linear map. This map may have additional properties, which we shall now describe. We shall say that F *preserves length* if we have

$$\|F(v)\| = \|v\|$$

for all v in V. Observe that this is equivalent to saying that

$$F(v) \cdot F(v) = v \cdot v$$

for all v in V (i.e. $\|F(v)\|^2 = \|v\|^2$ for all v in V).

We shall say that F *preserves the scalar product* if

$$F(v) \cdot F(w) = v \cdot w$$

for all elements v, w of V.

Exercise 1. If F satisfies any one of the above two properties, then it satisfies the other.

Proof. Hint: To go from the first to the second, use the hypothesis that $\|F(v + w)\|^2 = \|v + w\|^2$. To go from the second to the first, recall the argument of Chapter I which showed that "$v \perp w$" is equivalent with the relation "$\|v - w\| = \|v + w\|$".

A linear map F which satisfies any one of the above two properties, and hence satisfies both, is called an *orthogonal* map.

Exercise 2. Let V be a vector space with a scalar product. Let $\{v_1, \ldots, v_n\}$ and $\{w_1, \ldots, w_n\}$ be two orthonormal bases. Let F be a linear map of V into itself such that

$$F(v_i) = w_i$$

for $i = 1, \ldots, n$. Prove that F is orthogonal.

Exercise 3. Let V be a vector space with a scalar product. Let $\{v_1, \ldots, v_n\}$ be an orthonormal basis of V. Let F be a linear map of V into itself which is orthogonal. Show that $F(v_1), \ldots, F(v_n)$ is also an orthonormal basis.

Exercise 4. Let V be a vector space of dimension 2, with a scalar product, and let F be an orthogonal linear map of V into itself. Let $\{v_1, v_2\}$ and $\{w_1, w_2\}$ be two orthonormal bases of V such that $F(v_i) = w_i$ for $i = 1, 2$. Let a, b, c, d be numbers such that

$$w_1 = av_1 + bv_2, \qquad w_2 = cv_1 + dv_2.$$

Show that $a^2 + b^2 = 1$, $c^2 + d^2 = 1$, $ac + bd = 0$, $a^2 = d^2$, and $c^2 = b^2$.

Exercise 5. Let F and V be as in Exercise 4. Assume that $ad - bc > 0$. Show that there is a number θ such that

$$F(v_1) = (\cos \theta)v_1 + (\sin \theta)v_2,$$
$$F(v_2) = (-\sin \theta)v_1 + (\cos \theta)v_2.$$

(Referring to the next chapter, you will see that this means that F is a rotation. Conversely, when you have read the section on rotations in the next chapter, deduce that a rotation is an orthogonal map.)

Note. If $ad - bc < 0$, then the orthoganal map F does not correspond to a rotation. Give an example of such a map, and interpret it geometrically.

CHAPTER XII

Linear Maps and Matrices

When bases have been selected, it is possible to represent a linear map by a matrix, and conversely, every matrix gives rise to a linear map. We shall define addition and multiplication of linear maps and matrices, and see that these correspond to each other.

§1. *The linear map associated with a matrix*

Let V be a vector space, and let $\{v_1, \ldots, v_n\}$ be a basis of V. Let W be a vector space, and let $\{w_1, \ldots, w_m\}$ be a basis of W. Let

$$A = \begin{pmatrix} a_{11} & a_{12} & \cdots & a_{1n} \\ & \vdots & & \\ a_{m1} & a_{m2} & \cdots & a_{mn} \end{pmatrix}$$

be an $m \times n$ matrix. We shall define a linear map

$$L_A : V \to W,$$

depending on A, and the choice of bases for V and W.

Let $A_1, \ldots, A_m$ be the row vectors of the matrix A. Thus:

$$A_1 = (a_{11}, \ldots, a_{1n})$$
$$\vdots$$
$$A_m = (a_{m1}, \ldots, a_{mn}).$$

Let v be an element of V, and let $X = (x_1, \ldots, x_n)$ be its coordinates with respect to the given basis $v_1, \ldots, v_n$. We associate with v the element $L_A(v)$ of W given by the equation

$$L_A(v) = (A_1 \cdot X)w_1 + \cdots + (A_m \cdot X)w_m.$$

In other words, we may say that the i-th coordinate of $L_A(v)$ is $A_i \cdot X$. Thus L_A is a mapping from V into W.

THEOREM 1. *The mapping L_A is a linear mapping.*

Proof. Let u, v be elements of V. There exist unique numbers y_1, $\ldots, y_n$ and $x_1, \ldots, x_n$ such that we can write

$$u = y_1 v_1 + \cdots + y_n v_n, \qquad v = x_1 v_1 + \cdots + x_n v_n.$$

Then

$$u + v = (x_1 + y_1)v_1 + \cdots + (x_n + y_n)v_n.$$

We have:

$$L_A(u + v) = ((A_1 \cdot (X + Y))w_1 + \cdots + ((A_m \cdot (X + Y))w_m.$$

In other words, the i-th coordinate of $L_A(u + v)$ is $A_i \cdot (X + Y)$. We know that $A_i \cdot (X + Y) = A_i \cdot X + A_i \cdot Y$. Hence

$$\begin{aligned}
L_A(u + v) &= (A_1 \cdot X)w_1 + \cdots + (A_m \cdot X)w_m \\
&\qquad\qquad + (A_1 \cdot Y)w_1 + \cdots + (A_m \cdot Y)w_m \\
&= L_A(u) + L_A(v).
\end{aligned}$$

Let c be a number. Then

$$\begin{aligned}
L_A(cu) &= (A_1 \cdot cX)w_1 + \cdots + (A_m \cdot cX)w_m \\
&= c(A_1 \cdot X)w_1 + \cdots + c(A_m \cdot X)w_m \\
&= cL_A(u).
\end{aligned}$$

This proves our theorem.

Example 1. Let $V = \mathbf{R}^n$ and $W = \mathbf{R}^m$. We let

$$\left.\begin{aligned}
E_1 &= (1, 0, \ldots, 0) \\
E_2 &= (0, 1, \ldots, 0) \\
&\;\;\vdots \\
E_n &= (0, 0, \ldots, 1)
\end{aligned}\right\}\text{ (each vector having } n \text{ components).}$$

We also let

$$\left.\begin{aligned}
E_1' &= (1, 0, \ldots, 0) \\
E_2' &= (0, 1, \ldots, 0) \\
&\;\;\vdots \\
E_m' &= (0, 0, \ldots, 1)
\end{aligned}\right\}\text{ (each vector having } m \text{ components).}$$

Any vector in $\mathbf{R}^n$ can then be written in the form

$$(x_1, \ldots, x_n) = x_1 E_1 + \cdots + x_n E_n,$$

and any vector in $\mathbf{R}^m$ can be written in the form

$$(y_1, \ldots, y_m) = y_1 E_1' + \cdots + y_m E_m'.$$

If A is a matrix as before, and $L_A(X) = Y$, then we see that

$$(*)\qquad\begin{aligned}
y_1 &= a_{11}x_1 + \cdots + a_{1n}x_n \\
&\;\;\vdots \\
y_m &= a_{m1}x_1 + \cdots + a_{mn}x_n.
\end{aligned}$$

It is convenient at this point to define the multiplication of a matrix by a vector. Let $A = (a_{ij})$ be an $m \times n$ matrix, and let X be a *column* vector, with precisely n components.

$$X = \begin{pmatrix} x_1 \\ x_2 \\ \vdots \\ x_n \end{pmatrix}.$$

Then we define AX to be the column vector

$$Y = \begin{pmatrix} y_1 \\ y_2 \\ \vdots \\ y_m \end{pmatrix} = \begin{pmatrix} A_1 \cdot X \\ A_2 \cdot X \\ \vdots \\ A_m \cdot X \end{pmatrix}$$

whose coordinates $y_1, \ldots, y_m$ are given by $y_i = A_i \cdot X$. We see that the multiplication is obtained by taking the dot product of the *rows* of A with the *column* X:

$$\begin{pmatrix} a_{11} & a_{12} & \cdots & a_{1n} \\ a_{21} & a_{22} & \cdots & a_{2n} \\ & \vdots & & \\ a_{m1} & a_{m2} & \cdots & a_{mn} \end{pmatrix} \begin{pmatrix} x_1 \\ x_2 \\ \vdots \\ x_n \end{pmatrix} = \begin{pmatrix} y_1 \\ y_2 \\ \vdots \\ y_m \end{pmatrix}.$$

Example 2. Let $V = \mathbf{R}^3$ and $W = \mathbf{R}^2$. Let

$$A = \begin{pmatrix} 2 & 1 & -3 \\ 1 & 2 & 4 \end{pmatrix}.$$

Let

$$X = \begin{pmatrix} x_1 \\ x_2 \\ x_3 \end{pmatrix}$$

be a column vector. Then

$$AX = \begin{pmatrix} 2x_1 + x_2 - 3x_3 \\ x_1 + 2x_2 + 4x_3 \end{pmatrix}.$$

If

$$X = \begin{pmatrix} -2 \\ 1 \\ 2 \end{pmatrix}$$

then

$$AX = \begin{pmatrix} -9 \\ 8 \end{pmatrix}.$$

Let A and B be $m \times n$ matrices. It is a natural question to ask when they give rise to the same linear map, i.e. when $L_A = L_B$. The next theorem answers this question.

THEOREM 2. *Let A, B be $m \times n$ matrices. Let V, W be two vector spaces as above, and suppose that bases have been selected as above. If $L_A = L_B$, then $A = B$. In other words, if the matrices give rise to the same linear map, then they are equal.*

Proof. Let $\{v_1, \ldots, v_n\}$ and $\{w_1, \ldots, w_m\}$ be the bases of V and W respectively. Assume that $L_A = L_B$. Let $A_1, \ldots, A_m$ be the row vectors of A, and let $B_1, \ldots, B_m$ be the row vectors of B. For any n-tuple $X = (x_1, \ldots, x_n)$, and $v = x_1 v_1 + \cdots + x_n v_n$, the expressions of $L_A(v)$ and $L_B(v)$ as linear combinations of $w_1, \ldots, w_m$ are equal. Hence their coordinates with respect to the basis $\{w_1, \ldots, w_m\}$ are equal. Hence

$$A_i \cdot X = B_i \cdot X$$

for all $i = 1, \ldots, m$. Hence $(A_i - B_i) \cdot X = O$ for all i and all X. Hence $A_i - B_i = O$, and $A_i = B_i$ for all i. Hence $A = B$.

It will be a good exercise to prove the next theorem.

THEOREM 3. *Let V, W be vector spaces. Let $\{v_1, \ldots, v_n\}$ be a basis for V, and let $\{w_1, \ldots, w_m\}$ be a basis for W. Let A, B be two $m \times n$ matrices, and let L_A, L_B be the associated linear maps from V into W, relative to these bases. Then for any element v of V, and any number c, we have:*

$$L_{A+B}(v) = L_A(v) + L_B(v)$$
$$L_{cA}(v) = cL_A(v).$$

We could omit the v in the statement of Theorem 3, and simply write

$$L_{A+B} = L_A + L_B,$$
$$L_{cA} = cL_A.$$

In this manner, we see that the rule L, which to each $m \times n$ matrix A associates the linear map L_A, is itself a linear map, from the vector space of $m \times n$ matrices into the vector space of linear maps from $\mathbf{R}^n$ into $\mathbf{R}^m$.

Let us denote the vector space of $m \times n$ matrices by $\mathfrak{M}_{m,n}$, and let us denote by $\mathfrak{L}_{m,n}$ the vector space of linear maps from $\mathbf{R}^n$ into $\mathbf{R}^m$. Then the assertion of Theorem 3 is equivalent with the assertion that

$$L : \mathfrak{M}_{m,n} \to \mathfrak{L}_{m,n}$$

is itself a linear map.

1. In each case, find the vector $L_A(X)$.

(a) $A = \begin{pmatrix} 2 & 1 \\ 1 & 0 \end{pmatrix}$, $X = (3, -1)$ (b) $A = \begin{pmatrix} 1 & 0 \\ 0 & 0 \end{pmatrix}$, $X = (5, 1)$

(c) $A = \begin{pmatrix} 1 & 1 \\ 0 & 1 \end{pmatrix}$, $X = (4, 1)$ (d) $A = \begin{pmatrix} 0 & 0 \\ 0 & 1 \end{pmatrix}$, $X = (7, -3)$

2. Let X be the indicated column vector, and A the indicated matrix. Find AX as a column vector.

(a) $X = \begin{pmatrix} 3 \\ 2 \\ 1 \end{pmatrix}$, $A = \begin{pmatrix} 1 & 0 & 1 \\ 2 & 1 & 1 \\ 2 & 0 & -1 \end{pmatrix}$ (b) $X = \begin{pmatrix} 1 \\ 1 \\ 0 \end{pmatrix}$, $A = \begin{pmatrix} 2 & 1 & 5 \\ 0 & 1 & 1 \end{pmatrix}$

(c) $X = \begin{pmatrix} x_1 \\ x_2 \\ x_3 \end{pmatrix}$, $A = \begin{pmatrix} 0 & 1 & 0 \\ 0 & 0 & 0 \end{pmatrix}$ (d) $X = \begin{pmatrix} x_1 \\ x_2 \\ x_3 \end{pmatrix}$, $A = \begin{pmatrix} 0 & 0 & 0 \\ 1 & 0 & 0 \end{pmatrix}$

3. Let

$$A = \begin{pmatrix} 2 & 1 & 3 \\ 4 & 1 & 5 \end{pmatrix}.$$

Find AX for each of the following values of X.

(a) $X = \begin{pmatrix} 1 \\ 0 \\ 0 \end{pmatrix}$ (b) $X = \begin{pmatrix} 0 \\ 1 \\ 1 \end{pmatrix}$ (c) $X = \begin{pmatrix} 0 \\ 0 \\ 1 \end{pmatrix}$.

4. Let

$$A = \begin{pmatrix} 3 & 7 & 5 \\ 1 & -1 & 4 \\ 2 & 1 & 8 \end{pmatrix}.$$

Find AX for each of the values of X given in Exercise 3.

5. Let

$$X = \begin{pmatrix} 0 \\ 1 \\ 0 \\ 0 \end{pmatrix} \quad \text{and} \quad A = \begin{pmatrix} a_{11} & \cdots & a_{14} \\ & \vdots & \\ a_{m1} & \cdots & a_{m4} \end{pmatrix}.$$

What is AX?

6. Let X be a column vector having all its components equal to 0 except the i-th component which is equal to 1. Let A be an arbitrary matrix, whose size is such that we can form the product AX. What is AX?

§2. The matrix associated with a linear map

Let V, W be vector spaces. Let $F : V \to W$ be a linear map of V into W. We shall see how we can associate a matrix with F. Such a matrix will depend on a choice of bases for V, W.

Let $\{v_1, \ldots, v_n\}$ be a basis of V and let $\{w_1, \ldots, w_m\}$ be a basis of W. Each one of $F(v_1), \ldots, F(v_n)$ is an element of W. Hence each one can be written as a linear combination of $w_1, \ldots, w_m$. Thus:

$$F(v_1) = a_{11}w_1 + \cdots + a_{m1}w_m$$
$$\vdots$$
$$F(v_n) = a_{1n}w_1 + \cdots + a_{mn}w_m.$$

The array

$$\begin{pmatrix} a_{11} & a_{21} & \cdots & a_{m1} \\ a_{12} & a_{22} & \cdots & a_{m2} \\ & \vdots & & \\ a_{1n} & a_{2n} & \cdots & a_{mn} \end{pmatrix}$$

is a matrix. The *transpose* of this matrix will be called the *matrix* associated with the mapping F (relative to our choice of bases).

The transpose of the above matrix is therefore the matrix

$$A = \begin{pmatrix} a_{11} & a_{12} & \cdots & a_{1n} \\ & \vdots & & \\ a_{m1} & a_{m2} & \cdots & a_{mn} \end{pmatrix}.$$

The reason for taking the transpose will become clear in a moment.

Let $v = x_1v_1 + \cdots + x_nv_n$ be an element of V. Since F is linear, we obtain

$$F(v) = x_1F(v_1) + \cdots + x_nF(v_n).$$

Using the expression for $F(v_1), \ldots, F(v_n)$ given above in terms of $w_1, \ldots, w_m$, we find that

$$F(v) = x_1(a_{11}w_1 + \cdots + a_{m1}w_m) + \cdots + x_n(a_{1n}w_1 + \cdots + a_{mn}w_m),$$

and after collecting the coefficients of $w_1, \ldots, w_m$, we can rewrite this expression in the form

$$(a_{11}x_1 + \cdots + a_{1n}x_1)w_1 + \cdots + (a_{m1}x_1 + \cdots + a_{mn}x_n)w_m.$$

This is precisely equal to $L_A(v)$. Hence $F = L_A$!

In other words, let v be an element of V. Let X be its (vertical) coordinate vector relative to $\{v_1, \ldots, v_n\}$. Let A be the matrix associated to F relative to the chosen bases. Then the coordinate vector of $F(v)$ relative to the basis $\{w_1, \ldots, w_m\}$ is AX.

In view of Theorem 3 of the preceding section, we see that our matrix A is the unique matrix such that $F = L_A$. One could also prove the uniqueness of such a matrix A by a direct argument, using the fact that the values of F are determined by its values on basis elements.

Example 1.   Let $F:\mathbf{R}^3 \to \mathbf{R}^2$ be the projection, in other words the mapping such that $F(x_1, x_2, x_3) = (x_1, x_2)$. Then the matrix associated with F relative to the usual bases is

$$\begin{pmatrix} 1 & 0 & 0 \\ 0 & 1 & 0 \end{pmatrix}.$$

Example 2.   Let $F:\mathbf{R}^n \to \mathbf{R}^n$ be the identity. Then the matrix associated with F relative to the usual bases is the matrix

$$\begin{pmatrix} 1 & 0 & 0 & \cdots & 0 \\ 0 & 1 & 0 & \cdots & 0 \\ & & \vdots & & \\ 0 & 0 & 0 & \cdots & 1 \end{pmatrix},$$

having components equal to 1 on the diagonal, and 0 otherwise.

This matrix is called the *unit* matrix (or unit $n \times n$ matrix), and is sometimes denoted by I_n or I if the dimension is not specified..

Let $\mathfrak{B} = \{v_1, \ldots, v_n\}$ be a basis for the vector space V, and let $\mathfrak{B}' = \{w_1, \ldots, w_m\}$ be a basis for the vector space W. We shall denote by

$$M_{\mathfrak{B}'}^{\mathfrak{B}}(F)$$

the matrix associated with a linear map F of V into W, relative to the bases $\mathfrak{B}$ and $\mathfrak{B}'$. If these bases are fixed throughout a discussion, then we may write simply $M(F)$.

Warning. Assume that $V = W$, but that we work with two bases $\mathfrak{B}$ and $\mathfrak{B}'$ of V which are distinct. Then the matrix associated with the identity mapping of V into itself relative to these two distinct bases will *not* be the unit matrix!

Example 3.   *Rotations.* We shall encounter two situations. First, we shall pick two different coordinate systems differing by a rotation. The identity mapping will then have an associated matrix which is not the unit matrix. Second, we shall discuss the matrix associated with a rotation, with respect to a fixed basis.

Case 1.   Let us start with our coordinate system in the plane as usual. Let $E_1 = (1, 0)$ and $E_2 = (0, 1)$ be the unit vectors. We consider another coordinate system obtained by rotating the given coordinate system counterclockwise by an angle θ. Then the unit vectors are moved into two new unit vectors E_1' and E_2'.

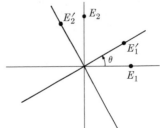

From the picture, we see that

$$E_1' = (\cos \theta)E_1 + (\sin \theta)E_2,$$
$$E_2' = (-\sin \theta)E_1 + (\cos \theta)E_2.$$

If we multiply the first equation by $\cos \theta$, if we multiply the second by $-\sin \theta$, and add, we find:

$$E_1 = (\cos \theta)E_1' - (\sin \theta)E_2'.$$

Similarly,

$$E_2 = (\sin \theta)E_1' + (\cos \theta)E_2'.$$

Let $Id:\mathbf{R}^2 \to \mathbf{R}^2$ be the identity mapping. Let $\mathfrak{B} = \{E_1, E_2\}$ and $\mathfrak{B}' = \{E_1', E_2'\}$. Then:

$$Id(E_1) = E_1 = (\cos \theta)E_1' + (-\sin \theta)E_2',$$
$$Id(E_2) = E_2 = (\sin \theta)E_1' + (\cos \theta)E_2'.$$

Consequently, the matrix associated with the identity mapping relative to the bases $\mathfrak{B}$ and $\mathfrak{B}'$ is

$$\begin{pmatrix} \cos \theta & \sin \theta \\ -\sin \theta & \cos \theta \end{pmatrix}.$$

Case 2. Let us keep our standard coordinate system, with basis $\mathfrak{B} = \{E_1, E_2\}$. Let $F:\mathbf{R}^2 \to \mathbf{R}^2$ be the mapping obtained by rotating the plane through an angle θ (counterclockwise). Then:

$$F(E_1) = E_1' = (\cos \theta)E_1 + (\sin \theta)E_2,$$
$$F(E_2) = E_2' = (-\sin \theta)E_1 + (\cos \theta)E_2.$$

Hence the matrix associated with F relative to the bases $\mathfrak{B}$, $\mathfrak{B}$ is the transpose of the matrix in Case 1, namely:

$$\begin{pmatrix} \cos \theta & -\sin \theta \\ \sin \theta & \cos \theta \end{pmatrix}.$$

There is no avoiding the fact that the matrix in Case 1 turns out to be the transpose of the matrix in Case 2. Hence it is necessary always to be careful of the selection of bases to compute the matrix associated with a linear map.

The next theorem is the analogue of Theorem 3, §2.

THEOREM 4. *Let V, W be vector spaces. Let $\mathfrak{B}$ be a basis of V, and $\mathfrak{B}'$ a basis of W. Let f, g be two linear maps of V into W. Then $M(f + g) = M(f) + M(g)$. If c is a number, then $M(cf) = cM(f)$. (The associated matrix is taken relative to the given bases $\mathfrak{B}$ and $\mathfrak{B}'$.)*

The proof will be left as an exercise.

EXERCISES

1. Assume that $\mathbf{R}^n$, $\mathbf{R}^m$ have their usual bases. Find the matrix associated with the following linear maps.

(a) $F:\mathbf{R}^4 \to \mathbf{R}^2$ given by $F(x_1, x_2, x_3, x_4) = (x_1, x_2)$ (the projection).

(b) The projection from $\mathbf{R}^4$ to $\mathbf{R}^3$.

(c) $F:\mathbf{R}^2 \to \mathbf{R}^2$ given by $F(x, y) = (3x, 3y)$.

(d) $F:\mathbf{R}^n \to \mathbf{R}^n$ given by $F(X) = 7X$.

(e) $F:\mathbf{R}^n \to \mathbf{R}^n$ given by $F(X) = -X$.

(f) $F:\mathbf{R}^4 \to \mathbf{R}^4$ given by $F(x_1, x_2, x_3, x_4) = (x_1, x_2, 0, 0)$.

2. Let $\mathfrak{B} = \{E_1, E_2\}$ be the usual basis of $\mathbf{R}^2$, and let $\mathfrak{B}'$ be the basis obtained after rotating the coordinate system by an angle θ. Find the matrix associated to the identity relative to $\mathfrak{B}$, $\mathfrak{B}'$ for each of the following values of θ.

(a) $\pi/2$ (b) $\pi/4$ (c) π (d) $-\pi$ (e) $-\pi/3$

(f) $\pi/6$ (g) $5\pi/4$

3. In general, let $\theta > 0$. What is the matrix associated with the identity map, and rotation of bases by an angle $-\theta$ (i.e. clockwise rotation by θ)?

4. Let $X = (1, 2)$ be a point of the plane. Let F be the rotation through an angle of $\pi/4$. What are the coordinates of $F(X)$ relative to the usual basis $\{E_1, E_2\}$?

5. Same question when $X = (-1, 3)$, and F is the rotation through $\pi/2$.

6. In general, let F be the rotation through an angle θ. Let (x, y) be a point of the plane in the standard coordinate system. Let (x', y') be the coordinates of this point in the rotated system. Express x', y' in terms of x, y, and θ.

7. Let $X = (x, y)$ and let F be a rotation through an angle θ. Show that $\|X\| = \|F(X)\|$ (i.e. that F preserves norms).

8. In each of the following cases, let $D = d/dt$ be the derivative. We give a set of linearly independent functions $\mathfrak{B}$. These generate a vector space V, and D is a linear map from V into itself. Find the matrix associated with D relative to the bases $\mathfrak{B}$, $\mathfrak{B}$.

(a) $\{e^t, e^{2t}\}$ (b) $\{1, t\}$ (c) $\{e^t, te^t\}$

(d) $\{1, t, t^2\}$ (e) $\{1, t, e^t, e^{2t}, te^{2t}\}$ (f) $\{\sin t, \cos t\}$

9. Let $\mathfrak{M}$ be the vector space of $m \times n$ matrices. What is its dimension?

10. Let V, W be vector spaces of dimensions n, m, respectively. What is the dimension of the vector space of linear maps from V into W?

11. Let V be a vector space of dimension n. What is the dimension of the space of linear maps from V into $\mathbf{R}$?

§3. Composition of linear mappings

Let U, V, W be sets. Let $F:U \to V$ be a mapping, and let $G:V \to W$ be a mapping. Then we can form a composite mapping from U into W in the same way that we formed composite functions. The value of this composite mapping at an element u of U is $G(F(u))$. The composite mapping is defined by the rule: Associate with the element u of U the element $G(F(u))$. This composite mapping will be denoted by $G \circ F$.

Example 1. If $f: \mathbf{R} \to \mathbf{R}$ is a function and $g: \mathbf{R} \to \mathbf{R}$ is also a function, then $g \circ f$ is the composite function, as studied long ago.

Example 2. Let $F: \mathbf{R} \to \mathbf{R}^2$ be the mapping given by

$$F(t) = (t, t^2),$$

and let $G: \mathbf{R}^2 \to \mathbf{R}$ be the mapping given by $G(x, y) = xy$.   Then $G(F(t)) = tt^2 = t^3$. Thus $(G \circ F)(t) = t^3$.

Example 3. Let $X: \mathbf{R} \to \mathbf{R}^3$ be the mapping given by

$$X(t) = (t, e^t, 2 \sin t).$$

Let $F: \mathbf{R}^3 \to \mathbf{R}$ be the mapping (function) given by

$$F(x, y, z) = x^2 y + z.$$

Then $F(X(t)) = t^2 e^t + 2 \sin t$. We can also write this $(F \circ X)(t)$.

Example 4. Let U be the vector space of differentiable functions (of one variable t), and let $U = V = W$. Let $F: U \to U$ be the mapping which to each function f associates its square [i.e. $F(f) = f^2$], and let $D: U \to U$ be the derivative. Then for any differentiable function f, we have

$$(D \circ F)(f) = 2ff',$$

denoting by f' the derivative of f.

Example 5. Let $U = V = W$ be the vector space of functions having derivatives of all orders. Let D be the derivative. Then

$$(D \circ D)(f) = f''$$

is the second derivative. Also, $(D \circ D \circ D)(f) = f''' = f^{(3)}$ is the third derivative. In general, we could write $D^n f = f^{(n)}$. Thus D^n is the iteration of D taken n times.

THEOREM 5. *Let U, V, W be vector spaces. Let*

$$F: U \to V \qquad and \qquad G: V \to W$$

be linear mappings. Then the composite mapping $G \circ F$ is also a linear mapping.

Proof. This is very easy to prove. Let u, v be elements of U. Since F is linear, we have $F(u + v) = F(u) + F(v)$. Hence

$$(G \circ F)(u + v) = G(F(u + v)) = G(F(u) + F(v)).$$

Since G is linear, we obtain

$$G(F(u) + F(v)) = G(F(u)) + G(F(v)).$$

Hence

$$(G \circ F)(u + v) = (G \circ F)(u) + (G \circ F)(v).$$

Next, let c be a number. Then

$$
\begin{aligned}
(G \circ F)(cu) &= G(F(cu)) \\
&= G(cF(u)) \quad \text{(because } F \text{ is linear)} \\
&= cG(F(u)) \quad \text{(because } G \text{ is linear)}.
\end{aligned}
$$

This proves that $G \circ F$ is a linear mapping.

The next theorem states that some of the rules of arithmetic concerning the product and sum of numbers also apply to the composition and sum of linear mappings.

THEOREM 6. *Let U, V, W be vector spaces. Let*

$$F : U \to V$$

be a linear mapping, and let G, H be two linear mappings of V into W. Then

$$(G + H) \circ F = G \circ F + H \circ F.$$

If c is a number, then

$$(cG) \circ F = c(G \circ F).$$

If $T : U \to V$ is a linear mapping from U into V, then

$$G \circ (F + T) = G \circ F + G \circ T.$$

The proofs are all simple. We shall just prove the first assertion and leave the others as exercises.

Let u be an element of U. We have:

$$
\begin{aligned}
((G + H) \circ F)(u) = (G + H)(F(u)) &= G(F(u)) + H(F(u)) \\
&= (G \circ F)(u) + (H \circ F)(u).
\end{aligned}
$$

By definition, it follows that $(G + H) \circ F = G \circ F + H \circ F$.

It may happen that $U = V = W$. Let $F : U \to U$ and $G : U \to U$ be two linear mappings. Then we may form $F \circ G$ and $G \circ F$. It is not always true that these two composite mappings are equal. As an example, let $U = \mathbf{R}^3$. Let F be the linear mapping given by

$$F(x, y, z) = (x, y, 0)$$

and let G be the linear mapping given by

$$G(x, y, z) = (x, z, 0).$$

Then $(G \circ F)(x, y, z) = (x, 0, 0)$, but $(F \circ G)(x, y, z) = (x, z, 0)$.

The following theorem applies to all mappings.

THEOREM 7. *Let U, V, W, S be sets. Let*

$$F : U \to V, \qquad G : V \to W, \qquad and \qquad H : W \to S$$

be mappings. Then

$$H \circ (G \circ F) = (H \circ G) \circ F.$$

Proof. Here again, the proof is very simple. By definition, we have, for any element u of U:

$$(H \circ (G \circ F))(u) = H((G \circ F)(u)) = H(G(F(u))).$$

On the other hand,

$$((H \circ G) \circ F)(u) = (H \circ G)(F(u)) = H(G(F(u))).$$

By definition, this means that $(H \circ G) \circ F = H \circ (G \circ F)$.

§4. *Multiplication of matrices*

We shall now define the product of matrices. Let $A = (a_{ij})$, $i = 1, \ldots, m$ and $j = 1, \ldots, n$ be an $m \times n$ matrix. Let $B = (b_{jk})$, $j = 1, \ldots, n$ and $k = 1, \ldots, s$ be an $n \times s$ matrix.

$$A = \begin{pmatrix} a_{11} & \cdots & a_{1n} \\ & \vdots & \\ a_{m1} & \cdots & a_{mn} \end{pmatrix}, \qquad B = \begin{pmatrix} b_{11} & \cdots & b_{1s} \\ & \vdots & \\ b_{n1} & \cdots & b_{ns} \end{pmatrix}.$$

We define the product AB to be the $m \times s$ matrix whose ik-coordinate is

$$\sum_{j=1}^{n} a_{ij}b_{jk} = a_{i1}b_{1k} + a_{i2}b_{2k} + \cdots + a_{in}b_{nk}.$$

If $A_1, \ldots, A_m$ are the row vectors of the matrix A, and if $B^1, \ldots, B^s$ are the column vectors of the matrix B, then the ik-coordinate of the product AB is therefore equal to $A_i \cdot B^k$. Thus

$$AB = \begin{pmatrix} A_1 \cdot B^1 & \cdots & A_1 \cdot B^s \\ & \vdots & \\ A_m \cdot B^1 & \cdots & A_m \cdot B^s \end{pmatrix}.$$

Multiplication of matrices is therefore a generalization of the dot product.

Example 1. Let

$$A = \begin{pmatrix} 2 & 1 & 5 \\ 1 & 3 & 2 \end{pmatrix}, \qquad B = \begin{pmatrix} 3 & 4 \\ -1 & 2 \\ 2 & 1 \end{pmatrix}.$$

Then AB is a 2×2 matrix, and computations show that

$$AB = \begin{pmatrix} 2 & 1 & 5 \\ 1 & 3 & 2 \end{pmatrix} \begin{pmatrix} 3 & 4 \\ -1 & 2 \\ 2 & 1 \end{pmatrix} = \begin{pmatrix} 15 & 15 \\ 4 & 12 \end{pmatrix}.$$

Example 2. Let

$$C = \begin{pmatrix} 1 & 3 \\ -1 & -1 \end{pmatrix}.$$

Let A, B be as in Example 1. Then:

$$BC = \begin{pmatrix} 3 & 4 \\ -1 & 2 \\ 2 & 1 \end{pmatrix} \begin{pmatrix} 1 & 3 \\ -1 & -1 \end{pmatrix} = \begin{pmatrix} -1 & 5 \\ -3 & -5 \\ 1 & 5 \end{pmatrix}$$

and

$$A(BC) = \begin{pmatrix} 2 & 1 & 5 \\ 1 & 3 & 2 \end{pmatrix} \begin{pmatrix} -1 & 5 \\ -3 & -5 \\ 1 & 5 \end{pmatrix} = \begin{pmatrix} 0 & 30 \\ -8 & 0 \end{pmatrix}.$$

Compute $(AB)C$. What do you find?

Let A be an $m \times n$ matrix and let B be an $n \times 1$ matrix, i.e. a column vector. Then AB is again a column vector.

Let A be a $1 \times n$ matrix, i.e. a row vector, and let B be an $n \times s$ matrix. Then AB is a row vector.

If A is a square matrix, then we can form the product AA, which will be a square matrix of the same size as A. It is denoted by A^2. Similarly, we can form A^3, A^4, and in general, A^n for any positive integer n. We define $A^0 = I$ (the unit matrix of the same size as A).

THEOREM 8. *Let A, B, C be matrices. Assume that A, B can be multiplied, and A, C can be multiplied. Then A, $B + C$ can be multiplied, and we have:*

$$A(B + C) = AB + AC.$$

If x is a number, then

$$A(xB) = x(AB).$$

Proof. Let A_i be the i-th row of A, and let B^k, C^k be the k-th column of B and C respectively. Then $B^k + C^k$ is the k-th column of $B + C$. By definition, the ik-component of AB is $A_i \cdot B^k$, the ik-component of AC is $A_i \cdot C^k$, and the ik-component of $A(B + C)$ is $A_i \cdot (B^k + C^k)$. Since

$$A_i \cdot (B^k + C^k) = A_i \cdot B^k + A_i \cdot C^k,$$

our first assertion follows. As for the second, observe that the k-th column of xB is xB^k. Since

$$A_i \cdot xB^k = x(A_i \cdot B^k),$$

our second assertion follows.

THEOREM 9. *Let A, B, C be matrices such that A, B can be multiplied and B, C can be multiplied and B, C can be added. Then A, BC can be multiplied, so can AB, C, and we have*

$$(AB)C = A(BC).$$

Proof. Let $A = (a_{ij})$ be an $m \times n$ matrix, let $B = (b_{jk})$ be an $n \times r$ matrix, and let $C = (c_{kl})$ be an $r \times s$ matrix. The product AB is an $m \times r$ matrix, whose ik-component is equal to the sum

$$a_{i1}b_{1k} + a_{i2}b_{2k} + \cdots + a_{in}b_{nk}.$$

We shall abbreviate this sum using our $\sum$ notation by writing

$$\sum_{j=1}^{n} a_{ij}b_{jk}.$$

By definition, the il-component of $(AB)C$ is equal to

$$\sum_{k=1}^{r} \left[\sum_{j=1}^{n} a_{ij}b_{jk} \right] c_{kl} = \sum_{k=1}^{r} \left[\sum_{j=1}^{n} a_{ij}b_{jk}c_{kl} \right].$$

The sum on the right can also be described as the sum of all terms

$$a_{ij}b_{jk}c_{kl},$$

where j, k range over all integers $1 \leq j \leq n$ and $1 \leq k \leq r$ respectively.

If we had started with the jl-component of BC and then computed the il-component of $A(BC)$ we would have found exactly the same sum, thereby proving the theorem.

We have one final result relating linear maps and matrices.

THEOREM 10. *Let V, W, U be vector spaces. Let $\mathcal{B}$, $\mathcal{B}'$, $\mathcal{B}''$ be bases for V, W, U respectively. Let*

$$F : V \to W \qquad and \qquad G : W \to U$$

be linear maps. Then

$$M_{\mathcal{B}''}^{\mathcal{B}'}(G) M_{\mathcal{B}'}^{\mathcal{B}}(F) = M_{\mathcal{B}''}^{\mathcal{B}}(G \circ F).$$

(*Note*. Relative to our choice of bases, the theorem expresses the fact that composition of mappings corresponds to multiplication of matrices.)

Proof. We shall see that Theorem 10 follows from Theorem 9. Let A be the matrix associated with F relative to the bases $\mathcal{B}$, $\mathcal{B}'$ and let B be the matrix associated with G relative to the bases $\mathcal{B}'$, $\mathcal{B}''$. Let v be an element of V and let X be its (column) coordinate vector relative to $\mathcal{B}$. Then the coordinate vector of $F(v)$ relative to $\mathcal{B}'$ is AX. By definition, the coordinate vector of $G(F(v))$ relative to $\mathcal{B}'$ is $B(AX)$, which, by Theorem 9, is equal to $(BA)X$. But $G(F(v)) = (G \circ F)(v)$. Hence the coordinate vector of $(G \circ F)(v)$ relative to the basis $\mathcal{B}''$ is $(BA)X$. By definition, this means that BA is the matrix associated with $G \circ F$, and proves our theorem.

Remark. In many applications, one deals with linear maps of a vector space V into itself. If a basis $\mathcal{B}$ of V is selected, and $F : V \to V$ is a linear map, then the matrix

$$M_{\mathcal{B}}^{\mathcal{B}}(F)$$

is usually called the matrix associated with F relative to $\mathcal{B}$ (instead of saying relative to $\mathcal{B}$, $\mathcal{B}$). Cf. Exercise 13 to see how this matrix changes when the basis $\mathcal{B}$ is changed.

EXERCISES

1. Let I be the unit $n \times n$ matrix. Let A be an $n \times r$ matrix. What is IA? If A is an $n \times n$ matrix, what is AI?

2. Let O be the matrix all of whose coordinates are 0. Let A be a matrix of a size such that the product AO is defined. What is AO?

3. In each one of the following cases, find $(AB)C$ and $A(BC)$.

(a) $A = \begin{pmatrix} 2 & 1 \\ 3 & 1 \end{pmatrix}$, $B = \begin{pmatrix} -1 & 1 \\ 1 & 0 \end{pmatrix}$, $C = \begin{pmatrix} 1 & 4 \\ 2 & 3 \end{pmatrix}$

(b) $A = \begin{pmatrix} 2 & 1 & -1 \\ 3 & 1 & 2 \end{pmatrix}$, $B = \begin{pmatrix} 1 & 1 \\ 2 & 0 \\ 3 & -1 \end{pmatrix}$, $C = \begin{pmatrix} 1 \\ 3 \end{pmatrix}$

(c) $A = \begin{pmatrix} 2 & 4 & 1 \\ 3 & 0 & -1 \end{pmatrix}$, $B = \begin{pmatrix} 1 & 1 & 0 \\ 2 & 1 & -1 \\ 3 & 1 & 5 \end{pmatrix}$, $C = \begin{pmatrix} 1 & 2 \\ 3 & 1 \\ -1 & 4 \end{pmatrix}$

4. Let A, B be square matrices of the same size, and assume that $AB = BA$. Show that $(A + B)^2 = A^2 + 2AB + B^2$, and

$$(A + B)(A - B) = A^2 - B^2,$$

using the properties of matrices stated in Theorem 8.

5. Let

$$A = \begin{pmatrix} 1 & 2 \\ 3 & -1 \end{pmatrix}, \qquad B = \begin{pmatrix} 2 & 0 \\ 1 & 1 \end{pmatrix}.$$

Find AB and BA.

6. Let $C = \begin{pmatrix} 7 & 0 \\ 0 & 7 \end{pmatrix}$. Let A, B be as in Exercise 5. Find CA, AC, CB, and BC. State the general rule including this exercise as a special case.

7. Let $X = (1, 0, 0)$ and let

$$A = \begin{pmatrix} 3 & 1 & 5 \\ 2 & 0 & 1 \\ 1 & 1 & 7 \end{pmatrix}.$$

What is XA?

8. Let $X = (0, 1, 0)$, and let A be an arbitrary 3×3 matrix. How would you describe XA? What if $X = (0, 0, 1)$? Generalize to similar statements concerning $n \times n$ matrices, and their products with unit vectors.

9. Let A, B be the matrices of Exercise 1(a). Verify by computation that $^t(AB) = {}^tB\,{}^tA$. Do the same for 1(b) and 1(c). Prove the same rule for any two matrices A, B (which can be multiplied). If A, B, C are matrices which can be multiplied, show that $^t(ABC) = {}^tC\,{}^tB\,{}^tA$.

10. Let M be an $n \times n$ matrix such that $^tM = M$. Given two row vectors in n-space, say A and B define $\langle A, B \rangle$ to be AM^tB. (Identify a 1×1 matrix with a number.) Show that the conditions of a scalar product are satisfied, except possibly the condition concerning positivity. Give an example of a matrix M and vectors A, B such that AM^tB is negative (taking $n = 2$).

11. Let A be the matrix

$$\begin{pmatrix} 0 & 1 & 1 \\ 0 & 0 & 1 \\ 0 & 0 & 0 \end{pmatrix}.$$

Find A^2, A^3. Generalize to 4×4 matrices.

12. Take $V = W = U$ in Theorem 10. Let F and G be both equal to the identity mapping. Let $\mathfrak{B}$, $\mathfrak{B}'$ be bases of V. Show that

$$M_{\mathfrak{B}'}^{\mathfrak{B}} (Id) M_{\mathfrak{B}}^{\mathfrak{B}'} (Id) = I,$$

where I is the unit matrix.

13. Let V be a vector space, and $\mathfrak{B}$, $\mathfrak{B}'$ two bases. Let $F : V \to V$ be a linear map of V into itself. Let M be the matrix associated with F relative to the bases $\mathfrak{B}$, $\mathfrak{B}$, and let M' be the matrix associated with F relative to the bases $\mathfrak{B}'$, $\mathfrak{B}'$. Show that there exist matrices A and B such that $M' = AMB$, and $AB = BA = I$. (One usually writes $B = A^{-1}$.)

14. Let $A = (a_{ij})$, $i = 1, \ldots, m$ and $j = 1, \ldots, n$ be an $m \times n$ matrix. Let $B = (b_{jk})$, $j = 1, \ldots, n$ and $k = 1, \ldots, s$ be an $n \times s$ matrix. Let $AB = C$. Show that the k-th column C^k can be written

$$C^k = b_{1k} A^1 + \cdots + b_{nk} A^n.$$

(This will be useful in finding the determinant of a product.)

§5. *Applications to linear equations*

We can give one more interpretation to linear equations, using the notions of linear map and multiplication of matrices.

Let A be an $m \times n$ matrix, and let L_A be the linear map represented by the matrix A (relative to the usual bases of $\mathbf{R}^n$ and $\mathbf{R}^m$). Let X be a column vector in n-space. Then

$$L_A(X) = AX$$

is equal to the product of the matrix A times the vector X. Given a column vector B in m-space, we can say that the set of solutions of the inhomogeneous system

$$a_{11}x_1 + \cdots + a_{1n}x_n = b_1$$
$$\vdots$$
$$a_{m1}x_1 + \cdots + a_{mn}x_n = b_m$$

consists of all solutions X of the equation $L_A(X) = B$, or in terms of matrices,

$$AX = B.$$

If B is the O-vector, then X is the solution of the homogeneous system $AX = O$, or $L_A(X) = O$. In that case, we can say that the set of solutions of the homogeneous system is the kernel of L_A. In this manner, we see once more that it is a vector space.

If C is any solution of the inhomogeneous system $AX = B$, i.e. if $AC = B$, and Y is any solution of the homogeneous system, then $C + Y$ is a solution of $AX = B$. Conversely, if C, C' are two solutions of the equation $AX = B$, then there exists a vector Y such that $C' = C + Y$. Prove these assertions as an exercise (using the present interpretation of the system of linear equations). It may happen of course that the inhomogeneous system does not have a solution, i.e. the equations may be inconsistent. For instance:

$$2x + 3y = 1,$$
$$2x + 3y = 0$$

does not have a solution, even though the homogeneous system has a 1-dimensional space of solutions.

EXERCISE

1. Let A be an $m \times n$ matrix and B a column vector in m-space. If the system $AX = B$ has a solution, the dimension of the associated homogeneous system $AY = O$ is called the dimension of the space of solutions. Find this dimension for the following systems of equations.

(a) $2x + 3y - z = 1$

(b) $2x - y + z = 0$
     $2x + y + z = 5$

(c) $-x + 4y + z = 2$
     $3x + y - z = 0$

(d) $x - y + z = 1$
     $2x - 3y + z = 0$
     $x + y - z = 5$

CHAPTER XIII

Applications to Functions of
Several Variables

Having acquired the language of linear maps and matrices, we shall be able to define the derivative of a mapping, or rather, of a differentiable mapping. The theoretical considerations involved in the proof of the general chain rule of §3 become of course a little abstract. But you should note that it is precisely the availability of the notion of linear mapping which allows us to give a statement of the chain rule, and a proof, which runs exactly parallel to the proof for functions of one variable, as given in the *First Course*. The analysis profits from algebra, and conversely, the algebra of linear mappings finds a neat application which enhances its attractiveness.

§1. *The derivative as a linear map*

We shall interpret our notion of differentiability given in Chapter III in terms of linear mappings.

Let U be an open set in $\mathbf{R}^n$. Let f be a function defined on U. Let P be a point of U, and assume that f is differentiable at P. Then there is a vector A, and a function g such that for all small vectors H we can write

$$(1) \qquad f(P + H) = f(P) + A \cdot H + \|H\|g(H),$$

and

$$(2) \qquad \lim_{\|H\| \to 0} g(H) = 0.$$

The vector A, expressed in terms of coordinates, is none other than the vector of partial derivatives:

$$A = \operatorname{grad} f(P) = (D_1 f(P), \ldots, D_n f(P)).$$

We have seen in Example 3 of Chapter IX, §3 that there is a linear map L such that

$$L(H) = A \cdot H.$$

Our condition that f is differentiable may therefore be expressed by saying that there is a linear map $L : \mathbf{R}^n \to \mathbf{R}$ and a function g defined for sufficiently small H, such that

(3) $f(P + H) = f(P) + L(H) + \|H\|g(H)$

and

$$\lim_{\|H\| \to 0} g(H) = 0.$$

Up to now, we did not define the notion of derivative for functions of several variables. We now define the derivative of f at P to be this linear map, which we shall denote by $Df(P)$ or also $f'(P)$. This notation is therefore entirely similar to the notation used for functions of one variable. We could not make the definition before we knew what a linear map is. All the theory developed in Chapters II through VII could be carried out knowing only dot products, and this is the reason we postponed making the general definition of derivative until now.

If L is a linear map from one vector space into another, then it will be useful to omit some parentheses in order to simplify the notation. Thus we shall sometimes write Lv instead of $L(v)$. With this convention, we can write (3) in the form

(4) $f(P + H) = f(P) + Df(P)H + \|H\|g(H),$

or also

(5) $f(P + H) = f(P) + f'(P)H + \|H\|g(H).$

These ways of expressing differentiability are those which generalize to arbitrary mappings.

Let U be an open set in $\mathbf{R}^n$. Let $F : U \to \mathbf{R}^m$ be a mapping. Let P be a point of U. We shall say that F is *differentiable* at P if there exists a linear map

$$L : \mathbf{R}^n \to \mathbf{R}^m$$

and a mapping G defined for all vectors H sufficiently small, such that we have

(6) $F(P + H) = F(P) + LH + \|H\|G(H)$

and

(7) $\lim_{\|H\| \to 0} G(H) = 0.$

If such a linear mapping L exists, then we interpret (6) as saying that L approximates F up to an error term whose magnitude is small, near the point P.

A linear map L satisfying conditions (6) and (7) will be said to be *tangent* to F at P.

THEOREM 1. *Suppose that there exist linear maps L, M which are tangent to F at P. Then $L = M$. In other words, if there exists one linear map which is tangent to F at P, then there is only one.*

Proof. Suppose that there are two mappings G_1, G_2 such that for all sufficiently small H, we have

$$F(P + H) = F(P) + LH + \|H\|G_1(H),$$
$$F(P + H) = F(P) + MH + \|H\|G_2(H)$$

and

$$\lim_{\|H\|\to 0} G_1(H) = 0, \qquad \lim_{\|H\|\to 0} G_2(H) = 0.$$

We must show that for any vector Y we have $LY = MY$. Let t range over small positive numbers. Then tY is small, and $P + tY$ lies in U. Thus $F(P + tY)$ is defined. By hypothesis, we have

$$F(P + tY) = F(P) + L(tY) + \|tY\|G_1(tY),$$
$$F(P + tY) = F(P) + M(tY) + \|tY\|G_2(tY).$$

Subtracting, we obtain

$$O = L(tY) - M(tY) + \|tY\|[G_1(tY) - G_2(tY)].$$

Let $G = G_1 - G_2$. Since L, M are linear, we can write $L(tY) = tL(Y)$ and $M(tY) = tM(Y)$. Consequently, we obtain

$$tM(Y) - tL(Y) = t\|Y\|G(tY).$$

Take $t \neq 0$. Dividing by t yields

$$M(Y) - L(Y) = \|Y\|G(tY).$$

As t approaches 0, $G(tY)$ approaches O also. Hence the right-hand side of this last equation approaches O. But $M(Y) - L(Y)$ is a fixed vector, The only way this is possible is that $M(Y) - L(Y) = O$, in other words. $M(Y) = L(Y)$, as was to be shown.

If there exists a linear map tangent to F at P, we shall denote this linear map by $F'(P)$, or $DF(P)$ and call it the *derivative* of F at P. We may therefore write

$$F(P + H) = F(P) + F'(P)H + \|H\|G(H)$$

instead of (6).

In the next section, we shall see how the linear map $F'(P)$ can be computed, or rather how its matrix can be computed when we deal with vectors as n-tuples.

EXERCISES

1. Let $f: \mathbf{R} \to \mathbf{R}$ be a function, and let a be a number. Assume that there exists a linear map L tangent to f at a. Show that

$$L(1) = \lim_{h \to 0} \frac{f(a+h) - f(a)}{h}.$$

2. Conversely, assume that the limit

$$\lim_{h \to 0} \frac{f(a+h) - f(a)}{h}$$

exists and is equal to a number b. Let L_b be the linear map such that $L_b(x) = bx$ for all numbers x. Show that L_b is tangent to f at a. It is customary to identify the number b and the linear map L_b, and to call either one the derivative of f at a.

3. Going back to Chapter II, let $X(t)$ be a curve, defined for all numbers t, say. Discuss in a manner analogous to Exercises 1 and 2 the derivative dX/dt, and the linear map $L_t: \mathbf{R} \to \mathbf{R}^n$ which is tangent to X at t.

§2. The Jacobian matrix

Throughout this section, all our vectors will be vertical vectors. We let $D_1, \ldots, D_n$ be the usual partial derivatives. Thus $D_i = \partial/\partial x_i$.

Let $F: \mathbf{R}^n \to \mathbf{R}^m$ be a mapping. We can represent F by coordinate functions. In other words, there exist functions $f_1, \ldots, f_m$ such that

$$F(X) = \begin{pmatrix} f_1(X) \\ f_2(X) \\ \vdots \\ f_m(X) \end{pmatrix} = {}^t(f_1(X), \ldots, f_m(X)).$$

To simplify the typography, we shall sometimes write a vertical vector as the transpose of a horizontal vector, as we have just done.

We view X as a column vector, $X = {}^t(x_1, \ldots, x_n)$.

Let us assume that the partial derivatives of each function f_i $(i = 1, \ldots, m)$ exist. We can then form the matrix of partial derivatives:

$$\left(\frac{\partial f_i}{\partial x_j} \right) = \begin{pmatrix} \dfrac{\partial f_1}{\partial x_1} & \dfrac{\partial f_1}{\partial x_2} & \cdots & \dfrac{\partial f_1}{\partial x_n} \\ \dfrac{\partial f_2}{\partial x_1} & \dfrac{\partial f_2}{\partial x_2} & \cdots & \dfrac{\partial f_2}{\partial x_n} \\ & \vdots & & \\ \dfrac{\partial f_m}{\partial x_1} & \dfrac{\partial f_m}{\partial x_2} & \cdots & \dfrac{\partial f_m}{\partial x_n} \end{pmatrix} = \begin{pmatrix} D_1 f_1(X) & \cdots & D_n f_1(X) \\ & \vdots & \\ D_1 f_m(X) & \cdots & D_n f_m(X) \end{pmatrix}$$

$i = 1, \ldots, m$ and $j = 1, \ldots, n$. This matrix is called the *Jacobian* matrix of F, and is denoted by $M_F(X)$.

Example 1. Let $F : \mathbf{R}^2 \to \mathbf{R}^2$ be the mapping defined by

$$F(x, y) = \begin{pmatrix} x^2 + y^2 \\ e^{xy} \end{pmatrix}.$$

Find the Jacobian matrix $M_F(P)$ for $P = (1, 1)$.

The Jacobian matrix at an arbitrary point (x, y) is

$$\begin{pmatrix} 2x & 2y \\ ye^x & xe^y \end{pmatrix}.$$

Hence when $x = 1$, $y = 1$, we find:

$$M_F(1, 1) = \begin{pmatrix} 2 & 2 \\ e & e \end{pmatrix}.$$

Example 2. Let $F : \mathbf{R}^2 \to \mathbf{R}^3$ be the mapping defined by

$$F(x, y) = \begin{pmatrix} xy \\ \sin x \\ x^2 y \end{pmatrix}.$$

Find $M_F(P)$ at the point $P = (\pi, \pi/2)$.

The Jacobian matrix at an arbitrary point (x, y) is

$$\begin{pmatrix} y & x \\ \cos x & 0 \\ 2xy & x^2 \end{pmatrix}.$$

Hence

$$M_F\left(\pi, \frac{\pi}{2}\right) = \begin{pmatrix} \dfrac{\pi}{2} & \pi \\ -1 & 0 \\ \pi^2 & \pi^2 \end{pmatrix}.$$

THEOREM 2. *Let U be an open set in $\mathbf{R}^n$. Let $F : U \to \mathbf{R}^m$ be a mapping, having coordinate functions $f_1, \ldots, f_m$. Assume that each function f_i is differentiable at a point X of U. Then F is differentiable at X, and the matrix representing the linear map $DF(X) = F'(X)$ relative to the usual bases is the Jacobian matrix $M_F(X)$.*

Proof. For each integer i between 1 and n, there is a function g_i such that

$$\lim_{\|H\| \to 0} g_i(H) = 0,$$

and such that we can write

$$f_i(X + H) = f_i(X) + \operatorname{grad} f_i\,(X) \cdot H + \|H\| g_i(H).$$

We view X and $F(X)$ as vertical vectors. By definition, we can write

$$F(X + H) = {}^t(f_1(X + H), \ldots, f_m(X + H)).$$

Hence,

$$F(X + H) = F(X) + \begin{pmatrix} \operatorname{grad} f_1\,(X) \cdot H \\ \operatorname{grad} f_2\,(X) \cdot H \\ \vdots \\ \operatorname{grad} f_m\,(X) \cdot H \end{pmatrix} + \|H\| \begin{pmatrix} g_1(H) \\ g_2(H) \\ \vdots \\ g_m(H) \end{pmatrix}.$$

The term in the middle, involving the gradients, is precisely equal to the product of the Jacobian matrix, times H, i.e. to

$$M_F(X)H.$$

Let $G(H) = {}^t(g_1(H), \ldots, g_m(H))$ be the vector on the right. Then

$$F(X + H) = F(X) + M_F(X)H + \|H\| G(H).$$

As $\|H\|$ approaches 0, each coordinate of $G(H)$ approaches 0. Hence $G(H)$ approaches O; in other words,

$$\lim_{\|H\| \to 0} G(H) = O.$$

Hence the linear map represented by the matrix $M_F(X)$ is tangent to F at X. Since such a linear map is unique, we have proved our theorem.

EXERCISES

1. In each of the following cases, compute the Jacobian matrix of F.
   (a) $F(x, y) = (x + y, x^2 y)$ (b) $F(x, y) = (\sin x, \cos xy)$
   (c) $F(x, y) = (e^{xy}, \log x)$ (d) $F(x, y, z) = (xz, xy, yz)$
   (e) $F(x, y, z) = (xyz, x^2 z)$ (f) $F(x, y, z) = (\sin xyz, xz)$

2. Find the Jacobian matrix of the mappings in Exercise 1 evaluated at the following points.
   (a) $(1, 2)$ (b) $(\pi, \pi/2)$ (c) $(1, 4)$ (d) $(1, 1, -1)$
   (e) $(2, -1, -1)$ (f) $(\pi, 2, 4)$

Let A, B be two linearly independent elements in $\mathbf{R}^n$. Let P be a point in $\mathbf{R}^n$. The set of points of type

$$P + tA + uB,$$

where t, u are numbers, is called a *plane* spanned by A, B (or parallel to A and B), and passing through P. Let V, W be vector spaces. Let $L: V \to W$ be a linear map. We recall that the *kernel* of L is the set of all elements C of V such that $L(C) = O$.

3. Let A, B be two linearly independent elements of $\mathbf{R}^n$. Let $L:\mathbf{R}^n \to \mathbf{R}^m$ be a linear map, whose kernel consists of O only. Show that the image under L of the plane spanned by A and B and passing through P is also a plane.

4. Let A, B, L be as in Exercise 3. Let C be any vector in $\mathbf{R}^n$. Let F be the mapping defined by $F(X) = L(X) + C$. Show that the image under F of the plane passing through P and parallel to A, B is also a plane.

Let U be an open set in $\mathbf{R}^2$, and let $F:U \to \mathbf{R}^m$ be a differentiable map. The image of F is called a (parametric) *surface*, parametrized by F. Let P be a point of U. Let L be the derivative of F at P, i.e. $L = F'(P)$. Assume that the kernel of L is equal to O. The plane passing through $F(P)$ and parallel to $L(E_1)$, $L(E_2)$ is called the *tangent plane* to the surface at P.

5. Let $F:\mathbf{R}^2 \to \mathbf{R}^3$ be the mapping defined by

$$F(t, u) = (tu, t^2, u^2).$$

Find the equation of the tangent plane to the surface at $(1, 2)$.

6. Let $F:\mathbf{R}^2 \to \mathbf{R}^3$ be the mapping defined by

$$F(t, u) = (\cos t, \sin t, u).$$

Find the equation of the tangent plane to the surface at $(\pi, \pi/4)$.

7. Let $F:\mathbf{R}^2 \to \mathbf{R}^3$ be the mapping defined by

$$F(t, u) = (t, tu, tu + 1).$$

Find the equation of the tangent plane to the surface at $(2, -1)$.

8. Let U be the open set in $\mathbf{R}^2$ determined by the conditions

$$0 < \theta < 2\pi, \qquad 0 < r$$

[using (θ, r) as coordinates]. Let $F:U \to \mathbf{R}^2$ be the mapping defined by

$$x = r \cos \theta, \qquad y = r \sin \theta.$$

Find the Jacobian matrix of this mapping. After you have read the chapter on determinants, find the determinant of this matrix.

9. Let U be the open set in $\mathbf{R}^3$ determined by the conditions

$$0 < \theta < 2\pi, \qquad 0 < \phi < \pi, \qquad 0 < \rho$$

[using (θ, ϕ, ρ) as coordinates]. Let $F:U \to \mathbf{R}^3$ be the mapping defined by

$$x = \rho \sin \phi \cos \theta, \qquad y = \rho \sin \phi \sin \theta, \qquad z = \rho \cos \phi.$$

Find the Jacobian matrix of this mapping. After you have read the chapter on determinants, find the determinant of this matrix.

§3. *The chain rule*

In the *First Course*, we proved a chain rule for composite functions. Earlier in this book, a chain rule was given for a composite of a function and a vector. In this section, we give a general formulation of the chain rule for arbitrary compositions of mappings.

We shall need an auxiliary statement.

LEMMA. *Let* $L:\mathbf{R}^n \to \mathbf{R}^m$ *be a linear mapping. There exists a number* b *such that, for any vector* X, *we have*

$$\|LX\| \leqq b\|X\|.$$

Proof. We know that the mapping L can be represented by a matrix $A = (a_{ij})$. Let c be the maximum of all absolute values $|a_{ij}|$ of all the components of the matrix A. Let $X = {}^t(x_1, \ldots, x_n)$. Then $L(X) = AX$. The components of AX are given by

$$a_{11}x_1 + \cdots + a_{1n}x_n, \ldots, a_{m1}x_1 + \cdots + a_{mn}x_n.$$

Let us estimate these components, for instance the first,

$$
\begin{aligned}
|a_{11}x_1 + \cdots + a_{1n}x_n| &\leqq |a_{11}x_1| + \cdots + |a_{1n}x_n| \\
&\leqq c|x_1| + \cdots + c|x_n| \\
&\leqq nc\|X\|
\end{aligned}
$$

because $|x_j| \leqq \|X\|$ for all j. We obtain a similar estimate for all components of AX.

We find therefore

$$
\begin{aligned}
\|AX\|^2 &= (a_{11}x_1 + \cdots + a_{1n}x_n)^2 + \cdots + (a_{m1}x_1 + \cdots + a_{mn}x_n)^2 \\
&\leqq (nc)^2\|X\|^2 + \cdots + (nc)^2\|X\|^2 \\
&\leqq n(nc)^2\|X\|^2.
\end{aligned}
$$

Taking the square root, we obtain

$$\|AX\| \leqq b\|X\|$$

with the constant $b = \sqrt{n(nc)^2}$. Since $L(X) = AX$, we have proved our lemma.

Let U be an open set in $\mathbf{R}^n$, and let V be an open set in $\mathbf{R}^m$. Let $F:U \to \mathbf{R}^m$ be a mapping, and assume that all values of F are contained in V. Let $G:V \to \mathbf{R}^s$ be mapping. Then we can form the composite mapping $G \circ F$ from U into $\mathbf{R}^s$.

Let X be a point of U. Then $F(X)$ is a point of V by assumption. Let us assume that F is differentiable at X, and that G is differentiable at

$F(X)$. We know that $F'(X)$ is a linear map from $\mathbf{R}^n$ into $\mathbf{R}^m$, and $G'(F(X))$ is a linear map from $\mathbf{R}^m$ into $\mathbf{R}^s$. Thus we may compose these two linear maps to give a linear map

$$G'(F(X)) \circ F'(X)$$

from $\mathbf{R}^n$ into $\mathbf{R}^s$.

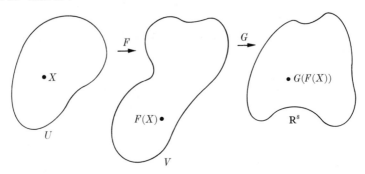

The next theorem tells us what the derivative of $G \circ F$ is in terms of the derivative of F at X, and the derivative of G at $F(X)$. Please observe how the statement and proof of the theorem will be entirely parallel to the statement and proof of the theorem for the chain rule in the *First Course*.

THEOREM 3. *Let U be an open set in $\mathbf{R}^n$, let V be an open set in $\mathbf{R}^m$. Let $F : U \to \mathbf{R}^m$ be a mapping such that all values of F are contained in V. Let $G : V \to \mathbf{R}^s$ be a mapping. Let X be a point of U such that F is differentiable at X. Assume that G is differentiable at $F(X)$. Then the composite mapping $G \circ F$ is differentiable at X, and its derivative is given by*

$$(G \circ F)'(X) = G'(F(X)) \circ F'(X).$$

Proof. By definition of differentiability, there exists a mapping Φ_1 such that

$$\lim_{\|H\| \to 0} \Phi_1(H) = O$$

and

$$F(X + H) = F(X) + F'(X) + \|H\|\Phi_1(H).$$

Similarly, there exists a mapping Φ_2 such that

$$\lim_{\|K\| \to 0} \Phi_2(K) = O,$$

and

$$G(Y + K) = G(Y) + G'(Y)K + \|K\|\Phi_2(K).$$

We let $K = K(H)$ be

$$F(X + H) - F(X) = F'(X)H + \|H\|\Phi_1(H).$$

Then:

$$G(F(X + H)) = G(F(X) + K)$$
$$= G(F(X)) + G'(F(X))K + \|K\|\Phi_2(K).$$

Using the fact that $G'(F(X))$ is linear, we can write:

$$(G \circ F)(X + H) = (G \circ F)(X) + G'(F(X))F'(X)H$$
$$+ \|H\|G'(F(X))\Phi_1(H) + \|H\| \frac{\|K\|}{\|H\|} \Phi_2(K).$$

If we put

$$\Phi(H) = G'(F(X))\Phi_1(H) + \frac{\|K\|}{\|H\|} \Phi_2(K),$$

then I contend that

$$\lim_{\|H\|\to 0} \Phi(H) = 0.$$

In fact, by the lemma, there is a number c such that

$$\|G'(F(X))\Phi_1(H)\| \leq c\|\Phi_1(H)\|,$$

and as $\|H\|$ approaches 0, the right-hand side of this inequality approaches 0.

Furthermore, $H/\|H\|$ has length 1. Hence, from the definition of $K(H)$, the quotient $K/\|H\|$ remains bounded. As $\|H\|$ approaches 0, so does $\|K\|$, and hence so does $\Phi_2(K)$. Consequently the second term

$$\frac{\|K\|}{\|H\|} \Phi_2(K)$$

appearing in the expression for $\Phi(H)$ approaches O as $\|H\|$ approaches 0. We have therefore shown that

$$\lim_{\|H\|\to 0} \Phi(H) = 0.$$

Since we have

$$(G \circ F)(X + H) = (G \circ F)(X) + G'(F(X))F'(X)H + \|H\|\Phi(H),$$

from the definition of differentiability, and tangent linear map, we conclude that the linear map

$$G'(F(X))F'(X)$$

is tangent to $G \circ F$ at X. It must therefore be equal to $(G \circ F)'(X)$, as was to be shown.

Remark. (To be read after the chapter on determinants.) You will recall that the chain rule in one variable had an analogue for integration, which was called "substitution" in the *First Course*. There is also an analogue in the present multidimensional case. Although we shall not state it with full precision, because it would require some notions which we have not discussed, nevertheless it is illuminating to see roughly in what context it holds, and we shall now describe this context.

Let U, V be two open sets in n-space. Let

$$G : U \to V \qquad \text{and} \qquad F : V \to U$$

be two differentiable mappings, whose partial derivatives are continuous, and such that the composite mapping $G \circ F$ is the identity mapping of V, and the composite mapping $F \circ G$ is the identity mapping of U. We then say that F, G are *inverse* to each other.

Denote the coordinate vector of a point in U by $X = (x_1, \ldots, x_n)$, and the coordinate vector of a point of V by $Y = (y_1, \ldots, y_n)$. Let f be a function on V. Then $f \circ G$ is a function on U, namely the function such that

$$(f \circ G)(X) = f(G(X)) = f(Y).$$

Let $J_F(X)$ denote the determinant of the Jacobian matrix of F at X, and call it the *Jacobian determinant*. Then J_F is a function on U. For a suitably restricted class of functions f, the *chain rule for integration* asserts that

$$\int_U \cdots \int f(G(X)) J_F(X)\, dX = \int_V \cdots \int f(Y)\, dY,$$

provided that the Jacobian determinant is positive at each point of U. Here, we abbreviate $dx_1 \cdots dx_n$ by dX, and similarly for dY. The integrals are multiple integrals, which are direct generalizations of the double integral in rectangular coordinates discussed in Chapter VIII, §1.

The integrals given in terms of polar and spherical coordinates can then be viewed as special cases of the above general chain rule. (Cf. Exercises 8 and 9.)

To develop the theory of integration and to give a proof for the chain rule requires a fairly elaborate machinery, which belongs properly to an Advanced Calculus course. Still, it may be quieting to many readers to see here already a more analytical reason for the integral given in terms of polar and spherical coordinates, than the geometric plausibility arguments given in Chapter VIII.

CHAPTER XIV

Determinants

We have worked with vectors for some time, and we have often felt the need of a method to determine when vectors are linearly independent. Up to now, the only method available to us was to solve a system of linear equations by the elimination method. In this chapter, we shall exhibit a very efficient computational method to solve linear equations, and determine when vectors are linearly independent.

It is sufficient to understand §1, §2, and §3 to be able to work with determinants. The formal rules which are used to compute them are very easy to state. Hence the proofs of §6 through §9, which require a somewhat higher level of abstraction, may be omitted without prejudice to the understanding of the computational aspects of determinants. The slight complication of notation is unavoidable when dealing with $n \times n$ matrices.

§1. Determinants of order 2

Before stating the general properties of an arbitrary determinant, we shall consider a special case.

Let

$$A = \begin{pmatrix} a & b \\ c & d \end{pmatrix}$$

be a 2×2 matrix. We define its determinant to be $ad - cb$. Thus the determinant is a number.

The determinant can be viewed as a function of the matrix A. It can also be viewed as a function of its two columns. Let these be A^1 and A^2 as usual. Then we write the determinant as

$$D(A), \qquad \text{Det } (A), \qquad \text{or} \qquad D(A^1, A^2).$$

The following properties are easily verified by direction computation, which you should carry out completely.

(1) As a function of the column vectors, the determinant is linear. This means: let b', d' be two numbers. Then

$$\text{Det } \begin{pmatrix} a & b + b' \\ c & d + d' \end{pmatrix} = \text{Det } \begin{pmatrix} a & b \\ c & d \end{pmatrix} + \text{Det } \begin{pmatrix} a & b' \\ c & d' \end{pmatrix}.$$

Furthermore, if t is a number, then

$$\text{Det} \begin{pmatrix} a & tb \\ c & td \end{pmatrix} = t \, \text{Det} \begin{pmatrix} a & b \\ c & d \end{pmatrix}.$$

The analogous properties also hold with respect to the first column.

(2) If the two columns are equal, then the determinant is equal to 0.

(3) If A is the unit matrix,

$$A = \begin{pmatrix} 1 & 0 \\ 0 & 1 \end{pmatrix},$$

then $\text{Det}(A) = 1$.

The determinant also satisfies the following additional properties.

(4) If one adds a multiple of one column to the other, then the value of the determinant does not change.

In other words, let t be a number. The determinant of the matrix

$$\begin{pmatrix} a + tb & b \\ c + td & d \end{pmatrix}$$

is the same as $D(A)$, and similarly when we add a multiple of the first column to the second.

(5) If the two columns are interchanged, then the determinant changes by a sign.

In other words, we have

$$\text{Det} \begin{pmatrix} a & b \\ c & d \end{pmatrix} = -\text{Det} \begin{pmatrix} b & a \\ d & c \end{pmatrix}.$$

(6) The determinant of A is equal to the determinant of its transpose, i.e. $D(A) = D({}^t A)$.

Explicitly, we have

$$\text{Det} \begin{pmatrix} a & b \\ c & d \end{pmatrix} = \text{Det} \begin{pmatrix} a & c \\ b & d \end{pmatrix}.$$

In the next section, we shall consider determinants of $n \times n$ matrices, and the analogous properties will give us a method for computing the determinant in general.

§2. *Properties of determinants*

Let A be an $n \times n$ matrix. It would be possible to define its determinant by a sum, just as we defined the determinant of a 2×2 matrix. However, to write such a sum is a little complicated, and it turns out that to find the value of a determinant, it is not necessary to have this expression. What is needed is a set of properties which can be used to compute it.

The *determinant*, denoted by D, or Det, is a function of square matrices, satisfying the properties listed below. In order to write down these properties, we settle first some notation.

Let $A = (a_{ij})$ be a square $n \times n$ matrix. Its determinant will be written $D(A)$, Det (A), or will also be denoted by surrounding the matrix with two vertical bars:

$$\text{Det } (a_{ij}) = \begin{vmatrix} a_{11} & \cdots & a_{1n} \\ \vdots & & \vdots \\ a_{n1} & \cdots & a_{nn} \end{vmatrix}.$$

If $A^1, \ldots, A^n$ are the column vectors of the matrix, we also write $D(A^1, \ldots, A^n)$ instead of $D(A)$.

We can now list the properties.

(1) As a function of the column vectors, the determinant is linear. This means: suppose that the j-th column A^j is equal to a sum of two column vectors, say $A^j = C + C'$. Then

$$D(A^1, \ldots, C + C', \ldots, A^n)$$
$$= D(A^1, \ldots, C, \ldots, A^n) + D(A^1, \ldots, C', \ldots, A^n).$$

Furthermore, if t is a number, then

$$D(A^1, \ldots, tA^j, \ldots, A^n) = tD(A^1, \ldots, A^j, \ldots, A^n).$$

Observe that if we let $t = 0$, then we conclude that when one of the columns is the zero vector, the determinant is equal to 0.

(2) If two columns are equal, then $D(A) = 0$.

(3) If A is the unit matrix, then $D(A) = 1$.

The main theorem in this chapter will be the following.

There exist determinants satisfying properties (1), (2), and (3). Such determinants are uniquely determined, and also satisfy properties (4) through (7) below.

Since properties (1) through (7) are the only ones needed to compute determinants, we shall state the rest of them and give some applications before considering the existence and uniqueness proofs.

(4) If one adds a multiple of one column to another column, then the value of the determinant does not change.

(5) If two adjacent columns are interchanged, then the determinant changes by a sign.

(6) The determinant of A is equal to the determinant of its transpose.

In view of (6), we conclude that the determinant satisfies properties (1) through (5) with respect to rows, i.e. each one of these properties is valid if we replace the word "column" by the word "row".

It is actually useful in practice to have one more rule, which gives us an analogue of the definition $ad - cb$ for 2×2 matrices. To explain this additional rule, we need one more notion.

Let i, j be a pair of integers between 1 and n. If we cross out the i-th row and j-th column in the $n \times n$ matrix A, we obtain an $(n - 1) \times (n - 1)$ matrix, which we shall denote by A_{ij}. It looks like this:

$$i \begin{pmatrix} a_{11} & \cdots & & \cdots & a_{1n} \\ \vdots & & & & \vdots \\ \hline & & a_{ij} & & \\ \vdots & & & & \vdots \\ a_{n1} & \cdots & & \cdots & a_{nn} \end{pmatrix}$$

Example 1. Let

$$A = \begin{pmatrix} 2 & 1 & 0 \\ 1 & 1 & 4 \\ -3 & 2 & 5 \end{pmatrix}.$$

Then

$$A_{11} = \begin{pmatrix} 1 & 4 \\ 2 & 5 \end{pmatrix}, \qquad A_{22} = \begin{pmatrix} 2 & 0 \\ -3 & 5 \end{pmatrix}, \qquad A_{31} = \begin{pmatrix} 1 & 0 \\ 1 & 4 \end{pmatrix}.$$

Our last rule may now be stated. It is called the *expansion rule according to the i-th row.*

(7) Let A be an $n \times n$ matrix as before. Then the determinant $D(A)$ is equal to:

$$(-1)^{i+1}a_{i1} \, \text{Det} \, (A_{i1}) + (-1)^{i+2}a_{i2} \, \text{Det} \, (A_{i2})$$
$$+ \cdots + (-1)^{i+n}a_{in} \, \text{Det} \, (A_{in})$$
$$= \sum_{j=1}^{n} (-1)^{i+j}a_{ij} \, \text{Det} \, (A_{ij}).$$

This sum can be described in words. For each element of the i-th row, we have a contribution of one term in the sum. This term is equal to $+$ or $-$ the product of this element, times the determinant of the matrix obtained from A by deleting the i-th row and the corresponding column. The sign $+$ or $-$ is determined according to the chess-board pattern:

$$\begin{pmatrix} + & - & + & - & \cdots \\ - & + & - & + & \cdots \\ + & - & + & - & \cdots \\ & & \cdots & & \end{pmatrix}$$

In view of (6), we could also expand the determinant according to the j-th column in an analogous manner.

Example 2. We shall write out the expansion of a 3×3 determinant according to the first column.

Let

$$A = \begin{pmatrix} a_{11} & a_{12} & a_{13} \\ a_{21} & a_{22} & a_{23} \\ a_{31} & a_{32} & a_{33} \end{pmatrix}.$$

Then $D(A)$ is equal to the sum:

$$a_{11} \begin{vmatrix} a_{22} & a_{23} \\ a_{32} & a_{33} \end{vmatrix} - a_{21} \begin{vmatrix} a_{12} & a_{13} \\ a_{32} & a_{33} \end{vmatrix} + a_{31} \begin{vmatrix} a_{12} & a_{13} \\ a_{22} & a_{23} \end{vmatrix}.$$

With all the above means at our disposal, we can now compute determinants very efficiently. In doing so, we try to apply the operations described in (4) to make as many entries in the matrix equal to 0. We try especially to make all but one element of a column (or row) equal to 0, and then expand according to that column (or row). The expansion will contain only one term, and reduces our computation to a determinant of smaller size.

Example 3. Compute $\begin{vmatrix} 3 & 0 & 1 \\ 1 & 2 & 5 \\ -1 & 4 & 2 \end{vmatrix}$.

We already have 0 in the first row. We subtract twice the second row from the third row. Our determinant is then equal to

$$\begin{vmatrix} 3 & 0 & 1 \\ 1 & 2 & 5 \\ -3 & 0 & -8 \end{vmatrix}.$$

We expand according to the second column. The expansion has only one term $\neq 0$, with a $+$ sign, and that is:

$$2 \begin{vmatrix} 3 & 1 \\ -3 & -8 \end{vmatrix}.$$

The 2×2 determinant can be evaluated by our definition $ad - cb$, and we find $2(-24 - (-3)) = -42$.

EXERCISES

1. Compute the following determinants.

(a) $\begin{vmatrix} 2 & 1 & 2 \\ 0 & 3 & -1 \\ 4 & 1 & 1 \end{vmatrix}$ (b) $\begin{vmatrix} 3 & -1 & 5 \\ -1 & 2 & 1 \\ -2 & 4 & 3 \end{vmatrix}$ (c) $\begin{vmatrix} 2 & 4 & 3 \\ -1 & 3 & 0 \\ 0 & 2 & 1 \end{vmatrix}$ *(cont.)*

(d) $\begin{vmatrix} 1 & 2 & -1 \\ 0 & 1 & 1 \\ 0 & 2 & 7 \end{vmatrix}$ (e) $\begin{vmatrix} -1 & 5 & 3 \\ 4 & 0 & 0 \\ 2 & 7 & 8 \end{vmatrix}$

2. Compute the following determinants.

(a) $\begin{vmatrix} 1 & 1 & -2 & 4 \\ 0 & 1 & 1 & 3 \\ 2 & -1 & 1 & 0 \\ 3 & 1 & 2 & 5 \end{vmatrix}$ (b) $\begin{vmatrix} -1 & 1 & 2 & 0 \\ 0 & 3 & 2 & 1 \\ 0 & 4 & 1 & 2 \\ 3 & 1 & 5 & 7 \end{vmatrix}$

(c) $\begin{vmatrix} 3 & 1 & 1 \\ 2 & 5 & 5 \\ 8 & 7 & 7 \end{vmatrix}$ (d) $\begin{vmatrix} 4 & -9 & 2 \\ 4 & -9 & 2 \\ 3 & 1 & 0 \end{vmatrix}$

3. Make up matrices yourself and find their determinants until you feel that you can compute determinants rapidly.

4. (a) Write out the expansion of a 3×3 determinant according to the second row in a manner similar to that of Example 2. (b) Write out the general formula for the expansion of an $n \times n$ matrix according to the i-th row.

5. Let x_1, x_2, x_3 be numbers. Show that

$$\begin{vmatrix} 1 & x_1 & x_1^2 \\ 1 & x_2 & x_2^2 \\ 1 & x_3 & x_3^2 \end{vmatrix} = (x_2 - x_1)(x_3 - x_1)(x_3 - x_2).$$

Generalize to the 4×4 case, and to the $n \times n$ case.

6. If $a(t)$, $b(t)$, $c(t)$, $d(t)$ are functions of t, one can form the determinant

$$\begin{vmatrix} a(t) & b(t) \\ c(t) & d(t) \end{vmatrix},$$

just as with numbers. Write out in full the determinant

$$\begin{vmatrix} \sin t & \cos t \\ -\cos t & \sin t \end{vmatrix}.$$

7. Write out in full the determinant

$$\begin{vmatrix} t+1 & t-1 \\ t & 2t+5 \end{vmatrix}.$$

8. Let $f(t)$, $g(t)$ be two functions having derivatives of all orders. Let $\varphi(t)$ be the function obtained by taking the determinant

$$\varphi(t) = \begin{vmatrix} f(t) & g(t) \\ f'(t) & g'(t) \end{vmatrix}.$$

Show that

$$\varphi'(t) = \begin{vmatrix} f(t) & g(t) \\ f''(t) & g''(t) \end{vmatrix}$$

(i.e. the derivative is obtained by taking the derivative of the bottom row).

9. Generalize Exercise 8 to the 3×3 case, and then to the $n \times n$ case. [*Hint:* Expand the following determinant according to the first row.]

$$\begin{vmatrix} f_1 & \cdots & f_n \\ f_1' & \cdots & f_n' \\ & \vdots & \\ f_1^{(n-1)} & \cdots & f_n^{(n-1)} \end{vmatrix}$$

10. Verify explicitly that the expression given for a 3×3 determinant in Example 2 satisfies properties (1), (2), (3) with respect to rows.

§3. *Cramer's rule*

The rules of §2 give us powerful tools to determine when vectors are linearly dependent.

THEOREM 1. *Let* $A^1, \ldots, A^n$ *be column vectors (of dimension n). If they are linearly dependent, then*

$$D(A^1, \ldots, A^n) = 0.$$

If $D(A^1, \ldots, A^n) \neq 0$, *then* $A^1, \ldots, A^n$ *are linearly independent.*

Proof. The second assertion is merely an equivalent formulation of the first. It will therefore suffice to prove the first. Assume that $A^1, \ldots, A^n$ are linearly dependent. We can find numbers $x_1, \ldots, x_n$ not all 0 such that

$$x_1 A^1 + \cdots + x_n A^n = O.$$

Suppose $x_j \neq 0$. Then

$$x_j A^j = -x_1 A^1 - \cdots - x_n A^n = \sum_{k \neq j} x_k A^k,$$

it being understood that the j-th term on the right-hand side does not appear. Dividing by x_j, we obtain A^j as a linear combination of $A^1, \ldots, A^n$ (omitting A^j). In other words, there are numbers $y_1, \ldots, y_n$ such that

$$A^j = y_1 A^1 + \cdots + y_n A^n = \sum_{k \neq j} y_k A^k,$$

the j-th term in the sum being omitted. We get:

$$D(A^1, \ldots, A^n) = D(A^1, \ldots, y_1 A^1 + \cdots + y_n A^n, \ldots, A^n),$$

which we can expand out using property (1). This yields

$$y_1 D(A^1, \ldots, A^1, \ldots, A^n) + \cdots + y_n D(A^1, \ldots, A^n, \ldots, A^n).$$

Here again, the j-term is omitted. In the other terms, we always have two equal columns, and hence each such term is equal to 0 by property (2). This proves Theorem 1.

THEOREM 2. *Let $A^1, \ldots, A^n$ be column vectors (of dimension n) such that $D(A^1, \ldots, A^n) \neq 0$. Let B be a column vector of dimension n also. Then there exist numbers $x_1, \ldots, x_n$ such that*

$$x_1 A^1 + \cdots + x_n A^n = B,$$

and for each j, we have

$$x_j = \frac{D(A^1, \ldots, B, \ldots, A^n)}{D(A^1, \ldots, A^n)},$$

where B occurs in the j-th column instead of A^j. In other words,

$$x_i = \frac{\begin{vmatrix} a_{11} & \ldots & b_1 & \ldots & a_{1n} \\ a_{21} & \ldots & b_2 & \ldots & a_{2n} \\ \vdots & & \vdots & & \vdots \\ a_{n1} & \ldots & b_n & \ldots & a_{nn} \end{vmatrix}}{\begin{vmatrix} a_{11} & \ldots & a_{ij} & \ldots & a_{1n} \\ a_{21} & \ldots & a_{2j} & \ldots & a_{2n} \\ \vdots & & \vdots & & \vdots \\ a_{n1} & \ldots & a_{nj} & \ldots & a_{nn} \end{vmatrix}}.$$

(The numerator is obtained from A by replacing the j-th column A^j by B. The denominator is the determinant of the matrix A.)

Theorem 2 gives us an explicit way to find the coordinates of B with respect to $A^1, \ldots, A^n$. In the language of linear equations, Theorem 2 allows us to solve explicitly in terms of determinants the system of n linear equations in n unknowns:

$$x_1 a_{11} + \cdots + x_n a_{1n} = b_1$$
$$\vdots \qquad\qquad \vdots \qquad \vdots$$
$$x_1 a_{n1} + \cdots + x_n a_{nn} = b_n.$$

Proof. According to Theorem 1, the vectors $A^1, \ldots, A^n$ are linearly independent, and hence constitute a basis of $\mathbf{R}^n$. Hence any vector B can be written as a linear combination of $A^1, \ldots, A^n$. Let B be written as in the statement of the theorem, and consider the determinant of the matrix obtained by replacing the j-th column of A by B. Then

$$D(A^1, \ldots, B, \ldots, A^n) = D(A^1, \ldots, x_1 A_1^1 + \cdots + x_n A_n^1, \ldots, A^n).$$

We use property (1) and obtain a sum:

$$D(A^1, \ldots, x_1 A^1, \ldots, A^n) + \cdots + D(A^1, \ldots, x_j A^j, \ldots, A^n)$$
$$+ \cdots + D(A^1, \ldots, x_n A^n, \ldots, A^n),$$

which by property (1) again, is equal to

$$x_1 D(A^1, \ldots, A^1, \ldots, A^n) + \cdots + x_j D(A^1, \ldots, A^n)$$
$$+ \cdots + x_n D(A^1, \ldots, A^n, \ldots, A^n).$$

In every term of this sum except the j-th term, two column vectors are equal. Hence every term except the j-th term is equal to 0, by property (2). The j-th term is equal to

$$x_j D(A^1, \ldots, A^n),$$

and is therefore equal to the determinant we started with, namely $D(A^1, \ldots, B, \ldots, A^n)$. We can solve for x_j, and obtain precisely the expression given in the statement of the theorem.

The rule of Theorem 2, giving us the solution to the system of linear equations by means of determinants, is known as *Cramer's rule*.

Example. Solve the system of linear equations:

$$3x + 2y + 4z = 1,$$
$$2x - y + z = 0,$$
$$x + 2y + 3z = 1.$$

We have:

$$x = \frac{\begin{vmatrix} 1 & 2 & 4 \\ 0 & -1 & 1 \\ 1 & 2 & 3 \end{vmatrix}}{\begin{vmatrix} 3 & 2 & 4 \\ 2 & -1 & 1 \\ 1 & 2 & 3 \end{vmatrix}}, \qquad y = \frac{\begin{vmatrix} 3 & 1 & 4 \\ 2 & 0 & 1 \\ 1 & 1 & 3 \end{vmatrix}}{\begin{vmatrix} 3 & 2 & 4 \\ 2 & -1 & 1 \\ 1 & 2 & 3 \end{vmatrix}}, \qquad z = \frac{\begin{vmatrix} 3 & 2 & 1 \\ 2 & -1 & 0 \\ 1 & 2 & 1 \end{vmatrix}}{\begin{vmatrix} 3 & 2 & 4 \\ 2 & -1 & 1 \\ 1 & 2 & 3 \end{vmatrix}}.$$

Observe how the column

$$B = \begin{pmatrix} 1 \\ 0 \\ 1 \end{pmatrix}$$

shifts from the first column when solving for x, to the second column when solving for y, to the third column when solving for z. The denominator in all three expressions is the same, namely it is the determinant of the matrix of coefficients of the equations.

The determinants involved are easy to compute. One finds:

$$x = \frac{-1}{5}, \qquad y = 0, \qquad z = \frac{2}{5}.$$

1. Write down systems of n linear equations in n unknowns (with $n = 3$ and $n = 4$) and solve them by determinants until you feel that you have absorbed the technique completely.

2. Let $A^1, \ldots, A^n$ be column vectors of dimension n and assume that they are linearly independent. Show that $D(A^1, \ldots, A^n) \neq 0$. [*Hint:* Express each one of the standard unit vectors $E_1, \ldots, E_n$ viewed as column vectors as linear combinations of $A^1, \ldots, A^n$. Using the fact that $D(E_1, \ldots, E_n) = 1$, and properties (1) and (2), prove the assertion.]

3. Let A be a triangular $n \times n$ matrix, say a matrix such that all components below the diagonal are equal to 0,

$$A = \begin{pmatrix} a_{11} & & & \\ 0 & a_{22} & & * \\ 0 & 0 & & \\ \vdots & \vdots & \ddots & \\ 0 & 0 & \cdots & 0 & a_{nn} \end{pmatrix}.$$

What is $D(A)$?

§4. *Inverse of a matrix*

Let A be an $n \times n$ matrix. If $\text{Det}\ (A) \neq 0$, then we say that A is a *non-singular* matrix. If B is a matrix such that $AB = I$ and $BA = I$ ($I = $ unit $n \times n$ matrix), then we say that B is an *inverse* of A, and we write $B = A^{-1}$. If there exists an inverse of A, then it is unique. Indeed, let C be an inverse of A. Then $CA = I$. Multiplying by B on the right, we obtain $CAB = B$. But $CAB = C(AB) = CI = C$. Hence $C = B$. A similar argument works for $AC = I$.

We shall see that property (7) allows us to construct an inverse for a non-singular matrix.

Let $A = (a_{ij})$ be a given $n \times n$ matrix. We had defined the matrix A_{ij} obtained from A by deleting the i-th row and j-th column. Let

$$b_{ij} = (-1)^{i+j} \text{Det}\ (A_{ji}).$$

(Note the reversal of indices!) Let $d = \text{Det}\ (A)$. The matrix dI is then diagonal:

$$dI = \begin{pmatrix} d & & & \\ & d & & 0 \\ & & \ddots & \\ 0 & & & d \end{pmatrix}.$$

THEOREM 3. *Let B be the matrix (b_{ij}). Then*

$$AB = BA = dI.$$

If $d \neq 0$, then $A^{-1} = \dfrac{1}{d}\ B$.

Proof. We shall use property (7). For any pair of indices i, k the ik-component of AB is

$$a_{i1}b_{1k} + a_{i2}b_{2k} + \cdots + a_{in}b_{nk}$$
$$= a_{i1}(-1)^{i+1} \text{Det}(A_{k1}) + \cdots + a_{in}(-1)^{i+n} \text{Det}(A_{kn}).$$

If $i = k$, then this sum is simply the expansion of the determinant according to the i-th row, and hence this sum is equal to d. If $i \neq k$, let $\overline{A}$ be the matrix obtained from A by replacing the k-th row by the i-th row, and leaving all other rows unchanged. If we delete the k-th row and j-th column from $\overline{A}$, we obtain the same matrix as by deleting the k-th row and j-th column from A. Thus

$$\overline{A}_{kj} = A_{kj},$$

and hence our sum above can be written

$$a_{i1}(-1)^{i+1} \text{Det}(\overline{A}_{k1}) + \cdots + a_{in}(-1)^{i+n} \text{Det}(\overline{A}_{kn}).$$

This is the expansion of the determinant of $\overline{A}$ according to the i-th row. By property (2), $\text{Det}(\overline{A}) = 0$. Hence this sum is 0. We have therefore proved that the ik-component of AB is equal to d if $i = k$ (i.e. if it is a diagonal component), and equal to 0 if $i \neq k$ (i.e. if it is off the diagonal).

Similarly, one can prove that $BA = dI$, thereby proving the first assertion in the theorem. The second assertion follows from the rule $\frac{1}{d}(AB) = A\left(\frac{1}{d}B\right)$. The inverse of the matrix A is therefore obtained by taking the transpose of the matrix

$$\left(\frac{(-1)^{i+j} \text{Det}(A_{ij})}{\text{Det}(A)}\right).$$

EXERCISES

1. Find the inverses of the matrices in Exercise 1, §2.

2. Using the fact that if A, B are two $n \times n$ matrices then $\text{Det}(AB) = \text{Det}(A) \text{Det}(B)$, prove that a matrix A such that $\text{Det}(A) = 0$ does not have an inverse. [The above-mentioned fact will be proved later.]

3. Write down explicitly the inverse of a 2×2 matrix

$$\begin{pmatrix} a & b \\ c & d \end{pmatrix}.$$

4. Verify explicitly the rule $D(AB) = D(A)D(B)$ for 2×2 matrices.

§5. *Proofs of some properties*

In this section, we shall prove properties (4) and (5) from properties (1) and (2). In fact, let us assume that our determinant satisfies (1) and only the following weaker version of property (2):

(2′) If two adjacent columns are equal, then the determinant is equal to 0.

We shall prove (5), (2), (4) in that order.

Let j be some integer, $1 \leqq j < n$. We shall first prove (5), namely: *If the j-th and $(j + 1)$-th columns are interchanged, then the determinant changes by a sign.*

In the matrix A, we replace the j-th and $(j + 1)$-th columns by $A^j + A^{j+1}$. We obtain a matrix with two equal adjacent columns, and by (2′) we have:

$$0 = D(\ldots, A^j + A^{j+1}, A^j + A^{j+1}, \ldots).$$

Expanding out using (1) repeatedly yields

$$0 = D(\ldots, A^j, A^j, \ldots) + D(\ldots, A^{j+1}, A^j, \ldots)$$
$$+ D(\ldots, A^j, A^{j+1}, \ldots) + D(\ldots, A^{j+1}, A^{j+1}, \ldots).$$

Using (2′), we see that two of these four terms are equal to 0, and hence that

$$0 = D(\ldots, A^{j+1}, A^j, \ldots) + D(\ldots, A^j, A^{j+1}, \ldots).$$

In this last sum, one term must be equal to minus the other, as desired.

Our original property (2) can now be proved easily. Indeed, assume that two columns of the matrix A are equal. We can change the matrix by a successive interchange of adjacent columns until we obtain a matrix with equal adjacent columns. (This could be proved formally by induction.) Each time that we make such an adjacent interchange, the determinant changes by a sign, which does not affect its being 0 or not. Hence we conclude by (2′) that $D(A) = 0$ if two columns are equal.

Let us now prove property (4). Consider two distinct columns, say the k-th and j-th columns A^k and A^j with $k \neq j$. Let t be a number. We add tA^j to A^k. By (1), the determinant becomes

$$D(\ldots, A^k + tA^j, \ldots) = D(\ldots, A^k, \ldots) + D(\ldots, tA^j, \ldots)$$
$$\uparrow \qquad\qquad\qquad\qquad \uparrow \qquad\qquad\qquad \uparrow$$
$$k \qquad\qquad\qquad\qquad\quad k \qquad\qquad\qquad\quad k$$

(the k points to the k-th column).

In both terms on the right, the indicated column occurs in the k-th place. But $D(\ldots, A^k, \ldots)$ is simply $D(A)$. Furthermore,

$$D(\ldots, tA^j, \ldots) = tD(\ldots, A^j, \ldots).$$
$$\uparrow \qquad\qquad\qquad \uparrow$$
$$k \qquad\qquad\qquad\quad k$$

Since $k \neq j$, the determinant on the right has two equal columns, because A^j occurs in the k-th place and also in the j-th place. Hence it is equal to 0. Hence

$$D(\ldots, A^k + tA^j, \ldots) = D(\ldots, A^k, \ldots),$$

thereby proving our property (4).

§6. *Uniqueness*

Before proceeding with the main part of the argument, we make some remarks on repeated linear maps, as in property (1). Consider first the case $n = 2$. If we have to expand

$$D(3A + 5B, 2A - B),$$

where A, B are 2-vectors, then using property (1), we obtain a sum of four terms, namely

$$D(3A, 2A - B) + D(5B, 2A - B)$$
$$= D(3A, 2A) + D(3A, -B) + D(5B, 2A) + D(5B, -B)$$
$$= 6D(A, A) - 3D(A, B) + 10D(B, A) - 5D(B, B).$$

Observe that we have used the fact that

$$D(A, -B) = -D(A, B),$$

taking $c = -1$ in property (1).

In such an expression, we note that $D(A, A) = 0$ and $D(B, B) = 0$. Thus only two terms remain to give a contribution which is not a priori equal to 0.

To give another example, let us expand

$$D(2A + B - C, 3E + F)$$

where A, B, C, E, F are vectors. Using (1) repeatedly, we obtain six terms, namely

$$6D(A, E) + 2D(A, F) + 3D(B, E) + D(B, F) - 3D(C, E) - D(C, F).$$

[As an exercise, prove this expansion writing out in detail each step as an application of property (1).]

The principle involved in expanding such determinants is the following. We select one term from the first column and one term from the second, and take the sum over all such terms. A proof for the general expansion rule for arbitrary n could be given by induction, but we shall omit it. Using expansions such as these, we shall now show that any function of $n \times n$ matrices satisfying properties (1), (2), (3) is uniquely determined, and we shall obtain an expansion for such functions.

Let A be an $n \times n$ matrix, with column vectors $A^1, \ldots, A^n$. Then we can write

$$A^1 = a_{11}E^1 + \cdots + a_{n1}E^n$$
$$\vdots \qquad \vdots \qquad\qquad \vdots$$
$$A^n = a_{1n}E^1 + \cdots + a_{nn}E^n,$$

where $E^1, \ldots, E^n$ are the unit column vectors. Then

$$D(A^1, \ldots, A^n) = D(a_{11}E^1 + \cdots + a_{n1}E^n, \ldots, a_{1n}E^1 + \cdots + a_{nn}E^n).$$

Using property (1), we can express this as a sum of terms

$$D(a_{\sigma(1),1}E^{\sigma(1)}, \ldots, a_{\sigma(n),n}E^{\sigma(n)}),$$

where $\sigma(1), \ldots, \sigma(n)$ denotes a choice of an integer between 1 and n for each value of $1, \ldots, n$. Thus σ is a mapping of the set of integers $\{1, \ldots, n\}$ into itself. By property (1), each one of the above terms can also be written

$$a_{\sigma(1),1} \cdots a_{\sigma(n),n} D(E^{\sigma(1)}, \ldots, E^{\sigma(n)}).$$

If some σ assigns the same integer to distinct values i, j between 1 and n, then the determinant on the right has two equal columns and hence is equal to 0. Consequently, we can take our sum only for those σ which are such that $\sigma(i) \neq \sigma(j)$ whenever $i \neq j$. Such σ are called *permutations*. Instead of saying that we take the sum for all permutations σ, we abbreviate the notation with the usual $\sum$ symbol. Thus we can write

$$D(A^1, \ldots, A^n) = \sum_\sigma a_{\sigma(1),1} \cdots a_{\sigma(n),n} D(E^{\sigma(1)}, \ldots, E^{\sigma(n)}).$$

The unit vectors $E^{\sigma(1)}, \ldots, E^{\sigma(n)}$ occur in a permutation of the standard arrangement $E^1, \ldots, E^n$. If we interchange successively two adjacent columns, we can reestablish the standard order for these unit vectors after a certain number of adjacent permutations. Each time that we permute two adjacent columns, the determinant changes by a sign. If $m(\sigma)$ is the number of transpositions of adjacent column vectors which have to be carried out to reestablish the standard ordering of the unit vectors, then

$$D(E^{\sigma(1)}, \ldots, E^{\sigma(n)}) = (-1)^{m(\sigma)} D(E^1, \ldots, E^n) = (-1)^{m(\sigma)}.$$

The sign $(-1)^{m(\sigma)}$ will be denoted by $\epsilon(\sigma)$ and will be called the sign of the permutation. Thus finally, we can write

(*) $$D(A^1, \ldots, A^n) = \sum_{\sigma} \epsilon(\sigma) a_{\sigma(1),1} \cdots a_{\sigma(n),n},$$

the sum being taken over all permutations of the integers $\{1, \ldots, n\}$. This expression shows that the value of the determinant is uniquely determined by properties (1), (2), (3), or even (1), (2'), (3) since we saw that (2) follows from these.

§7. *Determinant of a transpose*

Before proceeding any further, we make some comments on permutations. If σ, τ are two permutations of the integers $\{1, \ldots, n\}$ then we can form the composite permutation $\sigma \circ \tau$, such that $(\sigma \circ \tau)(i) = \sigma(\tau(i))$. Given a permutation σ, and an integer i, there exists a unique integer j such that $\sigma(j) = i$. (Here and afterwards, we let $i, j, \ldots$ denote integers between 1 and n.) We can define a permutation σ^{-1} by the rule: $\sigma^{-1}(i)$ is the unique j such that $\sigma(j) = i$. Then $\sigma \circ \sigma^{-1} = \sigma^{-1} \circ \sigma = id$ is the identity permutation (the permutation such that $id(i) = i$ for all i).

Instead of writing $\sigma \circ \tau$, we shall also write $\sigma\tau$. Our last remark can then be stated $\sigma\sigma^{-1} = \sigma^{-1}\sigma = id$.

A *transposition* is a permutation which interchanges two numbers and leaves the others fixed. Every permutation can be expressed as a product of transpositions. This can easily be seen as follows. Suppose we have a permutation $\{\sigma(1), \ldots, \sigma(n)\}$. If $n = \sigma(j)$ for some $j \neq n$, then we compose σ with the transposition τ which interchanges $\sigma(j)$ and $\sigma(j + 1)$. Then $\tau\sigma(j) = \sigma(j + 1)$. The effect of τ is to move n one step further to the right. We continue this until n reaches the last position. We then repeat the procedure, moving successively $n - 1$ furthest to the right, then $n - 2$, etc. Finally, we have a sequence of transpositions $\tau_1, \ldots, \tau_s$ such that $\tau_s\tau_{s-1} \cdots \tau_1\sigma = id$. Then $\sigma = \tau_1^{-1} \cdots \tau_{s-1}^{-1}\tau_s^{-1}$. Since the inverse of a transposition is a transposition, we have expressed σ as a product of transpositions.

When a permutation σ is expressed as a product of transpositions, then it can be shown that the parity of this number is always the same. In other words, suppose that

$$\sigma = \tau_1 \cdots \tau_r = \tau_1' \cdots \tau_s'$$

are two ways of expressing σ as a product of transpositions. If r is even, then so is s, and if r is odd, then s is odd also. (Hints for the proof will be given in an exercise.) Consequently, the number $(-1)^r$ is the same as $(-1)^s$, and is called the *sign* of σ. It is the number $\epsilon(\sigma)$ which occurred above. It is also sometimes written $\mathrm{sign}(\sigma)$.

If σ, σ' are two permutations, and we write

$$\sigma = \tau_1 \cdots \tau_r \qquad \text{and} \qquad \sigma' = \tau_1' \cdots \tau_s'$$

as products of transpositions, then

$$\sigma\sigma' = \tau_1 \cdots \tau_r \tau_1' \cdots \tau_s'.$$

Hence

$$\epsilon(\sigma\sigma') = (-1)^{r+s} = \epsilon(\sigma)\epsilon(\sigma').$$

The sign of a product of permutations is equal to the product of the signs.

In particular, since $\sigma\sigma^{-1} = id$, we obtain

$$1 = \epsilon(\sigma\sigma^{-1}) = \epsilon(\sigma)\epsilon(\sigma^{-1}).$$

Consequently $\epsilon(\sigma) = \epsilon(\sigma^{-1})$.

We return to our discussion of determinants, and to the expression (*) which we obtained.

Let σ be a permutation of $\{1, \ldots, n\}$. If $\sigma(j) = k$, then $\sigma^{-1}(k) = j$. We can therefore write

$$a_{\sigma(j),j} = a_{k,\sigma^{-1}(k)}.$$

In a product

$$a_{\sigma(1),1} \cdots a_{\sigma(n),n}$$

each integer k from 1 to n occurs precisely once among the integers $\sigma(1), \ldots, \sigma(n)$. Hence this product can be written

$$a_{1,\sigma^{-1}(1)} \cdots a_{n,\sigma^{-1}(n)},$$

and our sum (*) is equal to

$$\sum_\sigma \epsilon(\sigma^{-1}) a_{1,\sigma^{-1}(1)} \cdots a_{n,\sigma^{-1}(n)},$$

because $\epsilon(\sigma) = \epsilon(\sigma^{-1})$. In this sum, each term corresponds to a permutation σ. However, as σ ranges over all permutations, so does σ^{-1} because a permutation determines its inverse uniquely. Hence our sum is equal to

$$(**) \qquad \sum_\sigma \epsilon(\sigma) a_{1,\sigma(1)} \cdots a_{n,\sigma(n)}.$$

The sum (**) is precisely the sum giving the expanded form of the determinant of the transpose of A. Hence we have proved property (6), namely

$$\text{Det } (A) = \text{Det } ({}^{t}A)$$

from properties (1), (2), (3).

So far, we have shown: *If D is any function of $n \times n$ matrices satisfying (1), our weak property (2′), and (3), then D satisfies (2), (4), (5), (6), and is uniquely determined.*

§8. Existence

We come to the question of existence. Do determinants exist at all? The answer is yes, and we prove this by induction.

When $n = 1$, we deal with 1×1 determinants, and all our properties are obvious if we define Det $(a) = a$, for any number a.

To prove our assertion in general, it will suffice to give an argument which allows us to proceed stepwise. Suppose therefore that we have been able to define determinants for all integers $< n$, satisfying our properties. Let A be an $n \times n$ matrix, $A = (a_{ij})$. Let i be an integer, $1 \le i \le n$. We define

$$(\text{***}) \qquad \Delta(A) = (-1)^{i+1}a_{i1} \text{ Det } (A_{i1}) + \cdots + (-1)^{i+n}a_{in} \text{ Det } (A_{in}).$$

Each A_{ij} is an $(n-1) \times (n-1)$ matrix. We shall prove that our function Δ satisfies properties (1), (3), and the weak version of property (2).

[Observe that (***) is the expression we would get from expanding a determinant according to the i-th row.]

Note that $\Delta(A)$ is a sum of terms

$$(-1)^{i+j}a_{ij} \text{ Det } (A_{ij})$$

as j ranges from 1 to n.

(1) Consider Δ as a function of the k-th column, and consider any term

$$(-1)^{i+j}a_{ij} \text{ Det } (A_{ij}).$$

If $j \ne k$, then a_{ij} does not depend on the k-th column, and Det (A_{ij}) depends linearly on the k-th column. If $j = k$, then a_{ij} depends linearly on the k-th column, and Det (A_{ij}) does not depend on the k-th column. In any case, our term depends linearly on the k-th column. Since $\Delta(A)$ is a sum of such terms, it depends linearly on the k-th column, and property (1) follows.

(2′) We prove the weak property 2. Suppose two adjacent columns of A are equal, namely $A^{k} = A^{k+1}$. Let j be an index $\ne k$ or $k+1$. Then the matrix A_{ij} has two adjacent equal columns, and hence its determinant is equal to 0. Thus the term corresponding to an index $j \ne k$ or $k+1$

gives a zero contribution to $\Delta(A)$. The other two terms can be written

$$(-1)^{i+k}a_{ik}\, \text{Det}\, (A_{ik}) + (-1)^{i+k+1}a_{i,k+1}\, \text{Det}\, (A_{i,k+1}).$$

The two matrices A_{ik} and $A_{i,k+1}$ are equal because of our assumption that the k-th column of A is equal to the $(k+1)$-th column. Similarly, $a_{ik} = a_{i,k+1}$. Hence these two terms cancel since they occur with opposite signs. This proves the weak property (2').

(3) Let A be the unit matrix. Then $a_{ij} = 0$ unless $i = j$, in which case $a_{ii} = 1$. Each A_{ij} is the unit $(n-1) \times (n-1)$ matrix. The only term in the sum (***) which gives a non-zero contribution is

$$(-1)^{i+i}a_{ii}\, \text{Det}\, (A_{ii}),$$

which is equal to 1. This proves property (3).

From §6 we conclude that Δ is the unique determinant function satisfying (1), (2), (3). Furthermore, Δ also satisfies the rule for the expansion of determinants according to rows, i.e. property (7) is satisfied. Everything is proved.

EXERCISES

1. Let $x_1, \ldots, x_n$ be variables and let σ be a permutation of the numbers $\{1, \ldots, n\}$. Then there is a number $\epsilon(\sigma)$, equal to $+1$ or -1, such that

$$\prod_{i<j}[x_{\sigma(j)} - x_{\sigma(i)}] = \epsilon(\sigma)\prod_{i<j}[x_j - x_i],$$

where the symbol $\prod$ means that one should take the product over all pairs of integers i, j such that $1 \leqq i < j \leqq n$. If τ is a transposition, show that $\epsilon(\tau) = -1$.

2. Show that $\epsilon(\sigma)$ is equal to $(-1)^m$, where m is the number of pairs (i, j) such that $1 \leqq i < j \leqq n$ and $\sigma(i) > \sigma(j)$. This number m is called the number of inversions of σ.

3. Let σ' be any permutation of $\{1, \ldots, n\}$. Substitute $\sigma'(k)$ for x_k in the product of Exercise 1. Conclude that

$$\epsilon(\sigma\sigma') = \epsilon(\sigma)\epsilon(\sigma').$$

4. A permutation σ of the integers $\{1, \ldots, n\}$ is sometimes denoted by $\begin{bmatrix} 1 & \cdots & n \\ \sigma(1) & \cdots & \sigma(n) \end{bmatrix}$. Thus $\begin{bmatrix} 1 & 2 & 3 \\ 2 & 1 & 3 \end{bmatrix}$ denotes the permutation σ such that $\sigma(1) = 2$, $\sigma(2) = 1$, $\sigma(3) = 3$. This permutation is in fact a transposition. Determine the sign of the following permutations.

(a) $\begin{bmatrix} 1 & 2 & 3 \\ 2 & 3 & 1 \end{bmatrix}$ (b) $\begin{bmatrix} 1 & 2 & 3 \\ 3 & 1 & 2 \end{bmatrix}$ (c) $\begin{bmatrix} 1 & 2 & 3 \\ 3 & 2 & 1 \end{bmatrix}$

(d) $\begin{bmatrix} 1 & 2 & 3 & 4 \\ 2 & 3 & 1 & 4 \end{bmatrix}$
(e) $\begin{bmatrix} 1 & 2 & 3 & 4 \\ 2 & 1 & 4 & 3 \end{bmatrix}$
(f) $\begin{bmatrix} 1 & 2 & 3 & 4 \\ 3 & 2 & 4 & 1 \end{bmatrix}$

5. In each one of the cases of Exercise 4, write the inverse of the permutation.

6. Show that the number of odd permutations of $\{1, \ldots, n\}$ for $n \geq 2$ is equal to the number of even permutations.

§9. Determinant of a product

We shall prove the important rule:

THEOREM 4. *Let A, B be two $n \times n$ matrices. Then*

$$\mathrm{Det}\ (AB) = \mathrm{Det}\ (A)\ \mathrm{Det}\ (B).$$

The determinant of a product is equal to the product of the determinants.

Proof. Let $A = (a_{ij})$ and $B = (b_{jk})$:

$$\begin{pmatrix} a_{11} & \cdots & a_{1n} \\ \vdots & & \vdots \\ a_{n1} & \cdots & a_{nn} \end{pmatrix} \begin{pmatrix} b_{11} & \cdots & b_{1k} & \cdots & b_{1n} \\ \vdots & & \vdots & & \vdots \\ b_{n1} & \cdots & b_{nk} & \cdots & b_{nn} \end{pmatrix}.$$

Let $AB = C$, and let C^k be the k-th column of C. Then by definition,

$$C^k = b_{1k}A^1 + \cdots + b_{nk}A^n.$$

Thus

$$\begin{aligned} D(AB) &= D(C^1, \ldots, C^n) \\ &= D(b_{11}A^1 + \cdots + b_{n1}A^n, \ldots, b_{1n}A^1 + \cdots + b_{nn}A^n). \end{aligned}$$

If we expand this out using property (1), we find a sum

$$\begin{aligned} \sum_{\sigma} D(b_{\sigma(1),1}A^{\sigma(1)}, \ldots, b_{\sigma(n),n}A^{\sigma(n)}) \\ = \sum_{\sigma} b_{\sigma(1),1} \cdots b_{\sigma(n),n} D(A^{\sigma(1)}, \ldots, A^{\sigma(n)}) \\ = \sum_{\sigma} \epsilon(\sigma) b_{\sigma(1),1} \cdots b_{\sigma(n),n} D(A^1, \ldots, A^n). \end{aligned}$$

According to the formula for determinants which we found, this is equal to $D(B)\ D(A)$, as was to be shown.

CHAPTER XV

Complex Numbers

One of the advantages of dealing with the real numbers instead of the rational numbers is that certain equations which have no solutions in the rational numbers have a solution in real numbers. For instance, $x^2 = 2$ is such an equation. However, we also know some equations having no solution in real numbers, for instance $x^2 = -1$, or $x^2 = -2$. In this chapter, we define a new kind of number where such equations have solutions. What we have simply called numbers in the preceding chapters will now be called *real* numbers. The new kind of numbers will be called *complex* numbers.

§1. Definition

The complex numbers are a set of objects which can be added and multiplied, the sum and product of two complex numbers being also a complex number, and satisfy the following conditions.

(1) Every real number is a complex number, and if α, β are real numbers, then their sum and product as complex numbers are the same as their sum and product as real numbers.

(2) There is a complex number denoted by i such that $i^2 = -1$.

(3) Every complex number can be written uniquely in the form $a + bi$ where a, b are real numbers.

(4) The ordinary laws of arithmetic concerning addition and multiplication are satisfied. We list these laws:

If α, β, γ are complex numbers, then $(\alpha\beta)\gamma = \alpha(\beta\gamma)$, and

$$(\alpha + \beta) + \gamma = \alpha + (\beta + \gamma).$$

We have $\alpha(\beta + \gamma) = \alpha\beta + \alpha\gamma$, and $(\beta + \gamma)\alpha = \beta\alpha + \gamma\alpha$.
We have $\alpha\beta = \beta\alpha$, and $\alpha + \beta = \beta + \alpha$.
If 1 is the real number one, then $1\alpha = \alpha$.
If 0 is the real number zero, then $0\alpha = 0$.
We have $\alpha + (-1)\alpha = 0$.

We shall now draw consequences of these properties. With each complex number $a + bi$, we associate the vector (a, b) in the plane. Let $\alpha = a_1 + a_2 i$ and $\beta = b_1 + b_2 i$ be two complex numbers. Then

$$\alpha + \beta = a_1 + b_1 + (a_2 + b_2)i.$$

Hence addition of complex numbers is carried out "componentwise" and corresponds to addition of vectors in the plane. For example, $(2 + 3i) + (-1 + 5i) = 1 + 8i$.

In multiplying complex numbers, we use the rule $i^2 = -1$ to simplify a product and to put it in the form $a + bi$. For instance, let $\alpha = 2 + 3i$ and $\beta = 1 - i$. Then

$$
\begin{aligned}
\alpha\beta = (2 + 3i)(1 - i) &= 2(1 - i) + 3i(1 - i) \\
&= 2 - 2i + 3i - 3i^2 \\
&= 2 + i - 3(-1) \\
&= 2 + 3 + i \\
&= 5 + i.
\end{aligned}
$$

Let $\alpha = a + bi$ be a complex number. We define $\bar{\alpha}$ to be $a - bi$. Thus if $\alpha = 2 + 3i$, then $\bar{\alpha} = 2 - 3i$. The complex number $\bar{\alpha}$ is called the *conjugate* of α. We see at once that

$$
\alpha\bar{\alpha} = a^2 + b^2.
$$

With the vector interpretation of complex numbers, we see that $\alpha\bar{\alpha}$ is the square of the distance of the point (a, b) from the origin.

We now have one more important property of complex numbers, which will allow us to divide by complex numbers other than 0.

If $\alpha = a + bi$ is a complex number $\neq 0$, and if we let

$$
\lambda = \frac{\bar{\alpha}}{a^2 + b^2}
$$

then $\alpha\lambda = \lambda\alpha = 1$.

The proof of this property is an immediate consequence of the law of multiplication of complex numbers, because

$$
\alpha \, \frac{\bar{\alpha}}{a^2 + b^2} = \frac{\alpha\bar{\alpha}}{a^2 + b^2} = 1.
$$

The number λ above is called the *inverse* of α, and is denoted by α^{-1} of $1/\alpha$. If α, β are complex numbers, we often write β/α instead of $\alpha^{-1}\beta$ (or $\beta\alpha^{-1}$), just as we did with real numbers. We see that we can divide by complex numbers $\neq 0$.

We define the *absolute value* of a complex number $\alpha = a_1 + ia_2$ to be

$$
|\alpha| = \sqrt{a_1^2 + a_2^2}.
$$

This absolute value is none other than the length of the vector (a_1, a_2).

In terms of absolute values, we can write

$$\alpha^{-1} = \frac{\bar{\alpha}}{|\alpha|^2}$$

provided $\alpha \neq 0$.

The triangle inequality for the length of vectors can now be stated for complex numbers. If α, β are complex numbers, then

$$|\alpha + \beta| \leq |\alpha| + |\beta|.$$

Another property of the absolute value is given in Exercise 5.

EXERCISES

1. Express the following complex numbers in the form $x + iy$, where x, y are real numbers.

(a) $(-1 + 3i)^{-1}$ (b) $(1 + i)(1 - i)$
(c) $(1 + i)i(2 - i)$ (d) $(i - 1)(2 - i)$
(e) $(7 + \pi i)(\pi + i)$ (f) $(2i + 1)\pi i$
(g) $(\sqrt{2}i)(\pi + 3i)$ (h) $(i + 1)(i - 2)(i + 3)$

2. Express the following complex numbers in the form $x + iy$, where x, y are real numbers.

(a) $(1 + i)^{-1}$ (b) $\dfrac{1}{3 + i}$ (c) $\dfrac{2 + i}{2 - i}$ (d) $\dfrac{1}{2 - i}$

(e) $\dfrac{1 + i}{i}$ (f) $\dfrac{i}{1 + i}$ (g) $\dfrac{2i}{3 - i}$ (h) $\dfrac{1}{-1 + i}$

3. Let α be a complex number $\neq 0$. What is the absolute value of $\alpha/\bar{\alpha}$? What is $\bar{\bar{\alpha}}$?

4. Let α, β be two complex numbers. Show that $\overline{\alpha\beta} = \bar{\alpha}\bar{\beta}$ and that $\overline{\alpha + \beta} = \bar{\alpha} + \bar{\beta}$.

5. Show that $|\alpha\beta| = |\alpha| \, |\beta|$.

6. Define addition of n-tuples of complex numbers componentwise, and multiplication of n-tuples of complex numbers by complex numbers componentwise also. If $A = (\alpha_1, \ldots, \alpha_n)$ and $B = (\beta_1, \ldots, \beta_n)$ are n-tuples of complex numbers, define their scalar product $\langle A, B \rangle$ to be

$$\alpha_1\bar{\beta}_1 + \cdots + \alpha_n\bar{\beta}_n$$

(note the complex conjugation!). Prove the following rules:

SP1. $\langle A, B \rangle = \overline{\langle B, A \rangle}$.
SP2. $\langle A, B + C \rangle = \langle A, B \rangle + \langle A, C \rangle$.
SP3. If α is a complex number, then

$$\langle \alpha A, B \rangle = \alpha\langle A, B \rangle \quad \text{and} \quad \langle A, \alpha B \rangle = \bar{\alpha}\langle A, B \rangle.$$

SP4. If $A = 0$ then $\langle A, A \rangle = 0$, and otherwise, $\langle A, A \rangle > 0$.

(Observe the complex conjugates which appear. The scalar product is defined as we have done in order to preserve the positivity of SP4. For that purpose, we are willing to allow the complex conjugate in SP1, instead of the rule $\langle A, B \rangle = \langle B, A \rangle$.)

§2. *Polar form*

Let $(x, y) = x + iy$ be a complex number. We know that any point in the plane can be represented by polar coordinates (θ, r). We shall now see how to write our complex number in terms of such polar coordinates.

Let θ be a real number. We define the expression $e^{i\theta}$ to be

$$e^{i\theta} = \cos \theta + i \sin \theta.$$

Thus $e^{i\theta}$ is a complex number.

For example, if $\theta = \pi$, then $e^{i\pi} = -1$. Also, $e^{2\pi i} = 1$, and $e^{i\pi/2} = i$. Furthermore, $e^{i(\theta + 2\pi)} = e^{i\theta}$ for any real θ.

Let x, y be real numbers and $x + iy$ a complex number. Let $r = x^2 + y^2$. If (θ, r) are the polar coordinates of the point (x, y) in the plane, then

$$x = r \cos \theta \quad \text{and} \quad y = r \sin \theta.$$

Hence

$$x + iy = r \cos \theta + ir \sin \theta = re^{i\theta}.$$

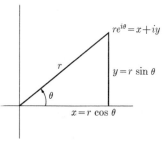

The expression $re^{i\theta}$ is called the *polar form* of the complex number $x + iy$.

The most important property of this polar form is given in Theorem 1. It will allow us to have a very good geometric interpretation for the product of two complex numbers.

THEOREM 1. *Let θ, φ be two complex numbers. Then*

$$e^{i\theta + i\varphi} = e^{i\theta} e^{i\varphi}.$$

Proof. By definition, we have

$$e^{i\theta + i\varphi} = e^{i(\theta + \varphi)} = \cos (\theta + \varphi) + i \sin (\theta + \varphi).$$

Using the addition formula for sine and cosine, we obtain:

$$\cos \theta \cos \varphi - \sin \theta \sin \varphi + i(\sin \theta \cos \varphi - \sin \varphi \cos \theta).$$

This is exactly the same expression as the one we obtain by multiplying out

$$(\cos \theta + i \sin \theta)(\cos \varphi + i \sin \varphi).$$

Our theorem is proved.

Theorem 1 justifies our notation, by showing that the exponential of complex numbers satisfies the same formal rule as the exponential of real numbers.

Let $\alpha = a_1 + ia_2$ be a complex number. We define e^α to be

$$e^{a_1} e^{ia_2}.$$

For instance, let $\alpha = 2 + 3i$. Then $e^\alpha = e^2 e^{3i}$.

THEOREM 2. *Let α, β be complex numbers. Then*

$$e^{\alpha + \beta} = e^\alpha e^\beta.$$

Proof. Let $\alpha = a_1 + ia_2$ and $\beta = b_1 + ib_2$. Then

$$e^{\alpha + \beta} = e^{(a_1 + b_1) + i(a_2 + b_2)} = e^{a_1 + b_1} e^{i(a_2 + b_2)}$$
$$= e^{a_1} e^{b_1} e^{ia_2 + ib_2}.$$

Using Theorem 1, we see that this last expression is equal to

$$e^{a_1} e^{b_1} e^{ia_2} e^{ib_2} = e^{a_1} e^{ia_2} e^{b_1} e^{ib_2}.$$

By definition, this is equal to $e^\alpha e^\beta$, thereby proving our theorem.

Theorem 2 is very useful in dealing with complex numbers. We shall now consider several examples to illustrate it.

Example 1. Find a complex number whose square is $4e^{i\pi/2}$.
Let $z = 2e^{i\pi/4}$. Using the rule for exponentials, we see that $z^2 = 4e^{i\pi/2}$.

Example 2. Let n be a positive integer. Find a complex number w such that $w^n = e^{i\pi/2}$.
It is clear that the complex number $w = e^{i\pi/2n}$ satisfies our requirement.

In other words, we may express Theorem 2 as follows. Let $z_1 = r_1 e^{i\theta_1}$ and $z_2 = r_2 e^{i\theta_2}$ be two complex numbers. To find the product $z_1 z_2$, we multiply the absolute values and add the angles. Thus

$$z_1 z_2 = r_1 r_2 e^{i(\theta_1 + \theta_2)}.$$

In many cases, this way of visualizing the product of complex numbers is more useful than that coming out of the definition.

EXERCISES

1. Put the following complex numbers in polar form.

   (a) $1 + i$ (b) $1 + i\sqrt{2}$ (c) -3 (d) $4i$
   (e) $1 - i\sqrt{2}$ (f) $-5i$ (g) -7 (h) $-1 - i$

2. Put the following complex numbers in the ordinary form $x + iy$.

   (a) $e^{3i\pi}$ (b) $e^{2i\pi/3}$ (c) $3e^{i\pi/4}$ (d) $\pi e^{-i\pi/3}$
   (e) $e^{2\pi i/6}$ (f) $e^{-i\pi/2}$ (g) $e^{-i\pi}$ (h) $e^{-5i\pi/4}$

3. Let α be a complex number $\neq 0$. Show that there are two distinct complex numbers whose square is α.

4. Let α be a complex number $\neq 0$. Let n be a positive integer. Show that there are n distinct complex numbers z such that $z^n = \alpha$. Write these complex numbers in polar form.

5. Let $\alpha = 1$ in Exercise 4. Plot all the complex numbers z such that $z^n = 1$ on a sheet of graph paper, for $n = 2, 3, 4$, and 5.

6. Let $a + bi$ be a complex number. Find real numbers x, y such that $(x + iy)^2 = a + bi$, expressing x, y in terms of a and b.

7. Let w be a complex number and suppose that z is a complex number such that $e^z = w$. Describe all complex numbers u such that $e^u = w$.

8. What are the complex numbers z such that $e^z = 1$?

9. If θ is real, show that

$$\cos \theta = \frac{e^{i\theta} + e^{-i\theta}}{2} \quad \text{and} \quad \sin \theta = \frac{e^{i\theta} - e^{-i\theta}}{2}.$$

10. A mapping from the real numbers into the complex numbers is called a complex valued function. Such a function can be written

$$F(t) = f(t) + ig(t),$$

where $f(t)$ and $g(t)$ are real valued functions. Define the derivative $F'(t)$ to be $f'(t) + ig'(t)$. [This corresponds to the derivative of the vector $(f(t), g(t))$.] The derivative $F'(t)$ (also written dF/dt) is defined only when both f, g are differentiable, of course, in which case we say that F is *differentiable*.

(a) Let F, G be complex valued functions which are differentiable. Define their sum in a natural way, and show that

$$\frac{d(F + G)}{dt} = F'(t) + G'(t).$$

If c is a complex number, show that

$$\frac{d(cF)}{dt} = cF'(t).$$

(b) Let F, G be complex valued functions which are differentiable. Define their product in a natural way, and show that

$$\frac{d(FG)}{dt} = F'(t)G(t) + F(t)G'(t).$$

(c) Let F be a differentiable complex valued function. Show that

$$\frac{d(e^{F(t)})}{dt} = F'(t)e^{F(t)}.$$

11. Let $F(t) = f(t) + ig(t)$ be a complex valued function of t, and assume that f, g are continuous. We then say that F is continuous. Define the indefinite integral as usual by

$$\int F(t)\, dt = \int f(t)\, dt + i \int g(t)\, dt.$$

(a) If there is a differentiable function G such that $F(t) = G'(t)$, show that $\int F(t)dt = G(t)$.

(b) Let α be a complex number $\neq 0$. Show that

$$\int e^{\alpha t}\, dt = \frac{e^{\alpha t}}{\alpha}.$$

(c) Let n be an integer. Find

$$\int_0^1 e^{2\pi i n t}\, dt.$$

12. Observe that the theory of bases, linear dependence, and determinants applies to n-tuples of complex numbers, and to vector spaces over the complex numbers, if one replaces the word "number" in the text by the word "complex number".

13. Compute the following determinants:

(a) $\begin{vmatrix} 1+i & i \\ 2 & -i \end{vmatrix}$
(b) $\begin{vmatrix} 2-i & -i \\ 4i & -2i \end{vmatrix}$

(c) Make up 3×3 determinants of complex numbers and find their value.

14. Are the vectors $(i, -1, 2+i)$, $(\pi i, i+1, -i)$, $(1, 1, 2)$ linearly independent over the complex numbers?

Appendix 1

Induction

In the course of several proofs, we have given a "stepwise" argument. One can formalise this type of argument, which is called *induction*.

Suppose that we wish to prove a certain assertion concerning positive integers n. Let $A(n)$ denote the assertion concerning the integer n. To prove it for all n, it suffices to prove the following.

(1) The assertion $A(1)$ is true (i.e. the assertion concerning the integer 1 is true).

(2) Assuming the assertion proved for all positive integers $\leqq n$, prove it for $n + 1$, i.e. prove $A(n + 1)$.

Step (2) is the procedure which allows us to proceed from one integer to the next, and step (1) gives us a starting point. We shall now give two examples.

THEOREM 1. *For all integers $n \geqq 1$, we have*

$$1 + 2 + \cdots + n = \frac{n(n + 1)}{2}.$$

Proof. By induction. The assertion $A(n)$ is the assertion of the theorem. When $n = 1$, it simply states that

$$1 = \frac{1(1 + 1)}{2},$$

and is clearly true. Assume now that the assertion of Theorem 1 is true for n. Then:

$$1 + 2 + \cdots + n + (n + 1) = \frac{n(n + 1)}{2} + (n + 1).$$

Putting the expression on the right of the equality sign over a common denominator 2, we see that it is equal to

$$\frac{n^2 + n + 2n + 2}{2} = \frac{(n + 1)(n + 2)}{2}.$$

Hence assuming $A(n)$, we have shown that

$$1 + 2 + \cdots + (n + 1) = \frac{(n + 1)(n + 2)}{2},$$

which is none other than assertion $A(n + 1)$. This proves our theorem.

201

THEOREM 2. *Every $n \times n$ matrix can be transformed into a matrix all of whose components are equal to 0 except those on the diagonal, which may be equal to 0 or 1, by means of the following operations: Interchanging two columns, multiplying a column by a non-zero number, adding one column to another, performing these operations on rows instead of columns.*

Proof. By induction. The assertion is trivially true for 1×1 matrices since in that case, there is only a diagonal component in the matrix. Assume the assertion proved for $(n - 1) \times (n - 1)$ matirces. We shall prove it for $n \times n$ matrices ($n \geqq 2$).

Let

$$A = \begin{pmatrix} a_{11} & \cdots & a_{1n} \\ \vdots & & \vdots \\ a_{n1} & \cdots & a_{nn} \end{pmatrix}$$

be an $n \times n$ matrix. If some element of the first column is not equal to zero, say $a_{i1} \neq 0$, we then interchange the i-th row and first row. We can then transform our matrix into another matrix whose 11-component is not equal to 0. Multiplying the first row by the inverse of the 11-component, we can achieve that this 11-component is equal to 1. We now multiply the first row by a_{i1} ($i > 1$) and subtract it from the i-th row for each integer i satisfying $2 \leqq i \leqq n$. This transforms our matrix into a matrix of type

$$\begin{pmatrix} 1 & b_{12} & \cdots & b_{1n} \\ 0 & & & \\ \vdots & & ** & \\ 0 & & & \end{pmatrix}$$

with 1 in the upper left-hand corner, and 0 in the first column and i-th row, $i \geqq 2$. We now multiply the first column by $-b_{1j}$ for each integer j such that $2 \leqq j \leqq n$ and add it to the j-th column. We then obtain a matrix of type

$$\begin{pmatrix} 1 & 0 & \cdots & 0 \\ 0 & & & \\ \vdots & & *** & \\ 0 & & & \end{pmatrix}$$

having a component 1 in the upper left-hand corner, and 0 otherwise in the first column and first row.

If every element of the first column was equal to 0 in the first place, and some element of the first row was not equal to 0, we carry out the preceding arguments on the transpose of the matrix, to transform our original matrix again into one of type

$$B = \begin{pmatrix} 1 & 0 & \cdots & 0 \\ 0 & & & \\ \vdots & & *** & \\ 0 & & & \end{pmatrix}.$$

If every element of the first column and first row of the original matrix was equal to 0, then we deal with a matrix of type

$$B = \begin{pmatrix} 0 & 0 & \cdots & 0 \\ 0 & & & \\ \vdots & & *** & \\ 0 & & & \end{pmatrix}.$$

In either one of the above cases, we end up with a matrix all of whose components on the first row and first column are equal to 0 except the 11-component.

The matrix denoted by *** in all cases is an $(n - 1) \times (n - 1)$ matrix. Hence by induction hypothesis, using the three operations on the rows and columns of ***, we can transform the matrix *** into a matrix all of whose components are equal to 0, except those on the diagonal, which are equal to 0 or 1. We can view an operation on rows or columns of *** as arising from an operation on the corresponding rows or columns of B (since the operations will not affect the components of B on the first column or first row, these being all equal to 0 except in the upper left-hand corner). We have now transformed our matrix into one of the desired type, thereby concluding the proof.

EXERCISES

1. Prove that for every positive integer n, we have

$$1^2 + \cdots + n^2 = \frac{n(n + 1)(2n + 1)}{6}.$$

2. Let $\binom{n}{k}$ denote the binomial coefficient, $\binom{n}{k} = \frac{n!}{k!(n - k)!}$, where n, k are integers ≥ 0, $0 \leq k \leq n$, and 0! is defined to be equal to 1. Prove the following assertions.

(a) $\binom{n}{k} = \binom{n}{n - k}$ (b) $\binom{n}{k - 1} + \binom{n}{k} = \binom{n + 1}{k}$ (for $k > 0$)

(c) $1 + \binom{n}{1} + \binom{n}{2} + \cdots + \binom{n}{n} = 2^n$

3. Let $P_1, \ldots, P_n$ be n points in m-space. Show that any convex set which contains $P_1, \ldots, P_n$ also contains all linear combinations

$$x_1 P_1 + \cdots + x_n P_n,$$

such that $0 \leq x_i \leq 1$ for all i, and $x_1 + \cdots + x_n = 1$. [*Hint:* Use induction, and the fact that if $x_n \neq 1$, then the above linear combination is equal to

$$(1 - x_n) \left(\frac{x_1}{1 - x_n} P_1 + \cdots + \frac{x_{n-1}}{1 - x_n} P_{n-1} \right) + x_n P_n.$$

4. Just for fun (you won't need induction), show that the set consisting of all linear combinations as in Exercise 3 is itself convex.

5. Let $f_1, \ldots, f_n$ be differentiable functions of one variable. Let f' denote the derivative of a function. Prove that the derivative of the product $f_1 \cdots f_n$ is equal to

$$(f_1 \cdots f_n)' = f_1' f_2 \cdots f_n + f_1 f_2' \cdots f_n + \cdots + f_1 \cdots f_n'.$$

Appendix 2

ϵ and δ again

Let V be a vector space. A *norm* on V is a function, which to each element v of V associates a number, denoted by $\|v\|$, satisfying the following properties:

N1. If $v \neq O$ then $\|v\| > 0$, and $\|O\| = 0$.
N2. If v_1, v_2 are elements of V, then

$$\|v_1 + v_2\| \leq \|v_1\| + \|v_2\|.$$

N3. If c is a number and v an element of V then

$$\|cv\| = |c|\,\|v\|.$$

In this book, we dealt with norms arising from scalar products, but it is convenient to study norms independently of scalar products. A vector space, together with a norm, is called a *normed vector space*.

Let V, W be two normed vector spaces. Let S be a (non-empty) subset of V, and let $F : S \to W$ be a mapping of S into W. Let v_0 be an element of V, and w an element of W. We shall say that $F(v)$ *approaches the limit w as v approaches v_0* if the following condition is satisfied:

Given a number $\epsilon > 0$, there exists a number $\delta > 0$ such that some element v of V lies in S and satisfies the inequality

$$\|v - v_0\| < \delta,$$

and for every element v of S unequal to v_0 satisfying this inequality, we have

$$\|F(v) - w\| < \epsilon.$$

We can also rephrase this in the usual manner as follows: We write

$$\lim_{u \to O} F(v_0 + u) = w$$

and say that *the limit of $F(v_0 + u)$ is w, as u approaches O*, if the following condition is satisfied:

Given $\epsilon > 0$, there exists $\delta > 0$ such that we can find an element $u \neq O$ of V for which $v_0 + u$ lies in S, and $\|u\| < \delta$. Furthermore, for every such u, we have

$$\|F(v_0 + u) - w\| < \epsilon.$$

It is then possible to prove in exactly the same manner as for functions of one variable the various theorems concerning the formal properties of limits. Of course, the theorem concerning the limit of a product will hold only when $W = \mathbf{R}$, and we can multiply functions. It should also be pointed out that a similar theorem holds when we take the dot product. The formulation is essentially the same as the ordinary one, and we state it as an example (but leave the proof as an exercise, using the Schwarz inequality).

Let W be a vector space with a scalar product, and let V be a normed vector space. Let S be a subset of V, and let F, $G:S \to W$ be two maps of S into W. Let v_0 be an element of V. Let

$$w = \lim_{v \to v_0} F(v) \quad \text{and} \quad w' = \lim_{v \to v_0} G(v).$$

Let $F \cdot G$ be the function on S defined by $(F \cdot G)(v) = F(v) \cdot G(v)$. Then

$$w \cdot w' = \lim_{v \to v_0} (F \cdot G)(v).$$

In dealing with vectors, we considered maps into $\mathbf{R}^n$. In that case, we have made use of the following result.

Let V be a normed vector space, and S a subset of V. Let $F:S \to \mathbf{R}^n$ be a mapping, and let $F_1, \ldots, F_n$ be its coordinate functions, i.e.

$$F(v) = \big(F_1(v), \ldots, F_n(v)\big).$$

Let $w = (w_1, \ldots, w_n)$ be an element of $\mathbf{R}^n$ and v_0 an element of V. Then

$$\lim_{v \to v_0} F(v) = w$$

if and only if, for every $i = 1, \ldots, n$ we have

$$\lim_{v \to v_0} F_i(v) = w_i.$$

Proof. Assume first that $\lim_{v \to v_0} F(v) = w$. Given $\epsilon > 0$, find $\delta > 0$ as in the definition of limits. Then whenever $\|v - v_0\| < \delta$ we have $\|F(v) - w\| < \epsilon$. Note that

$$F(v) - w = \big(F_1(v) - w_1, \ldots, F_n(v) - w_n\big).$$

If $X = (x_1, \ldots, x_n)$ is an n-tuple, then $|x_i| \leq \|X\|$. Hence for all i,

$$|F_i(v) - w_i| \leq \|F(v) - w\| < \epsilon.$$

This proves that $\lim_{v \to v_0} F_i(v) = w_i$.

Conversely, assume that these limits hold for each i. Given $\epsilon > 0$, find $\delta > 0$ such that whenever $\|v - v_0\| < \delta$ we have

$$|F_i(v) - w_i| < \frac{\epsilon}{\sqrt{n}}$$

for all $i = 1, \ldots, n$. Then

$$\|F(v) - w\| = \sqrt{\sum_{i=1}^{n} (F_i(v) - w_i)^2}$$
$$< \sqrt{n \frac{\epsilon^2}{n}}$$
$$< \epsilon.$$

This proves that $\lim_{v \to v_0} F(v) = w$.

Roughly speaking, what the preceding assertion means is that whenever two vectors are close together, their coordinates are also close together. Of course we have used this many times in the course of the book, but the purpose of the present appendix is to show how such notions can be reduced to notions concerning only numbers and elementary notions of logic.

Finally, let V, W be two normed vector spaces. Let S be a subset of V, and let v_0 be an element of S. Let $F : S \to W$ be a mapping. We say that F is *continuous* at v_0 if

$$\lim_{v \to v_0} F(v) = F(v_0),$$

or if v_0 is an isolated point of S. (*You* define what "isolated" means.) Again the theorems concerning continuous maps (sums, products if relevant, composition) are proved essentially without any change from the case of functions of one variable. We leave the proofs as exercises to the reader. (The point is that continuity is defined in terms of limits, and thus any property of limits immediately extends to the analogous property concerning continuity.)

In discussing error terms as in Chapter III, it is convenient to introduce certain abbreviations, and a convenient terminology to deal with orders of magnitude. We shall give here the relevant definitions.

We consider functions defined on subsets of n-space. A function f will be said to be *defined for small values of H* if there exists a number $c > 0$ such that f is defined for all H in n-space such that $H \neq O$ and $\|H\| < c$. *We shall say that f is $o(H)$* (which we read *"little oh of H"*) if

$$\lim_{\|H\| \to 0} \frac{f(H)}{\|H\|} = 0.$$

The following statements are then easy to prove, and are left as exercises. We assume that all functions involved are defined for small values of H.

(1) *If f_1, f_2 are two functions which are both $o(H)$, then so is $f_1 + f_2$.*

(2) *If f is $o(H)$, and C is a number > 0, then Cf is also $o(H)$.*

(3) *If f is $o(H)$, and if g is a function such that*

$$|g(H)| \leqq |f(H)|$$

for all sufficiently small values of H, then g is also $o(H)$.

(4) *A function f is $o(H)$ if and only if f can be written in the form*

$$f(H) = \|H\|g(H)$$

with some function g such that

$$\lim_{\|H\| \to 0} g(H) = 0.$$

In our definition of differentiability at a point, we could say that f is differentiable at X if and only if

$$f(X + H) = f(X) + \operatorname{grad} f(X) \cdot H + o(H).$$

Also observe that if $H = (h_1, \ldots, h_n)$, we have

$$|h_i| \leqq \|H\|$$

for every $i = 1, \ldots, n$. Using the o-notation, it is possible to rewrite in abbreviated form some of the proofs of Chapter III, and later proofs involved in Taylor's formula.

It is also clearly possible to define the o-notation for mappings with values in a normed vector space, and use the o-notation in the general formulation of differentiability as in Chapter XIII. Here again, it would be a good exercise to rewrite the relevant passages using this notation.

Appendix 3

Sine, Cosine, and Angle

In our two courses in calculus, the only notions for which geometric definitions were given were those of sine and cosine. As for angle, no definition was ever given, we just drew pictures. We have shown how to give definitions for all other notions in terms involving only properties of (real) numbers. Such definitions are called *analytic*. There is of course nothing wrong about using pictures, and it would be insane to have inhibitions about them, but it is reasonable to ask whether it is possible to develop the theory of angles, sine, and cosine without appeal to geometric intuition, i.e. give for these notions purely analytic definitions, and prove their properties purely analytically. This is possible, but involves a fair amount of theory which it is impossible to present in elementary courses, for obvious reasons (at least, granting the present sequence of courses in elementary schools). Still, it now seems worthwhile to show how the theory can be developed. To do so, we shall use theorems proved in this course, concerning both differentiation and linear algebra. These theorems and their proofs did not depend on the notions of sine, cosine, and angle, so that our logic is not circular. At the end, we shall recover all the usual properties.

By *number*, throughout this appendix, we shall mean *real number*. The proofs of §1 use only calculus, and except for Proposition 1, use only results proved in the *First Course*. The proofs of §2 use only results of linear algebra proved in the present volume, except for the last proposition, which relates the algebra and the calculus.

§1. The functions sin and cos

PROPOSITION 1. *There exists a unique pair of functions f, g defined for all numbers, which are differentiable, such that*

$$f' = g \quad \text{and} \quad g' = -f.$$

and such that $f(0) = 0$ and $g(0) = 1$.

Proof. There are a number of ways of proving the existence. One of them is to prove that the series

$$f(x) = \sum_{n=1}^{\infty} (-1)^n \frac{x^{2n+1}}{(2n+1)!} \quad \text{and} \quad g(x) = \sum_{n=0}^{\infty} (-1)^n \frac{x^{2n}}{(2n)!}$$

can be differentiated term by term. This is proved in every course in advanced calculus, and we shall omit the proof here. It is then clear that these functions satisfy our requirements.

Note. The fact about series quoted just now is rather easy to prove. It will be the only fact used in this appendix for which no proof has been given in our *Courses.* In this section, we shall make repeated application of the theorems concerning increasing and decreasing functions proved in the *First Course.*

As for uniqueness, let f_1, g_1 be functions such that

$$f_1' = g_1 \qquad \text{and} \qquad g_1' = -f_1,$$

and assume only that $f_1(0)^2 + g_1(0)^2 = 1$.

Differentiating the function $f_1^2 + g_1^2$, one finds 0. Hence this function is constant, and hence is equal to the constant 1.

Next we differentiate the functions $fg_1 - f_1g$ and $ff_1 + gg_1$. We find 0 in each case. Hence there exist numbers a, b such that

$$fg_1 - f_1g = a,$$
$$ff_1 + gg_1 = b.$$

We multiply the first equation by f, the second by g, and add. We multiply the first equation by g, the second by f, and subtract. We obtain the two equations:

(*)
$$g_1 = af + bg,$$
$$f_1 = bf - ag.$$

If we assume that f_1, g_1 satisfy the hypotheses of the proposition, then evaluating these functions at 0, we find the values for a, b to be $a = 0$ and $b = 1$. This proves our uniqueness statement.

In view of Proposition 1, we define the functions f and g in that proposition to be the *sine* and *cosine* functions respectively, and denote them by sin and cos.

PROPOSITION 2. *For all numbers x, y we have:*

(1) $$\sin^2 x + \cos^2 x = 1,$$

(2) $$\sin(-x) = -\sin x,$$

(3) $$\cos(-x) = \cos x,$$

(4) $$\sin(x + y) = \sin x \cos y + \cos x \sin y,$$

(5) $$\cos(x + y) = \cos x \cos y - \sin x \sin y.$$

Proof. The first formula has already been proved. To prove each pair of succeeding formulas, we make a suitable choice of functions f_1, g_1 and apply equations (*) of the proof of uniqueness. For instance, to prove (2) and (3), we let

$$f_1(x) = \cos(-x) \qquad \text{and} \qquad g_1(x) = \sin(-x).$$

Then we find numbers a, b as in the uniqueness proof such that equations (*) are satisfied. Taking the values of these functions at 0, we now find that $b = 0$ and $a = -1$. This proves what we want. To prove (4) and (5), we let y be a fixed number, and let

$$f_1(x) = \sin(x + y) \qquad \text{and} \qquad g_1(x) = \cos(x + y).$$

We determine the constants a, b as before, in equations (*), and find $a = -\sin y$, $b = \cos y$. Formulas (4) and (5) then drop out.

Since the functions sin and cos are differentiable, and since their derivatives are expressed in terms of each other, it follows that they are infinitely differentiable. In particular, they are continuous.

Since $\sin^2 x + \cos^2 x = 1$ for all x, it follows that the values of sin and cos lie between -1 and 1. Of course, we do not yet know that sin and cos take on all such values. This will be proved later.

Since the derivative of sin x at 0 is equal to 1, and since this derivative is continuous, it follows that the derivative of sin x (which is cos x) is > 0 for all numbers x in some open interval containing 0. Hence sin is strictly increasing in such an interval, and is strictly positive for all $x > 0$ in such an interval.

We shall now prove that there is a number $x > 0$ such that sin $x = 1$. In view of the relation between sin and cos, this amounts to proving that there exists a number $x > 0$ such that cos $x = 0$.

Suppose that no such number exists. Since cos is continuous, we conclude that cos x cannot be negative for any value of $x > 0$ (by the intermediate value theorem). Hence sin is strictly increasing for all $x > 0$, and cos is strictly decreasing for all $x > 0$. Let $a > 0$. Then

$$0 < \cos 2a = \cos^2 a - \sin^2 a < \cos^2 a.$$

By induction, one sees that $\cos(2^n a) < (\cos a)^{2^n}$ for all integers $n > 0$. Hence $\cos(2^n a)$ approaches 0 as n becomes large, because $0 < \cos a < 1$. Since cos is strictly decreasing for $x > 0$, it follows that cos x approaches 0 as x becomes large, and hence sin x approaches 1. In particular, there exists a number $b > 0$ such that

$$\cos b < \tfrac{1}{4} \qquad \text{and} \qquad \sin b > \tfrac{1}{2}.$$

Then $\cos 2b = \cos^2 b - \sin^2 b < (\frac{1}{4})^2 - (\frac{1}{2})^2 < 0$, contradiction, proving that there is a number $x > 0$ such that $\sin x = 1$, $\cos x = 0$.

The set of numbers $x > 0$ such that $\cos x = 0$ (or equivalently, $\sin x = 1$) is non-empty, bounded from below. Let c be its greatest lower bound. By continuity, we must have $\cos c = 0$. We *define* π to be the number $2c$. Thus $c = \pi/2$. (We follow the Greeks. Unfortunately, it would be more practical to define π as being equal to $4c$. This would get rid of an extraneous factor of 2 appearing in almost all formulas in mathematics involving π. However, it is too late in history to change the notation.) It is clear that $c > 0$, and by definition of the greatest lower bound, there is no number x such that

$$0 \leq x < \pi/2$$

and such that $\cos x = 0$, or $\sin x = 1$.

PROPOSITION 3. *For all x, we have*

$$\cos x = \sin\left(x + \frac{\pi}{2}\right) \qquad \text{and} \qquad \sin x = \cos\left(x - \frac{\pi}{2}\right).$$

Proof. Use (4) and (5) in Proposition 2.

PROPOSITION 4. *The functions* sin *and* cos *behave as described in the following table. We use "s.i." and "s.d." to abbreviate "strictly increasing" and "strictly decreasing" respectively.*

	$\theta \leq x \leq \frac{\pi}{2}$	$\frac{\pi}{2} \leq x \leq \pi$	$\pi \leq x \leq \frac{3\pi}{2}$	$\frac{3\pi}{2} \leq x \leq 2\pi$
sin	s.i. from 0 to 1	s.d. from 1 to 0	s.d. from 0 to −1	s.i. from −1 to 0
cos	s.d. from 1 to 0	s.d. from 0 to −1	s.i. from −1 to 0	s.i. from 0 to 1.

Proof. The behavior in the first column has already been proved in the course of our discussion concerning the definition of $\pi/2$. Consider the second column. The behavior of sin in the indicated interval comes from Proposition 3 (it is the same as the behavior of cos in the preceding column). In that interval, the derivative of cos is therefore negative, and cos is strictly decreasing. Furthermore, cos decreases from 0 to −1, since we must always have $\sin^2 x + \cos^2 x = 1$. We can now argue in a similar way concerning the behavior of sin in the interval of the third column, then the behavior of cos in the third column, and finally the fourth column.

The arguments are entirely similar to those used in going from the first to the second column, and can be left as exercises to the reader.

A function f is called *periodic*, and a number s is called a *period*, if $f(x + s) = f(x)$ for all numbers x.

PROPOSITION 5. *The functions* sin *and* cos *are periodic. The numbers* $2n\pi$ *(n equal to an integer) are periods, and every period is equal to* $2n\pi$ *for some integer n.*

Proof. From the fourth column of Proposition 4 [or by an easy direct argument, using (4) and (5) of Proposition 2], we know that $\sin 2\pi = 0$ and $\cos 2\pi = 1$. Hence

$$\sin (x + 2\pi) = \sin x \cos 2\pi + \cos x \sin 2\pi = \sin x,$$
$$\cos (x + 2\pi) = \cos x \cos 2\pi - \sin x \sin 2\pi = \cos x.$$

By induction, it follows that $2n\pi$ is a period for any integer n.

Let s_1, s_2 be periods for sin. Then one sees at once that $s_1 + s_2$ and $s_1 - s_2$ are periods. Let s be a period for sin. Consider the set of integers m such that $2m\pi \leqq s$. Taking m sufficiently large negative shows that this set is not empty, and is bounded from above by $s/2\pi$. Let n be its least upper bound. Then n is an integer, and $2n\pi \leqq s$ but $2(n + 1)\pi > s$. Let $t = s - 2n\pi$. Then t is a period, and $0 \leqq t < 2\pi$. We must have

$$\sin (0 + t) = \sin 0 = 0,$$
$$\cos (0 + t) = \cos 0 = 1.$$

From the table in Proposition 4, we see that this is possible only if $t = 0$, as was to be shown.

The preceding propositions give us all the usual properties of sin and cos.

We recall that a point (a, b) in 2-space is said to lie on the unit circle if $a^2 + b^2 = 1$. We see that for any number x, the point $(\cos x, \sin x)$ lies on the unit circle.

PROPOSITION 6. *Given a point (a, b) on the unit circle in 2-space, there exists a unique number t such that $0 \leqq t < 2\pi$ and such that $a = \cos t$, $b = \sin t$.*

Proof. We consider four different cases, according as a, b are $\geqq 0$ or $\leqq 0$. In any case, both a and b are between -1 and 1.

Consider for instance the case where $-1 \leqq a \leqq 0$ and $0 \leqq b \leqq 1$. From the table in Proposition 4, we see that there is only one possible column in which we could find a value of t satisfying our requirements, and that is the second column.

By the intermediate value theorem, we know that there is one number t such that

$$\frac{\pi}{2} \leqq t \leqq \pi$$

and $\sin t = b$. Since $\cos^2 x = 1 - \sin^2 x = 1 - b^2 = a^2$, and since both $\cos x$ and a are $\leqq 0$ in this interval, it follows that we must also have $\cos t = a$. This proves what we want.

The other cases are treated in an entirely similar way, and can be left to the reader.

We have now obtained a mapping from the real numbers into the plane $\mathbf{R}^2$, *such that the image of the mapping is equal to the unit circle, and such that each point on the unit circle is the image of exactly one number in the interval* $0 \leqq x < 2\pi$.

Using the periodicity of sin and cos, given a number c, we can conclude that every point on the unit circle is the image of exactly one number in the interval

$$c \leqq x < c + 2\pi.$$

Hence we conclude: If x_1, x_2 are two numbers such that

$$(\cos x_1, \sin x_1) = (\cos x_2, \sin x_2),$$

then there exists an integer n such that $x_2 = x_1 + 2n\pi$.

§2. *Angles*

For most of this section, we discuss the geometry of 2-space. This discussion is logically independent of calculus, and concerns only linear algebra. At the end we relate the geometry with our sin and cos functions.

Let V be a 2-dimensional vector space (over the real numbers), with a (positive definite) scalar product. By the unit circle in V we shall mean the set of all elements v of V such that $\|v\| = 1$. Thus the unit circle is just the set of unit vectors in V.

Let A be a non-zero element of V. The set of all elements tA, where t is a number $\geqq 0$, will be called a *half-line*, determined by A. If E is the unit vector in the direction of A, i.e.

$$E = \frac{A}{\|A\|},$$

then one sees at once that E determines the same half-line as A, and is the unique unit vector in V which does so. Thus to determine a half-line it is necessary and sufficient to specify the unit vector having the same direction.

We define an *angle* to be an ordered pair of half-lines $(L_1 L_2)$. If P is the unique point on the unit circle lying on the half-line L_1, and Q is the unique point on the unit circle lying on the half-line L_2, then we denote the angle $(L_1 L_2)$ also by the symbols $\angle PQ$.

Let $\mathfrak{B}$ and $\mathfrak{B}'$ be two bases of V. If $F : V \to V$ is a linear map, and if we let M be its associated matrix relative to $\mathfrak{B}$, $\mathfrak{B}$ (or as we also say, relative to $\mathfrak{B}$), and let M' be the associated matrix of F relative to $\mathfrak{B}'$, then we know that there exists a matrix N such that $M' = N M N^{-1}$. Using the rule concerning the product of determinants, we conclude that the determinant of M is equal to the determinant of M'. Hence the determinant does not depend on the choice of bases. We call it the determinant of F.

We recall that an orthogonal map is a linear map which preserves lengths (or scalar products).

PROPOSITION 7.   *The determinant of an orthogonal map F is equal to 1 or -1.*

Proof. Let $\{v_1, v_2\}$ be an orthonormal basis of V. Let a, b, c, d be numbers such that

$$F(v_1) = av_1 + bv_2,$$
$$F(v_2) = cv_1 + dv_2.$$

Since F is orthogonal, the lengths of $F(v_1)$ and $F(v_2)$ are equal to 1, and these two elements are perpendicular. This means that

$$a^2 + b^2 = 1, \qquad c^2 + d^2 = 1, \qquad ac + bd = 0.$$

Hence

$$1 = (a^2 + b^2)(c^2 + d^2) = a^2c^2 + b^2c^2 + a^2d^2 + b^2d^2,$$
$$0 = (ac + bd)^2 = a^2c^2 + 2abcd + b^2d^2.$$

From these we obtain

$$(ad - bc)^2 = 1,$$

thereby proving that the determinant squared is equal to 1. Hence the determinant itself is 1 or -1.

We define a *rotation* to be an orthogonal map whose determinant is equal to 1.

PROPOSITION 8.   *Let $\mathfrak{B}$ be an orthonormal basis of V, and let F be a linear map of V into itself. Then F is a rotation if and only if there exist numbers a, b such that $a^2 + b^2 = 1$, and such that the matrix of F relative to $\mathfrak{B}$ is*

$$\begin{pmatrix} a & -b \\ b & a \end{pmatrix}.$$

If F is a rotation, a, b are as above, and $\mathfrak{B}'$ is another orthonormal basis of V such that the linear map sending $\mathfrak{B}$ on $\mathfrak{B}'$ is a rotation, then

$$M_{\mathfrak{B}'}^{\mathfrak{B}'}(F) = M_{\mathfrak{B}}^{\mathfrak{B}}(F).$$

Proof. Assume first that F is a rotation, and let us keep the notation of Proposition 7. We have $ad - bc = 1$. Hence

$$-bc = 1 - ad, \qquad ac = -bd.$$

Multiplying the first of these equations by a, the second by b and adding yields

$$0 = a - a^2 d - b^2 d.$$

Since $a^2 + b^2 = 1$, we get $a = d$. From this it follows at once that $c = -b$, and our first assertion is proved. Conversely, it is trivially verified that a linear map represented by a matrix of the given type is a rotation.

Let now $\mathfrak{B}' = \{w_1, w_2\}$ be another orthonormal basis of V, and assume that it differs from $\{v_1, v_2\}$ by a rotation. By what we have just proved, there exist numbers x, y such that $x^2 + y^2 = 1$, and

$$v_1 = xw_1 + yw_2,$$
$$v_2 = -yw_1 + xw_2.$$

Thus the matrix

$$N = \begin{pmatrix} x & -y \\ y & x \end{pmatrix}$$

is equal to $M_{\mathfrak{B}}^{\mathfrak{B}'}(id)$ by definition. Since $N^{-1} = \begin{pmatrix} x & y \\ -y & x \end{pmatrix}$ (as one sees by a direct computation), it follows that

$$M_{\mathfrak{B}'}^{\mathfrak{B}'}(F) = \begin{pmatrix} x & y \\ -y & x \end{pmatrix}\begin{pmatrix} a & -b \\ b & a \end{pmatrix}\begin{pmatrix} x & -y \\ y & x \end{pmatrix},$$

and a direct computation shows that this is the same matrix as

$$\begin{pmatrix} a & -b \\ b & a \end{pmatrix},$$

thereby proving our proposition.

PROPOSITION 9. *Let F, G be two rotations. Then $F \circ G$ is a rotation. There exists an inverse F^{-1} for F, and F^{-1} is a rotation.*

Proof. The first assertion follows directly from the product rule for determinants. The second follows from the equations

$$1 = D(I) = D(FF^{-1}) = D(F)D(F^{-1}),$$

together with the assumption that $D(F) = 1$, provided we know that the inverse exists. The fact that an orthogonal linear map has an inverse, and that this inverse is orthogonal will be left as an exercise.

Let E_1 be a unit vector in V. The subspace of V which is perpendicular to E_1 has dimension 1 (because V has dimension 2). If E_2 is a unit vector generating this subspace, then any other vector perpendicular to E_1 can be written tE_2 for some number t. Hence there exist exactly two unit vectors in V perpendicular to E_1, and these are E_2, $-E_2$.

PROPOSITION 10. *Let P, A be unit vectors in V. Then there exists a unique rotation F such that $F(P) = A$.*

Proof. Let F_1, F_2 be rotations mapping P on A. Then

$$F_1^{-1}(F_2(P)) = P.$$

Hence $F_1^{-1}F_2$ is a rotation which leaves P fixed. If we can prove that such a rotation is the identity map, then we conclude that $F_1^{-1}F_2 = I$, and $F_2 = F_1$, as desired. Let G be a rotation leaving P fixed. Let E be a unit vector perpendicular to P. Then $\{P, E\}$ is a basis for V. Since G is orthogonal, it follows that $G(E)$ is perpendicular to P, hence is equal to E or $-E$. If $G(E)$ were equal to $-E$, then the determinant of G would be equal to -1, which is impossible. Hence $G(E) = E$. Hence G leaves both P, E fixed, and since G is linear, it must be the identity map. We have therefore proved our uniqueness statement.

As for existence, let E be as above, and let a, b be numbers such that

$$A = aP + bE.$$

There exists a unique linear map F such that $F(P) = A$ and $F(E) = -bP + aE$. Since A is a unit vector, we have $a^2 + b^2 = 1$, and hence the determinant of F is 1. Furthermore, $F(P)$ and $F(E)$ are perpendicular (their scalar product is obviously 0). Hence F is a rotation, and has the desired effect.

Our next task is to define the sine and cosine of an angle. For this we must consider an additional structure on the vector space, that of orientation.

Two orthonormal bases $\mathcal{B}$ and $\mathcal{B}'$ of V will be said to have the *same orientation* if the (unique) orthogonal map F sending $\mathcal{B}$ into $\mathcal{B}'$ is a rotation. If this orthogonal map is not a rotation, then we say that $\mathcal{B}$ and $\mathcal{B}'$ have *opposite orientation*.

Remark. If $\mathcal{B}$ and $\mathcal{B}'$ have the same orientation, and if $\mathcal{B}'$, $\mathcal{B}''$ have the same orientation, then $\mathcal{B}$ and $\mathcal{B}''$ have the same orientation. Furthermore, $\mathcal{B}$ has the same orientation as itself. If $\mathcal{B}$ and $\mathcal{B}'$ have the same orientation, then $\mathcal{B}'$ and $\mathcal{B}$ have the same orientation. These statements are easily proved, and the arguments will be left to the reader.

The set of all orthonormal bases of V having a given orientation will be said to determine an *orientation* of V. There exist exactly two orientations of V. (Trivial proof, left as an exercise.)

Let us now assume given an orientation on V. Let $\angle PQ$ be an angle. Of the two unit vectors which are perpendicular to P, exactly one of them, say E, will be such that $\{P, E\}$ has the given orientation (because $\{P, E\}$ and $\{P, -E\}$ have opposite orientations).

There exist numbers a, b such that

$$Q = aP + bE.$$

Since Q has length 1, we see that $Q \cdot Q = 1 = a^2 + b^2$. Thus relative to the basis $\{P, E\}$, we see that the point having coordinates (a, b) lies on the unit circle. We define the *cosine* of the angle $\angle PQ$ to be the number a, and the *sine* of the angle $\angle PQ$ to be the number b. We abbreviate these by cos and sin.

Let $\angle PQ$ and $\angle AB$ be two angles, and let F be the rotation such that $F(P) = A$. If $F(Q) = B$, then we shall say that $\angle PQ$ is *congruent to* $\angle AB$. It is easily proved that in that case, $\angle AB$ is congruent to $\angle PQ$. Trivially, $\angle PQ$ is congruent to itself. It is also easily proved that if $\angle PQ$ is congruent to $\angle AB$ and $\angle AB$ is congruent to $\angle CD$, then $\angle PQ$ is congruent to $\angle CD$. We shall leave these easy proofs as exercises.

PROPOSITION 11. *Two angles $\angle PQ$ and $\angle AB$ are congruent if and only if*

$$\cos \angle PQ = \cos \angle AB,$$
$$\sin \angle PQ = \sin \angle AB.$$

Proof. Assume first that the two angles are congruent, and let F be the rotation such that $F(P) = A$, $F(Q) = B$. Let E be the unit vector such that $\{P, E\}$ is the orthonormal basis having the given orientation. By definition, $\{F(P), F(E)\}$ has the same orientation. Let a, b be numbers such that

$$Q = aP + bE.$$

Since F is linear, we get

$$F(Q) = aF(P) + bF(E).$$

Since $F(P) = A$, it follows by definition that the cosines of our two angles are equal, and so are their sines.

The converse will be left as an exercise.

Let $\angle PQ$ be an angle. We define *minus* $\angle PQ$ to be the angle $\angle QP$, write it $-\angle PQ$, and also call it the *negative* of $\angle PQ$. We leave it as an exercise to prove that if two angles are congruent, then their negatives are congruent.

Let $\angle PQ$ and $\angle QR$ be two angles. We define their *sum* to be the angle $\angle PR$.

Let $\{P, E\}$ be an orthonormal basis having the given orientation. We call the angle $\angle PE$ a *positive right angle*. We call $\angle PQ$ a *flat* angle if $Q = -P$.

It is then possible to prove entirely within the context of linear algebra, directly from our definitions, all the properties of sines and cosines of angles which have been proved in §1 for the sin and cos functions (i.e. the properties of Propositions 2 and 3). All the relevant definitions have now been made. In fact, we note that the addition formula for the cosine function was proved in our *First Course* by a method which applies verbatim, since all the concepts involved in it have now received an analytic definition.

It is a good exercise for any one interested to carry out these proofs.

It is also possible to carry out the proofs by first relating directly our sines and cosines of angles with the sin and cos functions. This is done as follows.

PROPOSITION 12. *Assume that an orientation of V has been fixed. Given a number θ, let F_θ be the rotation whose associated matrix with respect to any orthonormal basis having the given orientation is*

$$\begin{pmatrix} \cos \theta & -\sin \theta \\ \sin \theta & \cos \theta \end{pmatrix}.$$

If θ, φ are numbers, then $F_{\theta+\varphi} = F_\theta F_\varphi = F_\varphi F_\theta$. Also, $F_{-\theta} = F_\theta^{-1}$. We have $F_\theta = F_\varphi$ if and only if θ and φ differ by a period $2n\pi$.

Proof. The fact that the matrix of a rotation is the same for two orthonormal bases having the same orientation was proved in Proposition 8. A direct multiplication of matrices will show that our assertions are true, using the properties of sin, cos proved in Proposition 2, §1.

Given an angle $\angle PQ$, we observe that we can find its sine and cosine as follows. We let F be the rotation such that $F(P) = Q$. By Proposition 12, there exists a number θ such that $F = F_\theta$. Then

$$\cos \angle PQ = \cos \theta \quad \text{and} \quad \sin \angle PQ = \sin \theta.$$

To each angle, we have associated a rotation, and hence a set of numbers of type $\theta + 2n\pi$. Conversely, given a rotation F and a point P on the unit circle, we can associate to these the angle $\angle PQ$ where $Q = F(P)$.

Let $\angle PQ$ be an angle and θ a number. We define the expression "$\angle PQ$ *has θ radians*" to mean that F_θ is the rotation associated with the angle $\angle PQ$. If $\varphi = \theta + 2n\pi$, and if $\angle PQ$ has θ radians, then $\angle PQ$ also has φ radians.

Using Proposition 12, it now follows trivially that the cosine of the sum of two angles satisfies the usual addition formula, if we use the analogous formula for the cos function, proved in Proposition 2, §1. We give the proof as an example.

Let $\angle PQ$ have θ radians, and $\angle QR$ have φ radians. Then $F_\theta(P) = Q$ and $F_\varphi(Q) = R$. Hence

$$F_{\theta+\varphi}(P) = F_\varphi(F_\theta(P)) = R.$$

Hence $\angle PR$ has $\theta + \varphi$ radians. Applying the formula

$$\cos{(\theta + \varphi)} = \cos{\theta}\cos{\varphi} - \sin{\theta}\sin{\varphi},$$

and the definitions, we get the addition formula for the cosine of the sum of two angles.

The addition formula for the sine is proved in the same way.

Answers to Exercises

ANSWERS TO EXERCISES

I am much indepted to Mr. I. Schochetman and Mr. J. Hennefeld for the answers to the exercises.

Chapter I, §1

	$A + B$	$A - B$	$3A$	$-2B$
1.	$(1, 0)$	$(3, -2)$	$(6, -3)$	$(2, -2)$
2.	$(-1, 7)$	$(-1, -1)$	$(-3, 9)$	$(0, -8)$
3.	$(1, 0, 6)$	$(3, -2, 4)$	$(6, -3, 15)$	$(2, -2, -2)$
4.	$(-2, 1, -1)$	$(0, -5, 7)$	$(-3, -6, 9)$	$(2, -6, 8)$
5.	$(3\pi, 0, 6)$	$(-\pi, 6, -8)$	$(3\pi, 9, -3)$	$(-4\pi, 6, -14)$
6.	$(15 + \pi, 1, 3)$	$(15 - \pi, -5, 5)$	$(45, -6, 12)$	$(-2\pi, -6, 2)$

Chapter I, §3

1. $5, 10, 30, 14, 10 + \pi^2, 245$ 2. $-3, 12, 2, -17, 2\pi^2 - 16, 15\pi - 10$
4. (b) and (d)   6. $\frac{2}{3}, \frac{2}{5}, 0$

Chapter I, §4

1. $\sqrt{5}, \sqrt{10}, \sqrt{30}, \sqrt{14}, \sqrt{10 + \pi^2}, \sqrt{245}$
2. $\sqrt{2}, 4, \sqrt{3}, \sqrt{26}, \sqrt{4\pi^2 + 58}, \sqrt{\pi^2 + 10}$
3. $(\frac{3}{2}, -\frac{3}{2}), (0, 3), \frac{2}{3}(-1, 1, 1), \frac{17}{26}(1, -3, 4),$

$$\frac{\pi^2 - 8}{2\pi^2 + 29}(2\pi, -3, 7), \qquad \frac{15\pi - 10}{\pi^2 + 10}(\pi, 3, -1)$$

4. $\frac{3}{5}(-2, 1), \frac{6}{5}(-1, 3), \frac{1}{5}(2, -1, 5), \frac{17}{14}(1, 2, -3),$

$$\frac{2\pi^2 - 16}{\pi^2 + 10}(\pi, 3, -1), \qquad \frac{3\pi - 2}{49}(15, -2, 4)$$

5. $0, 0$ 6. $\sqrt{\pi}, \sqrt{\pi}$ 7. $\sqrt{2\pi}$ 8. $\sqrt{2}$

Chapter I, §5

1. $X = (1, 1, -1) + t(3, 0, -4)$ 2. $X = (-1, 5, 2) + t(-4, 9, 1)$
3. $y = x + 8$ 4. $4y = 5x - 7$ 6. (c) and (d)
7. (a) $x - y + 3z = -1$ (b) $3x + 2y - 4z = 2\pi + 26$
   (c) $x - 5z = -33$
8. (a) $2x + y + 2z = 7$ (b) $7x - 8y - 9z = -29$
   (c) $y + z = 1$
9. $(3, -9, -5), (1, 5, -7)$ (others would be constant multiples of these)
10. (a) $2(t^2 + 5)^{1/2}$ 11. $(15t^2 + 26t + 21)^{1/2}, \sqrt{146/15}$
12. $(-2, 1, 5)$ 13. $(11, 13, -7)$
14. (a) $X = (1, 0, -1) + t(-2, 1, 5)$ (b) $X = (1, 0, 0) + t(11, 13, -7)$
15. (a) $-\frac{1}{3}$ (b) $-2/\sqrt{42}$ (c) $4/\sqrt{66}$ (d) $-\sqrt{2}/3$

16. $t = \dfrac{P \cdot N - Q \cdot N}{N \cdot N}$
17. $(1, 3, -2)$
18. $2/\sqrt{3}$

19. $(-4, \frac{11}{2}, \frac{15}{2})$
20. $\dfrac{\sqrt{2240}}{35}$

21. (a) $\frac{1}{2}(-3, 8, 1)$
(b) $(\frac{2}{3}, \frac{11}{3}, 0)$ $(\frac{1}{3}, \frac{13}{3}, 1)$

22. $\dfrac{P + Q}{2}$

Chapter I, §6

1. $(-4, -3, 1)$
2. $(-1, 1, -1)$
3. $(-9, 6, -1)$
4. 0
5. E_3, E_1, E_2 in that order.

Chapter II, §1

1. $(e^t, -\sin t, \cos t)$
2. $\left(2 \cos 2t, \dfrac{1}{1+t}, 1\right)$

3. $(-\sin t, \cos t)$
4. $(-3 \sin 3t, 3 \cos 3t)$
7. B
8. $y = \sqrt{3}x$ and $y = 0$
9. $ex + y + 2z = e^2 + 3$
10. $x + y = 1$
11. $[(X(t) - Q) \cdot (X(t) - Q)]^{1/2}$
12. $\sqrt{2}$
13. $2\sqrt{13}$

Chapter II, §2

2. (a) $\left(0, 1, \dfrac{\pi}{8}\right) + t(-4\ 0, 1)$
(b) $(1, 2, 1) + t(1, 2, 2)$

(c) $(e^3, e^{-3}, 3\sqrt{2}) + t(3e^3, -3e^{-3}, 3\sqrt{2})$
(d) $(1, 1, 1) + t(1, 3, 4)$

3. (a) $\dfrac{\pi\sqrt{17}}{8}$
(b) $\frac{3}{2}(\sqrt{41} - 1) + \dfrac{5}{4}\left(\log \dfrac{6 + \sqrt{41}}{5}\right)$

(c) $\frac{3}{2}e^2 - \frac{3}{2}e^{-2} + 6$

4. $\pi/2$
5. $(2, 0, 4)$ and $(18, 4, 12)$
6. (a) $x + 4z = \pi/2$
(b) $y = 2x$
(c) $-x + e^6y + \sqrt{2}\,e^3z = 6e^3$
(d) $2x - 2y + z = 1$

Chapter III, §2

	$\partial f/\partial x$	$\partial f/\partial y$	$\partial f/\partial z$
1.	y	x	1
2.	$2xy^5$	$5x^2y^4$	0
3.	$y \cos(xy)$	$x \cos(xy)$	$-\sin(z)$
4.	$-y \sin(xy)$	$-x \sin(xy)$	0
5.	$yz \cos(xyz)$	$xz \cos(xyz)$	$xy \cos(xyz)$
6.	yze^{xyz}	xze^{xyz}	xye^{xyz}
7.	$2x \sin(yz)$	$x^2z \cos(yz)$	$x^2y \cos(yz)$
8.	yz	xz	xz
9.	$z + y$	$z + x$	$x + y$
10.	$\cos(y - 3z)$	$-x \sin(y - 3z)$	$3x \sin(y - 3z)$
	$\quad + \dfrac{y}{\sqrt{1 - x^2y^2}}$	$\quad + \dfrac{x}{\sqrt{1 - x^2y^2}}$	

11. (1) $(2, 1, 1)$ (2) $(64, 80, 0)$ (6) $e^6(6, 3, 2)$
   (8) $(6, 3, 2)$ (9) $(5, 4, 3)$
12. (4) $(0, 0, 0)$ (5) $\pi \cos(\pi^2)(\pi, 1, 1)$ (7) $(2 \sin \pi^2, \ \pi \cos \pi^2, \ \pi \cos \pi^2)$
13. $(-1, -2, 1)$ 14. $yx^{y-1}, \ x^y \log x$

Chapter III, §3

6. $\displaystyle\lim_{h \to 0} g(h, k) = -1, \qquad \lim_{k \to 0} g(h, k) = 1$

   $\displaystyle\lim_{k \to 0} \lim_{h \to 0} g(h, k) = -1, \qquad \lim_{h \to 0} \lim_{k \to 0} g(h, k) = 1$

Chapter IV, §1

1. $\displaystyle\frac{\partial z}{\partial r} = \frac{\partial f}{\partial x}\frac{\partial u}{\partial r} + \frac{\partial f}{\partial y}\frac{\partial v}{\partial r}$ and $\displaystyle\frac{\partial z}{\partial t} = \frac{\partial f}{\partial x}\frac{\partial u}{\partial t} + \frac{\partial f}{\partial y}\frac{\partial v}{\partial t}$

2. (a) $\displaystyle\frac{\partial f}{\partial x} = 3x^2 + 3yz, \qquad \frac{\partial f}{\partial y} = 3xz - 2yz$

   $\displaystyle\frac{\partial f}{\partial s} = 3x^2 + (3 + 2s)yz - 3xz + 6sxy - 2sy^2$

   $\displaystyle\frac{\partial f}{\partial t} = 6x^2 + 8yz - 3xz + 6txy - 2ty^2$

  (b) $\displaystyle\frac{\partial f}{\partial x} = \frac{y^2 + 1}{(1 - xy)^2}, \qquad \frac{\partial f}{\partial y} = \frac{x^2 + 1}{(1 - xy)^2}$

   $\displaystyle\frac{\partial f}{\partial s} = \frac{(x^2 + 1)\sin(3t - s)}{(1 - xy)^2}$

   $\displaystyle\frac{\partial f}{\partial t} = \frac{2(y^2 + 1)\cos 2t - 3(x^2 + 1)\sin(3t - s)}{(1 - xy)^2}$

3. $\displaystyle\frac{\partial f}{\partial x} = \frac{x}{(x^2 + y^2 + z^2)^{1/2}}, \qquad \frac{\partial f}{\partial y} = \frac{y}{(x^2 + y^2 + z^2)^{1/2}}$

4. $\displaystyle\frac{\partial r}{\partial x_i} = \frac{x_i}{r}$

9. (a) $-X/r^3$ (b) $2X$ (c) $-3X/r^5$
   (d) $2e^{-r^2}X$ (e) $-X/r^2$ (f) $-4mX/r^{m+2}$

Chapter IV, §2

1.

	Plane	Line
(a)	$6x + 2y + 3z = 49$	$X = (6, 2, 3) + t(12, 4, 6)$
(b)	$x + y + 2z = 2$	$X = (1, 1, 0) + t(1, 1, 2)$
(c)	$13x + 15y + z = -15$	$X = (2, -3, 4) + t(13, 15, 1)$
(d)	$6x - 2y + 15z = 22$	$X = (1, 7, 2) + t(-6, 2, -15)$
(e)	$4x + y + z = 13$	$X = (2, 1, 4) + t(8, 2, 2)$
(f)	$z = 0$	$X = (1, \pi/2, 0) + t(0, 0, \pi/2 + 1)$

2. (a) $(3, 0, 1)$ (b) $X = (\log 3, 3\pi/2, -3) + t(3, 0, 1)$
    (c) $3x + z = 3 \log 3 - 3$
3. (a) $X = (3, 2, -6) + t(2, -3, 0)$ (b) $X = (2, 1, -2) + t(-5, 4, -3)$
    (c) $X = (3, 2, 2) + t(2, 3, 0)$
4. Distance $= \sqrt{[X(t) - Q]^2}$

Chapter IV, §3

1. (a) $\frac{5}{3}$ (b) max $= \sqrt{10}$, min $= -\sqrt{10}$
2. (a) $3/2\sqrt{5}$ (b) $\frac{48}{13}$ (c) $\sqrt{580}$

3. Increasing $\left(-\dfrac{9\sqrt{3}}{2}, -\dfrac{3\sqrt{3}}{2} \right)$,   decreasing $(9\sqrt{3}/2, \ 3\sqrt{3}/2)$

4. (a) $\left(\dfrac{3}{4 \cdot 6^{3/4}}, \ \dfrac{3}{2 \cdot 6^{7/4}}, \ \dfrac{-3}{6^{7/4}} \right)$ (b) $(1, 2, -1, 1)$

Chapter IV, §4

1. $\log \|X\|$ 2. $-1/2r^2$

Chapter V, §1

1. No   2. No   3. No   4. No

5. (a) r (b) $\log r$ (c) $\dfrac{r^{n+2}}{n+2}$ if $n \neq -2$

6. $2x^2 y$ 7. $x \sin xy$ 8. $x^3 y^2$
9. $x^2 + y^4$ 10. e^{xy} 11. $g(r)$
12. Given the vector field $F = (f_1, \ldots, f_n)$ in n-space, defined on a rectangle, centered at the origin, assume that

$$\frac{\partial f_i}{\partial x_j} = \frac{\partial f_j}{\partial x_i} \quad (\text{or} \quad D_j f_i = D_i f_j)$$

for all indices i, j. For $n = 3$, define $\varphi(x, y, z)$ to be

$$\int_0^x f_1(t, y, z)\, dt + \int_0^y f_2(0, t, z)\, dt + \int_0^z f_3(0, 0, t)\, dt,$$

and similarly for n variables. Using the hypothesis and the fact that a partial derivative of parameters can be taken in and out of an integral, you will find easily that φ is a potential function for F.

Conversely, given a vector field $F = (f_1, \ldots, f_n)$ on an open set U, if there exists a potential function, and if the partial derivatives of the functions f_i exist and are continuous, then the relations

$$\frac{\partial f_i}{\partial x_j} = \frac{\partial f_j}{\partial x_i}$$

must be satisfied for all i, j, for the same reason as that given in the text for two variables. This generalizes Theorem 2.

Chapter V, §2

1. $-369/10$ 2. $23/6$ 3. 0 4. 0 5. 54
6. $\sqrt{3C/2}$ 7. $4/3$ 8. $-\pi - \frac{8}{3}$ 9. $4/15$ 10. 4π
11. $3\pi/4$ 12. $-1/2$ 13. -56

14. Assume that $F = \text{grad } \varphi$ on U. Let C be a continuously differentiable curve between two points P and Q in U. By the chain rule, we have

$$F(C(t)) \cdot \frac{dC}{dt} = (\text{grad } \varphi)(C(t)) \cdot \frac{dC}{dt} = \frac{d\varphi(C(t))}{dt}.$$

Hence the integral of F along C is the integral of the derivative of $\varphi(C(t))$ taken between the corresponding limits, and hence is equal to $\varphi(Q) - \varphi(P)$. If the curve is closed, i.e. $Q = P$, this is equal to 0. In the piecewise continuously differentiable case, there is a sequence of continuously differentiable curves between points $\{P, P_1\}$, $\{P_1, P_2\}$, ..., $\{P_s, P\}$ and hence the integral is equal to

$$\varphi(P_1) - \varphi(P) + \varphi(P_2) - \varphi(P_1) + \cdots + \varphi(P) - \varphi(P_s) = 0.$$

15. First an observation. Let C be a continuously differentiable curve defined on the interval $[a, b]$, $a < b$. Let $C(a) = P$ and $C(b) = Q$. We can define a curve C^- by letting $C^-(t) = C(a + b - t)$, for all t in the interval $[a, b]$. Then $C^-(a) = Q$ and $C^-(b) = P$. Thus C^- goes from Q to P. We call C^- the negative of C. If we integrate along C^-, we also say that we integrate along C in reverse direction. A trivial application of the chain rule for functions of one variable shows that for any continuous vector field F, we have

$$-\int_C F = \int_{C^-} F = \int_b^a F(C(t)) \cdot \frac{dC}{dt} \, dt.$$

The same observation now is valid for a piecewise continuously differentiable curve.

Assume that the integral of F along any closed curve in U is 0. Let C_1, C_2 be two curves in U from a point P to a point Q in U. Then C_1 followed by C_2^- is a closed curve from P to P. Hence

$$\int_{C_1} F + \int_{C_2^-} F = 0.$$

By the previous observation, we see that the integral of F along C_1 is equal to the integral of F along C_2. Under our assumption, we can write

$$\int_P^Q F$$

to mean the integral of F from P to Q along any (piecewise continuously differentiable) curve from P to Q.

Let now P_0 be a fixed point of U, and define a function φ on U by the rule

$$\varphi(P) = \int_{P_0}^P F.$$

We must show that $D_i\varphi(P)$ exists for all P in U and if $F = (f_1, \ldots, f_n)$ is the representation of F by coordinate functions, then $D_i\varphi(P) = f_i(P)$. To do this, let E_i be one of the standard unit vectors. The Newton quotient of φ at P for the i-th variable is then

$$\frac{\varphi(P + hE_i) - \varphi(P)}{h}.$$

The integral of F from P_0 to $P + hE_i$ can be taken along a curve from P_0 to P, and then from P to $P + hE_i$. After cancellation of the integral from P_0 to P, we obtain

$$\frac{\varphi(P + hE_i) - \varphi(P)}{h} = \frac{\int_P^{P+hE_i} F(C) \cdot dC}{h},$$

taking the integral over the line segment $C(t) = P + tE_i$, with $0 \leq t \leq h$. Note that $dC/dt = E_i$. Hence $F(C(t)) \cdot C'(t) = f_i(C(t))$, and our Newton quotient is therefore equal to

$$\frac{\int_0^h f_i(C(t)) \, dt}{h}.$$

If g is a continuous function of *one* variable, then by the so-called fundamental theorem of calculus, we know that the derivative of the integral of g is equal to g, i.e.

$$\lim_{h \to 0} \frac{1}{h} \int_0^h g(t) \, dt = g(0).$$

We apply this to the function $g(t) = f_i(C(t)) = f_i(P + tE_i)$. We therefore obtain the limit

$$\lim_{h \to 0} \frac{\varphi(P + hE_i) - \varphi(P)}{h} = f_i(P).$$

This proves what we wanted.

Chapter VI, §1

	$\partial^2 f/\partial x^2$	$\partial^2 f/\partial y^2$	$\partial^2 f/\partial x \, \partial y$
1.	$y^2 e^{xy}$	$x^2 e^{xy}$	$yx e^{xy} + e^{xy}$
2.	$-y^2 \sin xy$	$-x^2 \sin xy$	$-xy \sin xy + \cos xy$
3.	$2y^3$	$6x^2 y$	$6xy^2 + 3$
4.	0	2	2
5.	$2e^{x^2+y^2} + 4x^2 e^{x^2+y^2}$	$e^{x^2+y^2}(2 + 4y^2)$	$4xy e^{x^2+y^2}$
6.	$2 \cos (x^2 + y)$ $-4x^2 \sin (x^2 + y)$	$-\sin (x^2 + y)$	$-2x \sin (x^2 + y)$
7.	$-(3x^2 + y)^2 \cos (x^3 + xy)$ $-6x \sin (x^3 + xy)$	$-x^2 \cos (x^3 + xy)$	$-(3x^2 + y)x \cos (x^3 + xy)$ $-\sin (x^3 + xy)$

8. $$\frac{\partial^2 f}{\partial x^2} = \frac{2(1 + (x^2 - 2xy)^2) - (2x - 2y)^2(x^2 - 2xy)}{(1 + (x^2 - 2xy)^2)^2}$$

$$\frac{\partial^2 f}{\partial y^2} = \frac{-(1 + (x^2 - 2xy)^2) - 2y(x^2 - 2xy)}{(1 + (x^2 - 2xy)^2)^2}$$

$$\frac{\partial^2 f}{\partial x \, \partial y} = \frac{-2(1 + (x^2 - 2xy)^2) - (2x - 2y)(x^2 - 2xy)(-2y)}{(1 + (x^2 - 2xy)^2)^2}$$

9. all three $= e^{x+y}$ 10. all three $= -\sin(x+y)$

11. 1   12. $2x$ 13. $e^{xyz}(1 + 3xyz + x^2y^2z^2)$

14. $(1 - x^2y^2z^2)\cos xyz - 3xyz \sin xyz$

15. $\sin(x+y+z)$ 16. $-\cos(x+y+z)$

17. $-\dfrac{48xyz}{(x^2+y^2+z^2)^4}$ 18. $6x^2 y$

Chapter VI, §2

1. $9D_1^2 + 12D_1D_2 + 4D_2^2$

2. $D_1^2 + D_2^2 + D_3^2 + 2D_1D_2 + 2D_2D_3 + 2D_1D_3$

3. $D_1^2 - D_2^2$ 4. $D_1^2 + 2D_1D_2 + D_2^2$

5. $D_1^3 + 3D_1^2D_2 + 3D_1D_2^2 + D_2^3$

6. $D_1^4 + 4D_1^3D_2 + 6D_1^2D_2^2 + 4D_1D_2^3 + D_2^4$

7. $2D_1^2 - D_1D_2 - 3D_2^2$ 8. $D_1D_2 - D_3D_2 + 5D_1D_3 - 5D_3^2$

9. $\left(\dfrac{\partial}{\partial x}\right)^3 + 12\left(\dfrac{\partial}{\partial x}\right)^2 \dfrac{\partial}{\partial y} + 48\dfrac{\partial}{\partial x}\left(\dfrac{\partial}{\partial y}\right)^2 + 64\left(\dfrac{\partial}{\partial y}\right)^3$

10. $4\left(\dfrac{\partial}{\partial x}\right)^2 + 4\dfrac{\partial}{\partial x}\dfrac{\partial}{\partial y} + \left(\dfrac{\partial}{\partial y}\right)^2$

11. $h^2\left(\dfrac{\partial}{\partial x}\right)^2 + 2hk\dfrac{\partial}{\partial x}\dfrac{\partial}{\partial y} + k^2\left(\dfrac{\partial}{\partial y}\right)^2$

12. $h^3\left(\dfrac{\partial}{\partial x}\right)^3 + 3h^2k\left(\dfrac{\partial}{\partial x}\right)^2 \dfrac{\partial}{\partial y} + 3hk^2\dfrac{\partial}{\partial x}\left(\dfrac{\partial}{\partial y}\right)^2 + k^3\left(\dfrac{\partial}{\partial y}\right)^3$

13. 8   14. 4   15. 4   16. 1

Chapter VI, §3

1. xy 2. 1   3. xy 4. $x^2 + y^2$

5. $1 + x + y + \dfrac{x^2}{2} + xy + \dfrac{y^2}{2}$ 6. $1 - \dfrac{y^2}{2}$ 7. x

8. $y + xy$ 9. $x + xy + 2y^2$ 10. Yes, 0

11. (a) Yes, 0   (b) Yes, 1   12. Yes, 0   13. Yes, 0

14. $1 + x + \dfrac{x^2}{2} - \dfrac{y^2}{2} + \dfrac{x^3}{6} - \dfrac{xy^2}{2}$ 15. 0

17. Terms up to degree 2 given in text. Term of degree 3 is $\frac{1}{3}(x+2y)^3$.

Chapter VI, §4

3. First observe that for each point X we have

$$f(X) - f(O) = \int_0^1 Df(tX)\, dt,$$

where $D = x_1 D_1 + \cdots + x_n D_n$. Assuming that $f(O) = 0$, and repeating the argument, assuming that $\nabla f(O) = 0$, we obtain

$$f(X) = \int_0^1 \int_1^1 t \, D^2 f(stX) \, ds \, dt.$$

Thus we find

$$f(X) = \sum_{i,j=1}^n h_{ij}(X) x_i x_j,$$

where

$$h_{ij}(X) = \int_0^1 \int_1^1 t \, D_i \, D_j f(stX) \, ds \, dt, \qquad \text{if} \quad i \neq j,$$

$$h_{ij}(X) = \int_0^1 \int_0^1 \tfrac{1}{2} t \, D_i \, D_j f(stX) \, ds \, dt, \qquad \text{if} \quad i = j.$$

We have $h_{ij} = h_{ji}$ because $D_i D_j = D_j D_i$.

6. (a) $X + t(Y - X)$

(b) By the mean value theorem applied to the function

$$g(t) = f(X + t(Y - X)),$$

we get

$$f(Y) - f(X) = (\operatorname{grad} f(Z)) \cdot (Y - X)$$

for some Z on the line segment. Now use the Schwarz inequality.

Chapter VII, §1

1. $(2, 1)$, neither max nor min
2. $((2n + 1)\pi, 1)$ and $(2n\pi, 1)$, neither max nor min
3. $(0, 0, 0)$, min, value 0
4. $(\sqrt{2}/2, \sqrt{2}/2)$, neither local max nor min. [Hint: Change variables, letting $u = x + y$ and $v = x - y$. Then the critical point is at $(\sqrt{2}, 0)$, and in the (u, v)-plane, near this point, the function increases in one direction, and decreases in the other.]
5. All points of form $(0, t, -t)$, neither max nor min.
6. All (x, y, z) with $x^2 + y^2 + z^2 = 2n\pi$ are local max, value 1.
   All (x, y, z) with $x^2 + y^2 + z^2 = (2n + 1)\pi$ are local min, value -1.
7. All points $(x, 0)$ and $(0, y)$ are mins, value 0.
8. $(0, 0)$, min, value 0.
9. (t, t), min, value 0.
10. $(0, n\pi)$, neither max nor min.
11. $(1/2, 0)$, neither max nor min.
12. $(0, 0, 0)$, max, value 1.
13. $(0, 0, 0)$, min, value 1.

Chapter VII, §2

1. $x^2 + 4xy - y^2$
2. At $((2n + 1)\pi, 1)$, $-xy$. At $(2n\pi, 1)$, $+xy$.
3. $x^2 + y^2 + z^2$
4. $\dfrac{1}{\sqrt{2}} e^{-1/2} \left(\dfrac{x^2}{2} + 3xy + \dfrac{y^2}{2} \right)$

5. $xy + xz$

6. At (a, b, c) such that $a^2 + b^2 + c^2 = 2n\pi$, the form is
$$-2(a^2x^2 + b^2y^2 + c^2z^2) - 4(abxy + acxz + bcyz).$$
At the point (a, b, c) such that $a^2 + b^2 + c^2 = (2n + 1)\pi$, the form is
$$2(a^2x^2 + b^2y^2 + c^2z^2) + 4(abxy + acxz + bcyz).$$

7. At points $(a, 0)$ we get a^2y^2. At points $(0, b)$, we get x^2b^2.

8. y^2 9. 0   10. $\pm xy$ 11. $x^2 + 2y^2$

12. $-x^2 - y^2 - z^2$ 13. $x^2 + y^2 + z^2$

Chapter VII, §3

1. Min $= -2$ at $(-1, -1)$, max $= 2$ at $(1, 1)$

2. Max $= \sqrt{3}$ at $\sqrt{3}/3(1, 1, 1)$, min $-\sqrt{3}$ at $-\sqrt{3}/3(1, 1, 1)$

3. Max $\frac{1}{2}$ at $(\sqrt{2}/2, \sqrt{2}/2)$ and $(-\sqrt{2}/2, -\sqrt{2}/2)$

4. Max at $(\frac{1}{2}, \frac{1}{3})$, no min

5. Min 0 at $(0, 0)$, max $2/e$ at $(0, \pm 1)$, rel. max at $(\pm 1, 0)$

6. Max $= 1$ at $(1, 0)$, min $= 1/9$ at $(3, 0)$

7. (a) max   (b) neither   (c) neither   (d) min

8. $t = (2n + 1)\pi$, so $(-1, 0, 1)$ and $(-1, 0, -1)$

Chapter VII, §4

1. $-1/\sqrt{2}$ 2. $1 + 1/\sqrt{2}$ 3. at $(\frac{5}{3}, \frac{2}{3}, \frac{1}{3})$ min $= 12$

4. $X = \frac{1}{3}(A + B + C)$, min value is $\frac{2}{3}(A^2 + B^2 + C^2 - AB - AC - BC)$

5. 45 at $\pm(\sqrt{3}, \sqrt{6})$ 6. $(\frac{2}{3})^{3/2}$ at $\sqrt{\frac{2}{3}}(1, 1, 1)$ 7. Min 0, max 0

8. Max at $(\pi/8, -\pi/8)$, value $2\cos^2(\pi/8)$; min at $(5\pi/8, 3\pi/8)$ value $\cos^2(5\pi/8) + \cos^2(3\pi/8)$

9. $(0, 0, \pm 1)$ 10. No min, max $= \frac{1}{4}$ at $(\frac{1}{2}, \frac{1}{2})$ 11. 1

14. $(x_1 \cdots x_n)^{1/n} \leqq \dfrac{x_1 + \cdots + x_n}{n}$

Chapter VIII, §1

1. (a) 12   (b) 11/5   (c) 1/10   (d) $2 + \pi^2/2$ (e) 5/6   (f) $\pi/4$

2. (a) $-3\pi/2$ (b) $e - 1/e$ (c) $\pi^2 - 40/9$ (d) 63/32

3. $9\frac{3}{4} - 28/3$

Chapter VIII, §2

1. $(e - 1)\pi$ 2. $3\pi/2$ 3. $\pi(1 - e^{-a^2})$ 4. π

5. $2ka^4/3$ 6. $3k\pi a^4/2$ 7. $k\pi/4$

Chapter VIII, §3

2. 0   3. $ka^4\pi$ 4. $2\pi k(b^2 - a^2)$ 5. $\pi ba^4/4$

6. $k\pi a^4/2$ 7. $\pi/8$ 8. $2\pi\left[-\dfrac{1}{3}\left(1 - r_0^2\right)^{3/2} + \dfrac{1}{3} - \dfrac{r_0^4}{4}\right]$,

where $r_0^2 = \dfrac{-1 + \sqrt{5}}{2}$

9. $\frac{2}{9}a^3(3\pi - 4)$ 10. πa^3

11. (a) $\pi/3$ (b) $2\pi\sqrt{2}/3$ (c) $\pi/2$ (d) $\pi/32$

12. (a) 25   (b) 15/2   (c) $7a^2b^3/3$

Chapter IX, §2

2. (a) $A - B$, $(1, -1)$ (b) $\frac{1}{2}A + \frac{3}{2}B$, $(\frac{1}{2}, \frac{3}{2})$
   (c) $A + B$, $(1, 1)$ (d) $3A + 2B$, $(3, 2)$
3. (a) $(\frac{1}{3}, -\frac{1}{3}, \frac{1}{3})$ (b) $(1, 0, 1)$ (c) $(\frac{1}{3}, -\frac{1}{3}, -\frac{2}{3})$
7. $(3, 5)$ 8. $(-5, 3)$

Chapter X, §1

1. $A + B = \begin{pmatrix} 0 & 7 & 1 \\ 0 & 1 & 1 \end{pmatrix}$, $3B = \begin{pmatrix} -3 & 15 & -6 \\ 3 & 3 & -3 \end{pmatrix}$

$-2B = \begin{pmatrix} 2 & -10 & 4 \\ -2 & -2 & 2 \end{pmatrix}$, $A + 2B = \begin{pmatrix} -1 & 12 & -1 \\ 1 & 2 & 0 \end{pmatrix}$

$2A + B = \begin{pmatrix} 1 & 9 & 4 \\ -1 & 1 & 3 \end{pmatrix}$, $A - B = \begin{pmatrix} 2 & -3 & 5 \\ -2 & -1 & 3 \end{pmatrix}$

$A - 2B = \begin{pmatrix} 3 & -8 & 7 \\ -3 & -2 & 4 \end{pmatrix}$, $B - A = \begin{pmatrix} -2 & 3 & -5 \\ 2 & 1 & -3 \end{pmatrix}$

2. $A + B = \begin{pmatrix} 0 & 0 \\ 2 & -2 \end{pmatrix}$, $3B = \begin{pmatrix} -3 & 3 \\ 0 & -9 \end{pmatrix}$

$-2B = \begin{pmatrix} 2 & -2 \\ 0 & 6 \end{pmatrix}$, $A + 2B = \begin{pmatrix} -1 & 1 \\ 2 & -5 \end{pmatrix}$

$A - B = \begin{pmatrix} 2 & -2 \\ 2 & 4 \end{pmatrix}$, $B - A = \begin{pmatrix} -2 & 2 \\ -2 & -4 \end{pmatrix}$

Chapter X, §2

3. $^{t}A = \begin{pmatrix} 1 & -1 \\ 2 & 0 \\ 3 & 2 \end{pmatrix}$, $^{t}B = \begin{pmatrix} -1 & 1 \\ 5 & 1 \\ -2 & -1 \end{pmatrix}$

4. $^{t}A = \begin{pmatrix} 1 & 2 \\ -1 & 1 \end{pmatrix}$, $^{t}B = \begin{pmatrix} -1 & 0 \\ 1 & -3 \end{pmatrix}$

7. Same   8. $\begin{pmatrix} 0 & 2 \\ 0 & -2 \end{pmatrix}$, same

9. $A + {}^{t}A = \begin{pmatrix} 2 & 1 \\ 1 & 2 \end{pmatrix}$, $B + {}^{t}B = \begin{pmatrix} -2 & 1 \\ 1 & -6 \end{pmatrix}$

11. Rows of A: $(1, 2, 3)$, $(-1, 0, 2)$. Columns of A:

$$\begin{pmatrix} 1 \\ -1 \end{pmatrix}, \quad \begin{pmatrix} 2 \\ 0 \end{pmatrix}, \quad \begin{pmatrix} 3 \\ 2 \end{pmatrix}$$

No answer given for the rest.

Chapter X, §5

4. dim 4

6. (a) $\dfrac{1}{\sqrt{3}} (1, 1, -1)$ and $\dfrac{1}{\sqrt{2}} (1, 0, 1)$

(b) $\dfrac{1}{\sqrt{6}} (2, 1, 1)$, $\dfrac{1}{5\sqrt{3}} (-1, 7, -5)$

7. $\dfrac{1}{\sqrt{6}} (1, 2, 1, 0)$ and $\dfrac{1}{\sqrt{31}} (-1, -2, 5, 1)$

8. $\dfrac{1}{\sqrt{2}} (1, 1, 0, 0)$, $\tfrac{1}{2}(1, -1, 1, 1)$, $\dfrac{1}{\sqrt{18}} (-2, 2, 3, 4)$

9. $\sqrt{80} (t^2 - 3t/4)$, $\sqrt{3}\, t$

10. $\sqrt{80} (t^2 - 3t/4)$, $\sqrt{3}\, t$, $10t^2 - 12t + 3$

11. (a) 1   (b) 1   (c) 0   (d) 2

12. $n - 1$ 13. $n - 2$

Chapter XI, §1

1. (a) $\cos x$ (b) e^x (c) $1/x$

2. (a) $e^x - 1$ (b) $\arctan x$ (c) $\sin x$

3. (a) 11   (b) 13   (c) 6

4. (a) $(e, 1)$ (b) $(1, 0)$ (c) $(1/e, -1)$

5. (a) $(e + 1, 3)$ (b) $(e^2 + 2, 6)$ (c) $(1, 0)$

6. (a) $(2, 0)$ (b) $(\pi e, \pi)$

7. (a) 1   (b) 11

8. ellipse $9x^2 + 4y^2 = 36$ 9. line $x = 2y$

10. circle $x^2 + y^2 = e^2$, circle $x^2 + y^2 = e^{2c}$

11. cylinder, radius 1, z-axis $=$ axis of cylinder

12. circle $x^2 + y^2 = 1$

Chapter XI, §2

1. All except (c), (g).

4. If u is one element such that $Tu = w$, then the set of all such elements is the set of elements $u + v$ where $Tv = 0$.

8. Only Ex. 8

9. If $F(A) = 0$, image $=$ point $F(P)$. If $F(A) \neq 0$, image is the line $F(P) + tF(A)$.

12. Parallelogram whose vertices are B, $3A$, $3A + B$, 0.

13. Parallelogram whose vertices are 0, $2B$, $5A$, $5A + 2B$.

Chapter XI, §3

2. $X = (1, 1, 0, -1) + t(1, -2, 1, 4) + u(3, -3, 1, 0)$
6. Constant functions
7. Ker D^2 = polynomials of deg ≤ 1, Ker D^n = polynomials of deg $\leq n - 1$
9. Constant multiples of e^x.   10. Constant multiples of e^{ax}.

Chapter XI, §5

1. (a) 2   (b) 2   (c) 2   (d) 1
3. n 4. (a) 1   (b) 2   (c) 1   (d) 0

Chapter XII, §1

1. (a) $(5, 3)$ (b) $(5, 0)$ (c) $(5, 1)$ (d) $(0, -3)$

2. (a) $\begin{pmatrix} 4 \\ 9 \\ 5 \end{pmatrix}$ (b) $\begin{pmatrix} 3 \\ 1 \end{pmatrix}$ (c) $\begin{pmatrix} x_2 \\ 0 \end{pmatrix}$ (d) $\begin{pmatrix} 0 \\ x_1 \end{pmatrix}$

3. (a) $\begin{pmatrix} 2 \\ 4 \end{pmatrix}$ (b) $\begin{pmatrix} 4 \\ 6 \end{pmatrix}$ (c) $\begin{pmatrix} 3 \\ 5 \end{pmatrix}$

4. (a) $\begin{pmatrix} 3 \\ 1 \\ 2 \end{pmatrix}$ (b) $\begin{pmatrix} 12 \\ 3 \\ 9 \end{pmatrix}$ (c) $\begin{pmatrix} 5 \\ 4 \\ 8 \end{pmatrix}$

5. Second column of A 6. i-th column of A

Chapter XII, §2

1. (a) $\begin{pmatrix} 1 & 0 & 0 & 0 \\ 0 & 1 & 0 & 0 \end{pmatrix}$ (b) $\begin{pmatrix} 1 & 0 & 0 & 0 \\ 0 & 1 & 0 & 0 \\ 0 & 0 & 1 & 0 \end{pmatrix}$ (c) $3I$

(d) $7I$ (e) $-I$ (f) $\begin{pmatrix} 1 & 0 & 0 & 0 \\ 0 & 1 & 0 & 0 \\ 0 & 0 & 0 & 0 \\ 0 & 0 & 0 & 0 \end{pmatrix}$

2. (a) $\begin{pmatrix} 0 & 1 \\ -1 & 0 \end{pmatrix}$ (b) $\dfrac{1}{\sqrt{2}}\begin{pmatrix} 1 & 1 \\ -1 & 1 \end{pmatrix}$ (c) $\begin{pmatrix} -1 & 0 \\ 0 & -1 \end{pmatrix}$

(d) $\begin{pmatrix} -1 & 0 \\ 0 & -1 \end{pmatrix}$ (e) $\dfrac{1}{2}\begin{pmatrix} 1 & -\sqrt{3} \\ \sqrt{3} & 1 \end{pmatrix}$ (f) $\dfrac{1}{2}\begin{pmatrix} \sqrt{3} & 1 \\ -1 & \sqrt{3} \end{pmatrix}$

(g) $\dfrac{1}{\sqrt{2}}\begin{pmatrix} -1 & -1 \\ 1 & -1 \end{pmatrix}$

3. $\begin{pmatrix} \cos\theta & -\sin\theta \\ \sin\theta & \cos\theta \end{pmatrix}$ 4. $\dfrac{1}{\sqrt{2}}(-1, 3)$ 5. $(-3, -1)$

6. $x' = x\cos\theta + y\sin\theta,\ y' = -x\sin\theta + y\cos\theta$

8. (a) $\begin{pmatrix} 1 & 0 \\ 0 & 2 \end{pmatrix}$ (b) $\begin{pmatrix} 0 & 1 \\ 0 & 0 \end{pmatrix}$ (c) $\begin{pmatrix} 1 & 1 \\ 0 & 1 \end{pmatrix}$

(d) $\begin{pmatrix} 0 & 1 & 0 \\ 0 & 0 & 2 \\ 0 & 0 & 0 \end{pmatrix}$ (e) $\begin{pmatrix} 0 & 1 & 0 & 0 & 0 \\ 0 & 0 & 0 & 0 & 0 \\ 0 & 0 & 1 & 0 & 0 \\ 0 & 0 & 0 & 2 & 1 \\ 0 & 0 & 0 & 0 & 2 \end{pmatrix}$ (f) $\begin{pmatrix} 0 & -1 \\ 1 & 0 \end{pmatrix}$

9. mn 10. mn 11. n

Chapter XII, §4

1. $IA = AI = A$ 2. 0

3. (a) $\begin{pmatrix} 3 & 2 \\ 4 & 1 \end{pmatrix}$ (b) $\begin{pmatrix} 1 & 0 \\ 1 & 4 \end{pmatrix}$ (c) $\begin{pmatrix} 3 & 3 & 37 \\ 1 & 1 & -18 \end{pmatrix}$

5. $AB = \begin{pmatrix} 4 & 2 \\ 5 & -1 \end{pmatrix}, \qquad BA = \begin{pmatrix} 2 & 4 \\ 4 & 1 \end{pmatrix}$

6. $AC = CA = \begin{pmatrix} 7 & 14 \\ 21 & -7 \end{pmatrix}, \qquad BC = CB = \begin{pmatrix} 14 & 0 \\ 7 & 7 \end{pmatrix}.$

If $C = xI$, where x is a number, then $AC = CA = xA$.

7. $(3, 1, 5)$, first row   8. Second row, third row, i-th row

11. $A^2 = \begin{pmatrix} 0 & 0 & 1 \\ 0 & 0 & 0 \\ 0 & 0 & 0 \end{pmatrix}, \qquad A^3 = 0$ matrix.   If $B = \begin{pmatrix} 0 & 1 & 1 & 1 \\ 0 & 0 & 1 & 1 \\ 0 & 0 & 0 & 1 \\ 0 & 0 & 0 & 0 \end{pmatrix}$ then

$B^2 = \begin{pmatrix} 0 & 0 & 1 & 1 \\ 0 & 0 & 0 & 1 \\ 0 & 0 & 0 & 0 \\ 0 & 0 & 0 & 0 \end{pmatrix}, \qquad B^3 = \begin{pmatrix} 0 & 0 & 0 & 1 \\ 0 & 0 & 0 & 0 \\ 0 & 0 & 0 & 0 \\ 0 & 0 & 0 & 0 \end{pmatrix}$ and $B^4 = 0.$

13. Let $A = M^{\mathcal{B}'}(id)$ and $B = M_{\mathcal{B}'}(id)$.

Chapter XII, §5

1. (a) 2   (b) 1   (c) 1   (d) 0

Chapter XIII, §2

1. (a) $\begin{pmatrix} 1 & 1 \\ 2xy & x^2 \end{pmatrix}$　　　　(b) $\begin{pmatrix} \cos x & 0 \\ -y\sin xy & -x\sin xy \end{pmatrix}$

(c) $\begin{pmatrix} ye^{xy} & xe^{xy} \\ 1/x & 0 \end{pmatrix}$　　　(d) $\begin{pmatrix} z & 0 & x \\ y & x & 0 \\ 0 & z & y \end{pmatrix}$　　　(e) $\begin{pmatrix} yz & xz & xy \\ 2xz & 0 & x^2 \end{pmatrix}$

(f) $\begin{pmatrix} yz\cos xyz & xz\cos xyz & yx\cos xyz \\ z & 0 & x \end{pmatrix}$

2. (a) $\begin{pmatrix} 1 & 1 \\ 4 & 1 \end{pmatrix}$　　(b) $\begin{pmatrix} -1 & 0 \\ -\dfrac{\pi}{2}\sin\dfrac{\pi}{2} & -\pi\sin\dfrac{\pi}{2} \end{pmatrix}$　　(c) $\begin{pmatrix} 4e^4 & e^4 \\ 1 & 0 \end{pmatrix}$

(d) $\begin{pmatrix} -1 & 0 & 1 \\ 1 & 1 & 0 \\ 0 & -1 & 1 \end{pmatrix}$　　(e) $\begin{pmatrix} 1 & -2 & -2 \\ -4 & 0 & 4 \end{pmatrix}$　　(f) $\begin{pmatrix} 8 & 4\pi & 2\pi \\ 4 & 0 & \pi \end{pmatrix}$

5. $4x - 4y - z = 0$　　　　6. $x = -1$　　　　7. $y - z = -1$

8. $-r$　　　　　　　　　　9. $-\rho^2 \sin\varphi$

Chapter XIV, §2

1. (a) -20　　　(b) 5　　　(c) 4　　　(d) 5　　　(e) -76

2. (a) -18　　　(b) 45　　　(c) 0　　　(d) 0

6. 1　　　　　　　　　　7. $t^2 + 8t + 5$

Chapter XIV, §3

3. The product $a_{11}a_{22}\cdots a_{nn}$

Chapter XIV, §4

1. (a) $-\dfrac{1}{20}\begin{pmatrix} 4 & 1 & -7 \\ -4 & -6 & 2 \\ 12 & 2 & 6 \end{pmatrix}$　　　(b) $\dfrac{1}{5}\begin{pmatrix} 2 & 23 & -11 \\ 1 & 19 & -8 \\ 0 & -10 & 5 \end{pmatrix}$

(c) $\dfrac{1}{4}\begin{pmatrix} 3 & 2 & -9 \\ 1 & 2 & -3 \\ -2 & -4 & 10 \end{pmatrix}$　　　(d) $\dfrac{1}{5}\begin{pmatrix} 5 & -16 & 3 \\ 0 & 7 & -1 \\ 0 & -2 & 1 \end{pmatrix}$

(e) $-\dfrac{1}{76}\begin{pmatrix} 0 & -19 & 0 \\ -32 & -14 & 12 \\ 28 & 17 & -20 \end{pmatrix}$

3. $\dfrac{1}{ad - bc} \begin{pmatrix} d & -b \\ -c & a \end{pmatrix}$

Chapter XIV, §8

4. (a) 1   (b) 1   (c) -1 (d) 1   (e) 1   (f) 1

5. (a) $\begin{bmatrix} 1 & 2 & 3 \\ 3 & 1 & 2 \end{bmatrix}$ (b) $\begin{bmatrix} 1 & 2 & 3 \\ 2 & 3 & 1 \end{bmatrix}$ (c) $\begin{bmatrix} 1 & 2 & 3 \\ 3 & 2 & 1 \end{bmatrix}$

(d) $\begin{bmatrix} 1 & 2 & 3 & 4 \\ 3 & 1 & 2 & 4 \end{bmatrix}$ (e) $\begin{bmatrix} 1 & 2 & 3 & 4 \\ 2 & 1 & 4 & 3 \end{bmatrix}$ (f) $\begin{bmatrix} 1 & 2 & 3 & 4 \\ 4 & 2 & 1 & 3 \end{bmatrix}$

Chapter XV, §1

1. (a) $-\dfrac{1}{10} - \dfrac{3}{10} i$ (b) 2

(c) $-1 + 3i$ (d) $-1 + 3i$

(e) $6\pi + (7 + \pi^2)i$ (f) $-2\pi + \pi i$

(g) $-3\sqrt{2} + \sqrt{2}\,\pi i$ (h) $-8 - 6i$

2. (a) $\dfrac{1}{2} - \dfrac{i}{2}$ (b) $\dfrac{3}{10} - \dfrac{i}{10}$

(c) $\dfrac{3}{5} + \dfrac{4}{5} i$ (d) $\dfrac{2}{5} + \dfrac{1}{5} i$

(e) $1 - i$ (f) $\dfrac{1}{2} + \dfrac{i}{2}$

(g) $-\dfrac{1}{5} + \dfrac{3}{5} i$ (h) $-\dfrac{1}{2} - \dfrac{i}{2}$

3. $1, \alpha$

Chapter XV, §2

1. (a) $\sqrt{2}\, e^{i\pi/4}$ (b) $\sqrt{3}\, e^{i(\arctan \sqrt{2})}$

(c) $3e^{i\pi}$ (d) $4e^{i\pi/2}$

(e) $\sqrt{3}\, e^{-i(\arctan \sqrt{2})}$ (f) $5e^{-i\pi/2}$

(g) $7e^{i\pi}$ (h) $\sqrt{2}\, e^{i5\pi/4}$

2. (a) -1 (b) $-\dfrac{1}{2} + \dfrac{\sqrt{3}}{2} i$

(c) $\dfrac{3}{\sqrt{2}} + \dfrac{3}{\sqrt{2}} i$ (d) $\dfrac{\pi}{2} - \dfrac{\sqrt{3}}{2} \pi i$

(e) $\dfrac{1}{2} + \dfrac{\sqrt{3}}{2} i$ (f) $-i$

(g) -1 (h) $-\dfrac{1}{\sqrt{2}} + \dfrac{1}{\sqrt{2}} i$

4. If $\alpha = re^{i\theta}$, then the n-th roots are

$$r^{1/n}e^{i(\theta+2\pi k)/n}, \qquad 0 \leq k \leq n - 1$$

6. $\sqrt{\dfrac{a + \sqrt{a^2 + b^2}}{2}} + \sqrt{\dfrac{-a + \sqrt{a^2 + b^2}}{2}}\, i$

7. All u such that $u = z + 2n\pi i$, n integer
8. All $z = 2n\pi i$ 11. (c) 0
13. (a) $1 - 3i$ (b) $-6 - 4i$ 14. Yes

Index

INDEX